The Faunal Connections between Europe and North America

BY CARL H. LINDROTH

The Faunal Connections

between

Europe and North America

BY

CARL H. LINDROTH

ALMQVIST & WIKSELL · STOCKHOLM

JOHN WILEY & SONS, INC., NEW YORK

PRINTED IN SWEDEN BY

Almqvist & Wiksells

BOKTRYCKERI AKTIEBOLAG

UPPSALA 1957

251445

To
My Wife

Foreword

I first encountered Carl Lindroth twenty-six years ago, by letter, when he wrote me in an effort to establish the identity of European and American species of *Micralymma*. The next year (1931) he published his fine book on the insects of Iceland, and since then I have followed his work with increasing interest and admiration. He has pursued much the same line of research that I have done—study of carabid beetles, not only their taxonomy but also special problems of their ecology, evolution, and zoogeography—so that I have had continual opportunities for direct and critical judgment. His studies of North European Carabidae culminated in 1949 with publication of the third part of his great work on "Fennoskandischen Carabidae". In 1948 he began to turn his attention to America, planning a series of collecting and study trips which have taken him to Newfoundland for two summers, to the M. C. Z. (the Museum of Comparative Zoology at Harvard, where I work) for several months during the winter of 1950–51, and elsewhere.

The present book on European and American faunal connections is important for two reasons. It is important because it is by Lindroth. He knows both sides of the subject (the European and American sides) better, I think, than anyone else has ever done; and he brings to the subject important new data derived from his first-hand knowledge of insects, especially carabid beetles. I know—and this is the reason I am writing this foreword—that much that has been written in the past about relationships of European and American insect faunas is untrustworthy, marred by misidentifications and other errors, while what Lindroth writes expecially about Carabidae can be trusted. His taxonomy stands the ultimate test: it describes situations as they really are in nature.

The other reason why this book is important is the growing importance of the north, which is drawing increasing numbers of biologists, other scientists, and "practical" people. This book describes, compares, and traces the history of the two best-known northern faunas, those of Europe and of eastern North America. The book may have no "practical" applications, but it is an important contribution to basic knowledge of the north.

P. J. DARLINGTON, JR.
Curator of Insects
Museum of Comparative Zoology
Harvard University.

Contents

CHAPTER I

List of land and freshwater animal species common to Europe and North America

CHAPTER II

The human transport of animals across the North Atlantic

CHAPTER III

The true, pre-human relationship between the Palaearctic and Nearctic faunas

FIG. I. River Oulankajoki in Kuusamo, NE Finland.
(Photo A. V. LUMIALA)

FIG. 2. Doctors Brook opposite St. John Island, NW Newfoundland.
(Photo ERNST PALMÉN)

Author's preface

The incentive to this book was given by entomological fieldwork in Iceland (1926 and 1929) and Newfoundland (1949 and 1951).

The former island has a veritable key position in the northern Atlantic, situated almost three times as far from the European mainland (Norway) as from Greenland but in spite of this inhabited by an almost purely European fauna. This fact leads to the assumption that a considerable part of the Icelandic fauna immigrated from Europe in an interglacial period when land had a greater extension in the North Atlantic. Parts of this faunal element apparently even succeeded in colonizing Greenland.

An attempt was made to investigate the insect fauna of Newfoundland from the same point of view, i.e. to discover a "European" element in the fauna of this island too. The results obtained were unexpected, in more ways than one, and it soon became clear that a satisfactory understanding of the faunal history of the islands in the North Atlantic called for a general faunistic survey of the continents of Europe and North America, at least for selected, sufficiently investigated and otherwise suitable groups of animals.

From this enlarged amount of data, the attempt to explain the trends of animal distribution in the islands considered was transformed into a comparison between the Palaearctic and the Nearctic terrestrial fauna as a whole. It was also necessary to consider the results obtained by botanists who, in biogeography, are often ahead of zoologists, to benefit by palaeozoological evidence (when available), and—finally—in order to understand the importance of dispersal of animals by human agencies, to get an idea of the North Atlantic trade during the last four centuries.

This was a diversified and fascinating study, but dangerous at the same time. It is perhaps to be regretted that a specialist in Carabid beetles, like the cobbler, is not always wise enough to stick to his last.

Introduction

A Scandinavian biologist travelling in Eastern Canada is at once struck by the close affinity of the nature of this country with that of his native land. Not only are the soft, levelled profiles of the landscape similar, as are the heavily ground rocks, the gentle hills of moraine, the countless lakes and ponds, the wide areas of bogs and fens—all vestiges of the simultaneous periods of glaciation—but the main stock of native animals and plants seems identical too.

This far-reaching coincidence is indisputable—and yet, largely fictitious. The specialist in zoological or botanical taxonomy, after a closer comparison, in most cases will find that the European and the North American representatives of the "species" after all are not quite identical. Whether he is inclined to regard them as different subspecies or prefers a specific separation, is often a matter of judgment only.

An excellent illustration of this is given by arboreous plants. There is no difficulty in using a common trivial name for almost any kind of tree occurring in northern regions of the two continents: in both of them grow alder, ash, aspen, birch, elm, hazel, maple, oak, pine, rowan, spruce, and several others; but no indigenous kind of tree is identical on both sides of the Atlantic—provided the common juniper (*Juniperus communis*) is not counted as a tree. With the possible exception of one of the birches (*Betula tortuosa*) and perhaps one alder (*Alnus incana*), botanists even regard all of them as different species.

The number of "Eur-American" species (the word used here regardless of a possible occurrence in Asia) may be greater within any of the two following groups of organisms:

(a) arctic or subarctic animals and plants which, on the whole, often tend to a circumpolar distribution;

(b) animals and plants at a lower evolutionary stage, e.g. many insects, arachnids, tardigrades, "worms", rotatorians, etc.; mosses, lichens, fungi, etc. These may in part be "older" as species and thus have had more time at their disposal for distribution. Due to their generally reduced size, often combined with the power of asexual reproduction, they may in part be more suited for a passive dispersal across the sea.

The following attempt to estimate the faunal exchange between Europe and North America had to be based on suffficient comparative knowledge of the taxonomy of the forms occurring in the two continents. Unfortunately, such a happy state of affairs has been reached in only few groups of animals. European and American zoologists are too inclined to work independently and a taxonomic study of a certain species group, to be useful in zoogeography, must be carried out by a specialist fully acquainted with both of the faunas. An attempt to compile a "complete" list of terrestrial (and limnic) animals common to Europe and North America would therefore be a hopeless enterprise. It was necessary to restrict the task to groups of animals which may be regarded as sufficiently worked through and to add some cases of special interest from other groups.

Marine animals and animals of the tidal zone were excluded from the investigation.

The bias of this study is also accentuated by the fact that the discussion often starts, taxonomically from Carabid beetles, geographically from Newfoundland. As an apology it may be pointed out that the insect family mentioned provides an unusually suitable subject to a student in zoogeography: (1) it is numerous in species, especially in northern regions; (2) these usually possess good specific and subspecific characters, above all in the male genitalia; (3) many species show a marked geographic variation; (4) the means of dispersal are unusually varying, many species being constantly short-winged, bound to the soil and conservative in distribution, others constantly long-winged, flying more or less regularly, whereas, in a third category, both long- and short-winged individuals occur which often results in a characteristic pattern of distribution of the two forms; (5) finally, the taxonomy of northern Carabidae is tolerably well-known in both continents. —As regards Newfoundland, this island has a key position in the understanding of the human transatlantic transport of animals and plants.

Chapter I

LIST OF LAND AND FRESHWATER ANIMAL SPECIES
COMMON TO EUROPE AND NORTH AMERICA

Introduction

This list is pronouncedly selective. It was necessary to restrict its content to animal groups sufficiently known with regard to taxonomy and distribution. In spite of this limited scope the groups considered are by no means equally well suited for the purpose. In some, as in birds, Carabid beetles, and certain Lepidoptera, specialists have made direct and careful comparisons between Old and New World forms, in others a modern revision is still needed and compilations had to be made from the often rather routine-stamped records of catalogues or from scattered revisions of smaller taxonomic units. I am fully aware that, owing to the extensiveness of the task, parts of the purely taxonomic literature have been overlooked, which is much regretted. Also, introduced species which have appeared more or less sporadically in either or both continents, for instance in hothouses, have certainly not been listed in full.

It is also evident that the species and subspecies concepts are not used identically in different groups of animals and direct comparisons of the zoogeographical significance of, for instance, a bird and an insect subspecies should be avoided. The criterion of a species seems to be especially obscure among mammals so that "species" of that group apparently often correspond to what is called "subspecies" in others.

Genera and species, under each higher taxonomical unit, are listed in alphabetical order. Names in brackets are synonyms. Subgeneric names have not been used.

Names in English, according to both American and European practice, if different, are added for vertebrates only.

The records of distribution are quite summary. Their main purpose is to show whether the species, in Eurasia as well as in America, is transcontinental or not. More detailed records, for instance of the occurrence in the British Isles, are particularly given within groups containing species which are introduced into North America. Subspecies, if any, are listed in geographical order: if numerous subspecies are described from a limited are, only their approximate number is given. Subspecies outside the actual area are omitted.

Only animals living (breeding) on the continent of both Europe and North America were considered. A species occurring only on the Bermudas or on the arctic islands of Canada as well as in Greenland, is not counted as "American"; similarly, a species confined to Iceland, the Faroes, Jan Mayen, and (or) Spitzbergen, not as "European". The British Isles, however, are counted as belonging to the European continent.

Freshwater animals occurring also in the sea, or regularly descending into the sea, are omitted.

Not included in the list are furthermore the following types of animals:

a. Domesticated animals. An enumeration is superfluous.

b. Animals introduced and released for the purpose of game, fur, or fishery. Examples: American Mink (*Mustela vison* Schreb.), Muskrat (*Ondatra* [*Fiber*] *zibethica* L.; fig. 5), and Rainbow Trout (*Salmo irideus* Gibb., s.l.), in Europe; European Hare (*Lepus europaeus* Pall.), and European Saibling (*Salvelinus alpinus* L.) in North America.

c. Animals used in "biological control" of noxious insects, plants, and other pests. Besides instances mentioned below (p. 121 a.f.), leaf-beetles of genus *Chrysomela* (*Chrysolina*) were imported to California against the European weed *Hypericum perforatum* (St. John's Wort).

d. "Pet animals", imported and released, for instance in order to still the nostalgia of emigrants. Examples: Starling (*Sturnus vulgaris* L.; fig. 4) and English or House Sparrow (*Passer domesticus* L.), in North America; the American "Robin" (*Turdus migratorius* L.), in Great Britain.

e. Animals imported for study or fancy and unintentionally escaped. Example: the Gypsy Moth (*Lymantria dispar* L.) 1868 or 1869 in North America, and probably several freshwater animals, released by aquarium fanciers.

f. Unintentionally imported animals which have not become established in the new continent. Most of them have been found in ports or in wares immediately after these have been unloaded, especially on the quarantine stations. Therefore the majority of cases reported by Kraepelin (1901) from Hamburg have been neglected whereas species found in hothouses (Kew Gardens, &c.) were considered. Several similar cases, however, may have been overlooked.

Summarising, the list below tries to give, within the animal groups considered, all species common to Europe and North America, and breeding (or supposed to breed) in both continents, which are not purposely brought across by man in either direction.

Species believed or stated to be unintentionally introduced into either or both continents are indicated by a cross (†), in doubtful cases put in brackets.

The author is anxious to receive any addition to or correction of the list, which can be sent under the address of: Zoological Institute, University, Lund, Sweden.

Mammalia—Mammals

The list was largely compiled from Anderson (1946), Ellerman & Morrison-Scott (1951), and Burt & Grossenheider (1952).

There is great confusion among mammologists concerning the definition of species and subspecies, the North American ones (e.g. Anderson, 1946) as a rule being inclined to assign specific value to rather small taxonomic units. Unfortunately no thorough comparison has been made between the Palaearctic and the Nearctic mammal fauna and the relations indicated below are therefore in some cases merely suggestive, especially in the Rodentia, where the opinions of specialists largely disagree.

The following Old World Rodentia, which according to Ellerman & Morrison-Scott (1951) "doubtless", "probably" or "perhaps" are represented also in North America, have been omitted pending further evidence:—*Clethrionomys glareolus* Schreb., *Marmota marmota* L.[1], and *Microtus agrestis* L.

Insectivora

? SOREX ARCTICUS Kerr[2]

(Arctic Shrew and Tundra Shrew)

sbsp. *lapponicus* Melander N Sweden.	sbsp. *europaeus* Strog. Kola Penins.	sbsp. *petschorae* Ognev NE Eur. Russ.	sbsp. *middendorffi* Ognev NW Sib.

sbsp. *ultimus* Allen NE Sib.	sbsp. *tundrensis* Merr. Alas., N. W. Terr.	*f. typ.* Gr. Bear L.–Nova Scot., S Labr.

Carnivora

ALOPEX LAGOPUS L.

(Arctic Fox)

(?) sbsp. *fuliginosus* Bechst. Icel.	sbsp. *spitzbergensis* B.–Ham. Spitzb.	*f. typ.* Norw.–Kamch.	sbsp. *beringensis* Merr. Bering Isl.

sbsp. *innuitus* Merr. Alas.–Huds. B.–Baffins L.	sbsp. *ungava* Merr. N Labr.	sbsp. *groenlandicus* Bechst. Ellesmere L., Greenl.

---

[1] Accepted as American by Rausch (1953, p. 116 a. f.).

[2] This arrangement of northern *Sorex* is quite tentative. The association of *petschorae*, *middendorffi*, and *ultimus* with *tundrensis* was made by Chaworth-Muster, according to

CANIS LUPUS L.

(Gray Wolf)

f. typ.	sbsp. *albus* Kerr	sbsp. *hattai* Kish.	Many sbspp.
Eurasian taiga.	Eurasian tundra.	Sakh., ? Kuril.	Alas.–Labr., arct. isl., N Greenl., in the mts. S to Mex.

Several more southern sbspp.

FELIS (LYNX) LYNX L.

(Lynx)

f. typ.	sbsp. *wrangeli* Ognev	sbsp. *canadensis* Kerr[1]	sbsp. *subsolanus* Bangs[1]
Eur.–Yenisei.	Sib. E of Yenisei.	Alas.–Labr., Nov. Scot.	Nfld.

4 more southern sbspp.

GULO GULO L.

(Wolverine; Glutton)

f. typ.	sbsp. *luscus* L. (incl. 3 forms)
Scand.–Ussuri, Sakhalin.	Alas.–Labr., arct. isl., S to Color.

MUSTELA ERMINEA L.

(Ermine; Shorttail Weasel; Stoat)

3 sbspp.	*f. typ.*	many sbspp.	sbsp. *orientalis* Ognev
Brit. Isl.	Fennoscand.	N Asia.	NE Sib., Jap., Sakhal., Kuril.
sbsp. *arctica* Merr.		sbsp. *richardsoni* Bonap. (and several other forms)	
? Kamch.; Alas., N Can. W of Huds. B., arct. isl. E to Ellesmere Isl., N & NE Greenl.		Huds. B.–Labr., Nov. Scot., Nfld.	

MUSTELA NIVALIS L.

(Least Weasel)

f. typ.	sbsp. *pygmaea* Allen	sbsp. *namiyei* Kur.	sbsp. *rixosa* Bangs[1] (incl. 3 forms)
Main part of Eur.	E Sib., Mong., Manch.	N Jap., Kuril.	Alas.–S Labr.

Several more southern sbspp.

Ellerman & Morrison-Scott (1951, p. 49), who themselves refer these forms, as well as *europaeus* and *lapponicus*, to *caecutiens* Laxm. Burt & Grossenheider (1952) think that *arcticus* and *tundrensis* are of the same species. If so, the former name has priority.

[1] Usually regarded as distinct species.

URSUS ARCTOS L.
(Brown Bear)

f. typ.	sbsp. *beringianus* Midd.	sbsp. *lasiotus* Gray	sbsp. *middendorfii* Merr.[1] (incl. many forms)[2]
Scand.–Stanovoi (Sib.).	E Sib., Manch., Kamch.	Mong., Manch., N Jap., Kuril.	Pacif. coast of Alas. –N Brit. Col.

About 4 more southern sbspp.

VULPES VULPES L.
(Red Fox)

f. typ.	Many sbspp.	sbsp. *beringiana* Midd.	sbsp. *fulva* Desm.[3] (incl. many forms)
Scand.	N Eur., N Asia	NE Sib., Kamch.	Alas.–Labr., Nfld., S to the Mexic. boundary.

Ungulata

ALCES ALCES L. (fig. 54)
(Moose; Engl.: Elk)

f. typ.	sbsp. *cameloides* and *pfizenmayeri* Zuk. M.–Edw.[4]	sbsp. *americanus* Clint.[4] (incl. 4 forms)
Eur.–Baikal.	Sib. E of Yenisei, Mong., Manch.	Alas.–Nov. Scot. (Nfld., introduced), S to Wyom.

CERVUS ELAPHUS L.

f. typ.	Many sbspp.	sbsp. *xanthopygus* M.–Edw.	sbsp. *canadensis* Erxl.[3]
(Red Deer)			(Elk or Wapiti)
Sweden.	C Asia, S Siber.	Mong., Manch., Amur, Ussuri.	Originally transamerican, now disjunct: Brit. Col.–N Calif., E to Manit., S to N. Mex.

Several other Europ. sbspp.

---

[1] Due to the many "species" described by Merriam, the taxonomy of N. American bears is very confused (cf. Simpson, 1945, p. 225, footnote).

[2] According to Rausch (1953, p. 95 a. f.) even the grizzly (*Ursus horribilis* Ord), with its forms, belongs to the species *U. arctos* L.

[3] Usually regarded as distinct species.

[4] Flerow (1934, p. 141 a.f.) treats *cameloides* (*pfizenmayeri* Zuk.) as sbsp. of *americanus*, which he regards as distinct species but, in 1952 (p. 207), he joins them as above. *Vide* also Peterson (1952).

RANGIFER TARANDUS L.[1] (fig. 53)
(Caribou; Reindeer)

f. typ.	sbsp. *platyrhynchus* Vrol.	sbsp. *sibiricus* Murr. (and 4 other sbspp.)	sbsp. *arcticus* Rich.[2] (incl. some minor forms)
N Eur.	Spitzb.	Ural Mts.–E Sib., Sakhal.	Arct. N Amer.: N & C Alas., Brit. Col.– N Labr. (*caboti* All.[2]) and Ellesmere Isl. (*pearyi* All.[2]).
	sbsp. *groenlandicus* Bor. W, N & NE Greenl.		

Rodentia (in widest sense)

CLETHRIONOMYS RUTILUS Pall.
(Tundra or Northern Redbacked Vole)

f. typ.	Many sbspp.	sbsp. *amurensis* Schrk.	sbsp. *jochelsoni* Allen
N Scand.–Baikal, Mong.	N Asia.	Amur, Sakhal.	Kolyma, Kamch.
	sbsp. *dawsoni* Merr.[2] Alas.–Huds. B., S to Brit. Col.		

DICROSTONYX TORQUATUS Pall.
(Collared Lemming)

f. typ.	sbsp. *lenae* Kerr	sbsp. *unalascensis* Merr[2].	sbsp. *groenlandicus* Traill[2]
N Russ.–N Sib.	Lena–Anadyr.	Aleut. Isl.	N. Amer. tundra: Alas.–Hudson B., arct. isl., Greenl.
	sbsp. *hudsonius* Pall.[2] N Labr.		

LEMMUS SIBIRICUS Kerr (*obensis* Brants)
(Brown Lemming)

f. typ.	3–4 sbspp.	sbsp. *kittlitzi* Midd.	sbsp. *trimucronatus* Rich.[2]
White Sea–W Sib.	NE Sib.	Kamch.	Alas. & Brit. Col., E to N Labr. & Baff. L.

---

[1] According to Flerow (1952, p. 222–247). Jacobi (1931) has a different arrangement of *Rangifer*.
[2] Usually regarded as distinct species.

LEPUS TIMIDUS L.

sbsp. *hibernicus* Bell Ireland.	sbsp. *scoticus* Hilzh. (Blue, Mountain, or Varying Hare) Scotland.	*f. typ.* Scand., N Russ.	Many sbspp. C Russ.–Kamch., Sakhal., N Japan, Kuril.
One or two more southern sbspp. in the Old World.	sbsp. *othus* Merr.[1] (Tundra Hare) W Alas.		sbsp. *arcticus* Ross[1] (Arctic Hare) NW Terr.–Labr., Nfld., arctic isl., Greenl.

MICROTUS OECONOMUS Pall.

(Tundra Vole; Root Vole)

sbsp. *ratticeps* Keys. & Blas. Scand., Russ., N C. Eur.	*f. typ.* (and several sbspp.) Sib., E to Kamch., Kuril.	sbsp. *yakutatensis* Merr. Alas.	Several sbspp. Alaskan islands.

sbsp. *macfarlani* Merr.
NW Terr.

MUS MUSCULUS L.

(House Mouse)

Cosmopolitan, probably native of Mediterr., E Eur. & Asia.

Eur. (generally). † N & C Amer. (generally).

RATTUS NORVEGICUS Berkenh.

(Norway or Brown Rat)

Cosmopolitan, possibly native of Palaearctic Asia.

† Eur. (generally). † N & C Amer. (generally).

RATTUS RATTUS L.

(Black or House Rat)

Almost cosmopolitan, native of Asia.

† Eur. (formerly generally). † N Amer. (both coasts).

Aves—Birds

The main source was Peters (I–VI, 1931–48), who gives an explicit, conservative account with high demands on "the species". For the *Passeriformes*, which Peters did not manage to complete before his death, Hartert (1910–38) and the North

---

[1] Usually regarded as distinct species.

American "Check-List" (1931), with subsequent Supplements in "The Auk", were the foremost substitutes. The British "Handbook" (1945) also rendered excellent service. Valuable information was obtained from Dr. Gustaf Rudebeck, Lund.

Only breeding areas were considered.

Gaviiformes

GAVIA (COLYMBUS) ADAMSII Gray
(White-billed Northern Diver; Yellow-billed Loon)
N Finl. (?), N Russ., N. Zeml., Arct.   Alas.–Mackenzie, Boothia Penins.
Sib. E to Bering Strait.

GAVIA (COLYMBUS) ARCTICA L.

f. typ.	sbsp. *viridigularis* Dwight	sbsp. *pacifica* Lawr.
(Black-throated Diver)	(Green-throated Loon)	(Pacific Loon)
Scand.–Yenisei, Altai.	NE Sib., Alas.	Alas.–Baffins L.

GAVIA (COLYMBUS) STELLATA Pont.
(Red-throated Diver or Loon)
Iceland–Scand.–Kamch.   Alas.–Nfld.–Greenl.

Podicipitiformes

PODICEPS (COLYMBUS) AURITUS L.
(Slavonian or Horned Grebe)

f. typ.	sbsp. *cornutus* Gmel.
Icel., Scotl., Scand.–Sakhalin.	Brit. Columbia–Magdalen Isl.

PODICEPS (COLYMBUS) CASPICUS Habl. (*nigricollis* Brehm)

f. typ.	sbsp. *californicus* Heerm.
(Black–necked Grebe)	(Eared Grebe)
Eur., Asia E to Amur.	W & NW N. Amer. E to Manitoba.

PODICEPS (COLYMBUS) GRISEIGENA Bodd.

f. typ.	sbsp. *holboelli* Reinh.
(Red-necked Grebe)	(Holboell's Grebe)
N. Eur., W. Sib.	E. Asia, N. Amer., E to Ungava.

Procellariiformes

FULMARUS GLACIALIS L. (fig. 27)

f. typ.	sbsp. *rodgersii* Cassin
(Fulmar Petrel; Atlantic Fulmar)	(Pacific Fulmar)
NE arct. N. Amer., Greenl., NW Eur.	NE Asia E to Bering Sea, Kuriles, islands off Alas.

OCEANODROMA LEUCORHOA Vieill.

f. typ.
(Fork-tailed or Leach's Petrel)
N Pacific (incl. Aleutian); N Atlantic:
Maine–Brit. Isl.

3 sbspp.
(Other American names)
Pacific coast of N. Amer.

PUFFINUS PUFFINUS Brünn.

f. typ.
(Manx Shearwater)
NW Eur. (incl. Iceland), Macaronesia;
Bermudas.

sbsp. *opisthomelas* Coues
(Black-vented Shearwater)
Islands off Lower Calif. & Mex.

Pelecaniformes

MORUS (SULA) BASSANUS L. (fig. 28)
(Gannet)

Brit. Isl., Faeroes, Iceland.   NE Canada, Nfld.

PHALACROCORAX CARBO L., *f. typ.*
(European Cormorant)

Nova Scot., Labr., Greenl.   Iceland, NW Eur. E to White Sea.
Other sbspp. farther south.

Ciconiiformes

CASMERODIUS (EGRETTA) ALBUS L.

f. typ.
(Great White Heron)
SE Eur., Asia.

Other sbspp. farther south.

sbsp. *egretta* Gmel.
(American Egret)
From Oregon and N. Carolina S to Pata-
gonia.

NYCTICORAX NYCTICORAX L.

f. typ.
(Night Heron)
C Eur.–Japan, &c.

sbsp. *hoactli* Gmel.
(Black-crowned Night Heron)
N. Amer. (greater part)–Argent., Hawaii.

PLEGADIS FALCINELLUS L., *f. typ.*
(Eastern Glossy Ibis)

S Eur., W & C Asia, Africa.   S N. Amer., C Amer.
One tropical sbsp.

Anseriformes

ANAS (DAFILA) ACUTA L.
(Pintail)

Iceland, Eur.–Kamch.   W & NW N. Amer., Greenl.

ANAS (NETTION) CRECCA L.

f. typ.	sbsp. *nimia* Friedm.	sbsp. *carolinensis* Gmel.
(European Teal)		(Green–winged Teal)
Eur.–Japan.	Aleutian Isl.	W & NW N. Amer.

ANAS PLATYRHYNCHA L.
(Common Mallard)

f. typ.   sbsp. *conboschas* Brehm
Eur.–Japan; N. Amer. (doubtful E of   Greenland.
Hudson Bay).

ANAS (CHAULELASMUS) STREPERUS L.
(Gadwall)

Iceland, Eur.–Kamch.   NW N. Amer. W of Hudson Bay (not Alas.).

ANSER ALBIFRONS Scop.
(White-fronted Goose)

f. typ.   sbsp. *flavirostris* Dalg. & Sc.
Icel.(?), NE Eur.–Bering Str.; arct.   W Greenland.
N. Amer.

AYTHYA (NYROCA) MARILA L.
(Greater Scaup Duck)

f. typ.	sbsp. *mariloides* Vig.	sbsp. *nearctica* Stejn.
Icel., N Eur.–Kamch.	Bering Island.	Aleut.–Hudson Bay.

BRANTA BERNICLA L.

f. typ.	sbsp. *nigricans* Lawr.	sbsp. *hrota* O. F. Müll.
(Dark-breasted Brent)	(Black Brent)	(Pale-breasted or American Brent)
N Eur.–Taimyr.	Taimyr–NW arct. Amer.	NE arct. Amer., Greenl., Spitzb.

BUCEPHALA (GLAUCIONETTA) CLANGULA L.
(Golden-eye)

f. typ.   sbsp. *americana* Bonap.
Scand.–Kamch.   Alas.–Maine.

CLANGULA HYEMALIS L.
(Long-tailed Duck; Old-squaw)

Icel., Faeroes, Orkney, arct. Eur.– Aleut., arct. N. Amer., Greenl.
Bering Str.

MELANITTA FUSCA L.

f. typ.	sbsp. *stejnegeri* Ridgw.	sbsp. *deglandi* Bonap.[1]
(Velvet Scoter)		(White-winged Scoter)
Scand.–Yenisei.	Altai–Kamch.	Alas.–E Canada.

MERGUS MERGANSER L.

f. typ.	sbsp. *americanus* Cass.
(Goosander)	(American Merganser)
Icel.–Kamch., Kuril.	Alas.–Nfld.

MERGUS SERRATOR L.
(Red-breasted Merganser)

f. typ.	sbsp. *schiøleri* Salom.
Icel.–Kamch.; Alas.–Labr.	Greenl.

OIDEMIA (MELANITTA) NIGRA L.

f. typ.	sbsp. *americana* Swain.
(Common Scoter)	(American Scoter)
Icel.–Taimyr.	NE Asia, Alas.–Nfld.

SOMATERIA MOLLISSIMA L.
(Common Eider)

f. typ.	sbsp. *v-nigrum* Gray	sbsp. *sedentaria* Snyd.	sbsp. *dresseri* Sha rpe
Icel.–N. Zeml.	NE Sib.; Alas.–Victoria Isl.	Huds. Bay.	Huds. Bay–Labr.

sbsp. *borealis* Brehm
Queb.–Greenl.

SOMATERIA SPECTABILIS L.
(King Eider)

Spitzb., N. Zeml.; Kola Penins.– Alas.–Labr.–Greenl.
Bering Strait.

SPATULA CLYPEATA L.
(Shoveller)

W Eur.–Ussuri. N. Amer., W of Hudson Bay.

---

[1] Often regarded as distinct species.

Falconiformes

ACCIPITER (ASTUR) GENTILIS L.
(Goshawk)

f. typ.	sbsp. *buteoides* Menzb.	sbsp. *albidus* Menzb.	sbsp. *atricapillus* Wils.
NW Eur.–N Russ. (Several sbspp. in other parts of Eur. and Asia).	NE Russ., W Sib.	NE Sib., Kamch.	Alas.–Nfld.

sbsp. *striatulus* Ridgw.
Pacific region of N. Amer.

AQUILA CHRYSAËTOS L.
(Golden Eagle)

f. typ.	2–3 sbspp. in	sbsp. *canadensis* L.
W Eur.–W Sib.	E Asia. Other sbspp. farther south.	Alas.–Ungava, S to Mex.

BUTEO LAGOPUS Pont.
(Rough-legged Hawk or Buzzard)

f. typ.	sbsp. *kamtchatkensis* Dement.	sbsp. *s.-johannis* Gmel.
N Eur.	N Sib.; NW Alas.	Alas.–Labr., Nfld.

CIRCUS CYANEUS L.

f. typ. (Hen-Harrier) Eur.–R. Lena.	sbsp. *taissiae* But. NE Sib.	sbsp. *hudsonius* L. (Marsh Hawk) Alas.–Nfld., S to Tex.

FALCO COLUMBARIUS L.
(Pigeon Hawk; Merlin)

sbsp. *aesalon* Tunst. Icel.(?), NW Eur.	sbsp. *regulus* Pall. NE Eur., W Sib.	sbsp. *insignis* Clark N Sib.	sbsp. *pacificus* Stegm. E Sib.
sbsp. *bendirei* Swann Alas.–Sask.	*f. typ.* Manit.–Nfld.		Two more southern sbspp. in N. Amer.

FALCO PEREGRINUS Tunst.

f. typ.	sbsp. *calidus* Lath.	sbsp. *pealei* Ridgw.	sbsp. *anatum* Bonap.
(Peregrine Falcon) W Eur.–Ural.	W Sib.–Kamch.	(Peale's Falcon) NW N. Amer.	(Duck Hawk) Alas.–Baff. L., S to Tex.; Greenl.

Many more southern sbspp.

FALCO RUSTICOLUS L.

(Gyrfalcon)

sbsp. *islandus* Brünn.	*f. typ.*	sbsp. *uralensis* Gmel.	sbsp. *obsoletus* Gmel. (incl. *candicans* Gmel.)
Iceland.	N Eur.	W Sib.–Bering Str., W Alaska.	Alas.–Labr., Greenl.

PANDION HALIAËTUS L.

(Osprey)

f. typ. Eur.–Kamch.	sbsp. *carolinensis* Gmel. Alas.–Labr., Nfld., S to Mex.

Other sbspp. farther south.

Galliformes

LAGOPUS LAGOPUS L.

(Willow Ptarmigan)

f. typ.	sbsp. *alexandrae* Grinn.	sbsp. *leucopterus* Tav.	sbsp. *alleni* Stejn.
Scand.–Kamch.; Alas.–Ungava.[1]	Alas., Brit. Col.	Arct. isl. of N. Amer.	Nfld.

LAGOPUS MUTUS Mont.

sbsp. *islandorum* Fab.	sbsp. *millaisi* Hart. (Scottish Ptarmigan)	*f. typ.*	sbsp. *hyperboreus* Sundev.
Iceland.	Scotland.	NW Eur.	Spitzb., Fr. Jos. Land.
Several sbspp.	sbsp. *rupestris* Gmel. *s. l.*[2] (Rock Ptarmigan)	sbsp. *welchi* Brewst.	2 sbspp.
N Asia.	Alas.–Ungava–Baff. L., Greenl. (3 sbspp.).	Nfld.	Greenland.

Gruiformes

GALLINULA CHLOROPUS L.

f. typ. (Moorhen)	sbsp. *indica* Blyth	sbsp. *cachinnans* Bangs (Florida Gallinule)
W Eur.–Ussuri, N Afr.	C, E, & S Asia.	Calif.–Ont., S to Mex.

Many sbspp. in southern regions of the Old & New World.

---

[1] The N. American form is referred to sbsp. *albus* Gmel. in Check List (1931).
[2] The N. American forms are often treated as species *rupestris* Gmel.

Charadriiformes, Charadrii

ARENARIA INTERPRES L.

f. typ.	sbsp. *morinella* L.[1]
(European Turnstone)	(Ruddy Turnstone)
Greenl., Icel., Eur.–Kamch., W Alas.	Arct. N. Amer.: Mackenzie–Baffins L.

CAPELLA GALLINAGO L.

sbsp. *faeroensis* Brehm	*f. typ.*	sbsp. *delicata* Ord
(Faeroe Snipe)	(European or Common Snipe)	(American or Wilson's Snipe)
Icel., Faeroes.	Scand.–Kamch.–Japan.	Alas.–Nfld.

CHARADRIUS ALEXANDRINUS L.

(Snowy or Kentish Plover)

f. typ.	sbsp. *nivosus* Cass.	sbsp. *tenuirostris* Lawr.
Brit. Isl., Scand.–Bering Str.	Wash.–Lower Calif.	C & SE U.S.A., West Ind.

Many sbspp. farther south.

CHARADRIUS HIATICULA L.

f. typ.	sbsp. *tundrae* Lowe	sbsp. *semipalmatus* Bonap.[2]
(Ringed Plover)		(Semipalmated Plover)
W Eur.	Spitzb., N Scand.–Chukchi Penins.	Bering Str.–Baff. L.–Nov. Scot.

sbsp. *psammodroma* Salom.[3]
Baffins L., Greenl., Icel., Faeroes.

EROLIA (PELIDNA, CALIDRIS) ALPINA L.

sbsp. *arctica* Schiøl.	sbsp. *schinzii* Brehm	*f. typ.*	sbsp. *centralis* But.
	(Southern Dunlin)	(Northern Dunlin)	
N Greenl.	E Greenl., Icel., Faeroes, W Eur.	Scand.–Sib.: Yalmal; Spitzb., N. Zeml.	Yenisei–Yana.

sbsp. *pacifica* Coues
(Red-backed Sandpiper)
NE Asia; Alas.–Hudson Bay.

EROLIA (ARQUATELLA, CALIDRIS) MARITIMA Brünn.[4]

(Purple Sandpiper)

Icel., Faeroes, arct. Eur. isl., Scand.–Taimyr.	Arct. isl. of N. Amer.: Melville Isl.–Ellesm. Isl., Greenl.

[1] "A very unsatisfactory race" (Peters, 1934, p. 271).
[2] Often regarded as distinct species.
[3] Very doubtfully distinguished from *forma typica*.
[4] *E. ptilocnemis* Coues, with its races, from NE Sib. and Alaska, is sometimes regarded as a sbsp. of *maritima*.

HAEMATOPUS OSTRALEGUS L.
(Oyster-catcher)

sbsp. *malacophaga*	sbsp. *occidentalis*	*f. typ.*	2 sbspp.
Salom.	Neum.		
Icel., Faeroes.	Brit. Isl.	N & C Eur.	N Asia.

3 sbspp.
Both coasts of N. America.

Other sbpp. farther south.

HIMANTOPUS HIMANTOPUS L.
(Stilt)

f. typ.	sbsp. *mexicanus* P. L. S. Müll.
Mediterr., S Russ.–China.	Oregon–Peru.

Several sbspp. farther south.

LIMOSA LAPPONICA L.

f. typ.	sbsp. *baueri* Naum.
(Bar-tailed Godwit)	(Pacific Godwit)
N Scand.–Taimyr.	NE Asia, Alaska.

LOBIPES (PHALAROPUS) LOBATUS L.
(Northern or Red-necked Phalarope)

Icel.–Hebr., Spitzb., Scand.–Sakhalin. Alas.–Labr., W Greenl.

NUMENIUS (PHAEOPUS) PHAEOPUS L.

sbsp. *islandicus* Brehm	*f. typ.*	sbsp. *variegatus* Scop.	sbsp. *hudsonicus* Lath.
	(Whimbrel)		(Hudsonian Curlew)
Icel., Faeroes.	Scand.–W Sib.	E Sib.	Arct. N. Amer. W of Hudson Bay.

SQUATAROLA SQUATAROLA L.
(Black-bellied or Grey Plover)

Kanin Penins.–E Sib.   Alas.–Baffins L.

Charadriiformes, Lari

CATHARACTA (STERCORARIUS) SKUA Brünn., *f. typ.*
(Northern or Great Skua)

Arct. NE N. Amer. (perhaps not permanent), Greenl. (ditto), Icel.–Orkney.
Several other sbspp. in the southern hemisphere.

CHLIDONIAS NIGRA L.
(Black Tern)

f. typ.   sbsp. *surinamensis* Gmel.
Eur., W Sib.   Alas.–New York.

GELOCHELIDON NILOTICA Gmel.
(Gull-billed Tern)

f. typ.   sbsp. *vanrossemi* Bancr.   sbsp. *aranea* Wils.
Eur. (local)–S Mong.,   Calif.   Atl. coast of N. Amer.:
and farther south.   Virg.–Tex., W. Ind.
                             Other sbspp. farther south.

HYDROPROGNE CASPIA Pall. (*tschegrava* auctt.)
(Caspian Tern)

Eur.–Ussuri, Afr.   N. Amer. (local): Calif., C Can., Atl. coast.

LARUS ARGENTATUS Pont.
(Herring Gull)

f. typ.   sbsp. *omissus* Pleske   5 sbspp.   sbsp. *smithsonianus*
                                                             Coues
NW Eur.   N Fennoscand.   Russ.–Sib.   Alas.–Maine.

                   sbsp. *thayeri* W. S. Brks.   Several sbspp. farther south.
                   Arct. isl. of N. Amer.

LARUS CANUS L.

f. typ.   sbsp. *kamtschatschensis*   sbsp. *brachyrhynchus* Rich.
                             Bonap.
(Common Gull)   (Short-billed Gull)
Eur.: Faeroes–Kanin   Siber.–Kamch.   NW N. Amer.
Penins.

LARUS HYPERBOREUS Gunn.
(Glaucous Gull)

Jan Mayen, Spitzb., Kola Penins.–   Alas.–N Greenl.
Petchora, arct. Sib.

LARUS MARINUS L.
(Great Black-backed Gull)

Atl. coast of N. Amer. (Nova Scot.–   Greenl.–Icel.–NW Eur., E to Petchora.
Labr.).

RISSA TRIDACTYLA L.

(Kittiwake)

f. typ.
Arct. isl. of NE N. Amer., Greenl.,
Spitzb., Icel.–NW Eur., Sib. isl.

sbsp. *pollicaris* Ridgw.
NE Sib., Bering Sea, Aleut.

STERCORARIUS LONGICAUDUS Vieill.

(Long-tailed Jaeger or Skua)

Spitzb., Scand.–Sib. (incl. New Sib. Isl.).

Alas.–Labr.–Greenl.

STERCORARIUS PARASITICUS L.

(Parasitic Jaeger; Arctic Skua)

Icel., Spitzb., Scand.–Commander Isl.

Alas.–Baffins L., Greenl.

STERCORARIUS POMARINUS Temm.

(Pomarine Jaeger; Pomatorhine Skua)

Kanin Penins., N. Zeml., N Sib.

Alas.–Baffins L., W Greenl.

STERNA ALBIFRONS Pall. (*minuta* L.)

f. typ.	sbsp. *browni* Mearns	sbsp. *athalassos* Burl. & Low.	sbsp. *antillarum* Less.
(Little Tern)	(Brown's Tern)		(Least Tern)
Brit. Isl.–N Russ. –Tarbagatai.	Calif.–Mex.	Inland of U.S.A.	Atl. coast of N. Amer.: Mass.– Venez.

Other sbspp. farther south.

STERNA DOUGALLII Mont., *f. typ.*

(Roseate Tern)

Atl. coasts of Eur. and N. Amer., N to Denm. and Nova Scot., S to Azor. and Venez. Also farther south, in part other sbspp.

STERNA HIRUNDO L.

(Common Tern)

f. typ.
N. Amer. W to Gr. Slave
L., S to Venez.; Eur. N
to N Scand., W Sib.

sbsp. *minussensis* Sushk.
C Asia.

sbsp. *longipennis* Nordm.
NE Asia.

STERNA PARADISAEA Pont. (*macrura* Naum.)

(Arctic Tern)

Icel., N Eur. (S to Holl.), N Asia–
Commander Isl.

Alas.–Baffins L., Greenl.

THALASSEUS (STERNA) SANDVICENSIS Lath.

f. typ.
(Sandwich Tern)
W & S Eur.

sbsp. *acuflavidus* Cab.
(Cabot's Tern)
Atl. coast of N. Amer.: Virg.–W. Ind.

Charadriiformes, Alcae

ALCA TORDA L.
(Razor-billed Auk; Razorbill)

f. typ.
Nova Scot.–Labr., Greenl., Icel., NW Eur.–White Sea.

sbsp. *britannica* Ticeh.
Faeroes, Brit. Isl., W France.

CEPPHUS (URIA) GRYLLE L.[1]
(Black Guillemot)

sbsp. *atlantis* Salom.
Maine–Labr.; Icel., W Scand.–Brit. Isl.

f. typ.
Baltic Sea.

sbsp. *mandti* Mandt
NE Greenl., Spitzb., N. Zeml., arct. Sib.

sbsp. *ultimus* Salom.
Arct. isl. of N. Amer., N Labr., N Greenl.

sbsp. *arcticus* Brehm
Labr., Baffins L., Greenl.

FRATERCULA ARCTICA L.

f. typ.
(Atlantic Puffin)
Ungava–Maine; S Greenl., Icel., Bear Isl., N Norway.

sbsp. *naumanni* Nort.
(Large-billed Puffin)
N Greenl., Spitzb., N. Zeml., Kola Penins.

sbsp. *grabae* Brehm
(Southern Puffin)
Faeroes, Brit. Isl., W France, S Scand.

URIA AALGE Pont.

f. typ.

(Atlantic Murre; Northern Guillemot)
Nova Scot.–Labr.; Greenl., Icel.– Scotl., Heligol., Scand., N. Zeml.

4 sbspp.

NW Eur.

sbsp. *inornata* Salom.

NE Asia; Alas.– Wash.

sbsp. *californica* Bryant
(Californian Murre)

Calif.

---

[1] The sbspp. of *Cepphus grylle* seem to be little pronounced and have often been treated differently.

URIA LOMVIA L.

f. typ.
(Brünnich's Murre or Guillemot)
NE Can. (Huds. Str.–Gulf St. Lawr.);
Greenl., Icel., Spitzb., Fr. Jos. L.,
Kola Penins., N. Zeml., Taimyr.

sbsp. *arra* Pall.
(Pallas's Murre)
E arct. Sib. (S to Japan); Alaska.

Strigiformes

AEGOLIUS (CRYPTOGLAUX) FUNEREUS L.

f. typ.	sbsp. *sibiricus* But.	sbspp. *jakutorum* & *magnus*, But.	sbsp. *richardsoni* Bonap.
(Tengmalm's Owl)			(Richardson's Owl)
Eur.–Ob (Sib.).	C Sib.–Sakhalin.	NE Sib.	Alas.–Nova Scot.

ASIO FLAMMEUS Pont., *f. typ.*
(Short-eared Owl)

Brit. Isl.–Sakhalin.

Aleut., Alas.–Ungava, New Jersey, Greenl.
Several more southern sbspp. in the New World.

ASIO OTUS L.
(Long-eared Owl)

f. typ.
Brit. Isl.–Japan.

sbsp. *wilsonianus* Less.
Brit. Col.–Nfld.

NYCTEA SCANDIACA L. (*nyctea* L.) (fig. 49)
(Snowy Owl)

Scand.–Bering Str.

Alas.–Ungava, Greenl.

SURNIA ULULA L.
(Hawk Owl)

f. typ.	sbsp. *tianschanica* Smallb.	sbsp. *caparoch* P. L. S. Müll.
Scand.–Kamch.	C Asia.	Alas.–Ungava.

STRIX (SCOTIAPTEX) NEBULOSA J. R. Forst.
(Great Gray Owl)

sbsp. *lapponica* Thunb.
N Scand.–Sakhalin.

f. typ.
Alas.–N Ontario.

TYTO ALBA Scop.

(Barn Owl)

f. typ.	sbsp. *guttata* Brehm	sbsp. *pratincola* Bonap.
Brit. Isl., France, Mediterr.	S Swed., Germ.–W Russ., Balcan.	Transamerican in U.S.A., S to C Amer.

Numerous more southern sbspp.

Piciformes

PICOIDES TRIDACTYLUS L. (fig. 50)

(Three-toed Woodpecker)

f. typ.	sbsp. *crissoleucus* Reich.	sbsp. *albidior* Stejn.	sbsp. *sakhalinensis* But.
Scand.–Amur & Korea.	N Sib.	Kamch.	Sakhalin.

3 more southern sbspp. in Asia.

sbsp. *fasciatus* Baird	sbsp. *dorsalis* Baird	sbsp. *bacatus* Bangs
Alas.–Mont.	Rocky Mts.	Mackenzie–Nfld.

Passeriformes

ACANTHIS (CARDUELIS) FLAMMEA L. (*linaria* L.)[1]

(Common or Mealy Redpoll)

f. typ.	sbsp. *holboellii* Brehm	sbsp. *fuscescens* Coues	sbsp. *rostrata* Coues
Eur., Sib.; Alas. – Ungava.	N Sib.	NE Labr., Baffins L.	Greenl., ? Icel. ("*islandica* Htz.")

ACANTHIS (CARDUELIS) HORNEMANNII Holb.[1]

(Hornemann's Redpoll)

sbsp. *exilipes* Coues	*f. typ.*
N Scand.-N Japan. Alas.–Ungava.	Greenl., Icel., Jan Mayen, Spitzb.

ANTHUS SPINOLETTA L.

sbsp. *kleinschmidti* Hart.	sbsp. *littoralis* Brehm (Scandinavian Rock-Pipit)	*f. typ.* (Water-Pipit)	sbsp. *blakistoni* Swinh.
Faeroes.	Coasts of Scand.	C & S Eur.	C Asia.
sbsp. *japonicus* Temm. & Schleg.		sbsp. *rubescens* Tunst. (American Pipit)	
Lena R.–Kamch., Kuril.		Alas.–Nfld., S to New Mex., Greenl.	

[1] The specific distinction between *flammea* and *hornemanni*, as well as the validity of their "races", is still disputed.

BOMBYCILLA GARRULUS L.
(Waxwing)

f. typ.	sbsp. *pallidiceps* Reich. (doubtfully distinct)	sbsp. *cedrorum* Vieill.
Scand.–E Sib.	Alas.–Manit.	Brit. Col.–Nova Scot.

CALCARIUS LAPPONICUS L.

f. typ.	sbsp. *coloratus* Ridgw.	sbsp. *alascensis* Ridgw.	sbsp. *subcalcaratus* Brehm
(Lapland Longspur)		(Alaska Longspur)	
N Scand., N Asia; Mackenzie–N Queb.	NE Asia.	Alas.–Mackenzie.	Greenl.

CERTHIA FAMILIARIS L.
(Creeper or Tree-creeper)

sbsp. *britannica* Ridgw.	*f. typ.*	several sbspp.	sbsp. *orientalis* Dom.
Brit. Isl.	N Eur.	C Asia.	E Sib., Sakh., N Japan, Kuril.

7 sbspp.
N. & C. Amer.: Alas.–New York.

CORVUS CORAX L.
(Raven)

sbsp. *islandicus* Hntz.	*f. typ.*	several sbspp.	sbsp. *behringianus* Dyb.
Icel.	Eur.–W Sib.	N Asia.	Bering Str.

sbsp. *principalis* Rigdw.
Alas.–Ellesm. L., Greenl.; S to Georgia.

sbsp. *sinuatus* Wagl.
Brit. Col.–C. Amer; E to Mississippi.

EREMOPHILA (OTOCORIS) ALPESTRIS L.

sbsp. *flava* Gmel. (Shore-Lark)	several sbspp.	*f. typ.* (Horned Lark)
N Eur., N Asia E to Transbaik.	Alas.–Huds. Bay, S to Colombia.	Huds. Bay–Nfld., Greenl.(?)

Many sbspp. in southern mts. of Palaearctic region.

HIRUNDO (CHELIDON) RUSTICA L.

f. typ.	sbsp. *gutturalis* Scop.	sbsp. *tytleri* Jerd.	sbsp. *erythrogaster* Bodd.
(European Swallow)			(Barn Swallow)
Eur.–Yenisei, N Afr.	Transbaik.–Sakhal.; Japan.	NE Sib., Kamch.	Alas.–Queb., S to Mex.

LANIUS EXCUBITOR L.

f. typ.	sbsp. *mollis* Ev.	sbsp. *invictus* Grinn.	sbsp. *borealis* Vieill.
(Great Grey Shrike)		(Northwestern Shrike)	(Northern Shrike)
Eur.–R. Ob.	Yenisei–Kamch.	Alas.–Sask.	Huds. Bay–Queb.

Numerous southern Palaearctic sbspp.

LOXIA CURVIROSTRA L.[1]
(Crossbill)

f. typ.	sbsp. *japonica* Ridgw.	sbsp. *pusilla* Glog.	sbsp. *percna* Bent
Eur.–E Sib.	Ussuri, Kuril., N Japan.	Alas.–Queb.	Nova Scot., Nfld.

Many southern sbspp. in both continents.

LOXIA LEUCOPTERA Gmel.

sbsp. *bifasciata* Brehm	*f. typ.*
(Two-barred Crossbill)	(White-winged Crossbill)
N Eur.–Kamch.	Alas.–Nova Scot.

LUSCINIA (CYANOSYLVIA) SUECICA L.
(Red-spotted Bluethroat)

f. typ.	sbsp. *robusta* But.
Scand.–Yenisei.	E Sib.; W Alas.

Several southern Palaearctic sbspp.

MOTACILLA FLAVA L.

f. typ.	sbsp. *thunbergi* Billb.	Several sbspp.	sbsp. *simillima* Hart.
(Blue-headed Wagtail)	(Grey-headed W.)		
Eur., N to C Scand.	Scand.–R. Ob.	N Asia.	Kamch.
sbsp. *alascensis* Ridgw.		Several southern Palaearctic sbspp.	
(Yellow Wagtail)			
NE Sib.; W Alas.			

OENANTHE (SAXICOLA) OENANTHE L.
(Wheatear)

sbsp. *leucorrhoa* Gmel.	sbsp. *schiöleri* Salom.	*f. typ.*
NE N. Amer. S to N Queb., W Greenl.	E Greenl., Icel., Faeroes.	Eur.–Bering Str.; Alas.

Several southern Palaearctic sbspp.

---

[1] Dr. W. L. Brown, Harvard, informs me that the arrangement of N. American sbspp. of *Loxia curvirostra* is in need of revision.

PARUS (PENTHESTES) ATRICAPILLUS L.

sbsp. *colletti* Stejn.	sbsp. *borealis* Sel.	Several sbspp.	sbsp. *kamtschat-kensis* Bonap.
	(Northern Willow-Tit)		
W Norway.	Scand.–N Russia.	N & C Asia.	Kamch.
sbsp. *turneri* Ridgw.	sbsp. *septentrionalis* Harr.	sbsp. *occidentalis* Baird	f. typ.
(Yukon Chickadee) N Alas.	(Long-tailed Ch.) Alas.–Manit., S to N. Mex.	(Oregon Ch.) Brit. Col.–Calif.	(Black-capped Ch.) Ont.–N. Engl.

sbsp. *bartletti* Aldr. & Nutt.   Many sbspp. farther south.
Nfld.

PARUS (PENTHESTES) CINCTUS Bodd.

f. typ.	sbsp. *obtectus* Cab.	sbsp. *alaskensis* Pražák[1]
		(Alaska Chickadee)
N Scand.–W Sib.	Yenisei–Kamch.	NE Sib.(?); Alas., Mackenzie.

PHYLLOSCOPUS (ACANTHOPNEUSTE) BOREALIS Blas.

f. typ.	sbsp. *xanthodryas* Swinh.	sbsp. *examinandus* Stres.	sbsp. *kennicotti* Baird
(Eversmann's Warbler)			(Willow Warbler)
N Scand.–E Sib.	N Japan, Kuril.	Kamch., Kuril.	W Alas.

PICA PICA L.
(Magpie)

f. typ.	sbsp. *hemileucoptera* Stegm.	sbsp. *leucoptera* Gould	sbsp. *kamtschatica* Stejn.
W Eur.–Ural.	W Sib.–Irkutsk.	E Sib.	Kamch.

sbsp. *hudsonia* Sab.   sbsp. *nuttalli* Aud.
Alas.–Manit. (casual farther E), S to   Calif.
New Mex.

PINICOLA ENUCLEATOR L.
(Pine-Grosbeak)

f. typ.	sbsp. *pacata* Bangs.	sbsp. *kamtschat-kensis* Dyb.	6–7 sbspp.
(incl. sbsp. *stschur* Port.)			
Scand.–W Sib.	E Sib.	Kamch., Sakhalin.	Transamerican: Alas.–Nfld., S to New Mex.

---

[1] *P. hudsonicus* Forst., with its races, is sometimes referred to *cinctus*.

PLECTROPHENAX (PASSERINA) NIVALIS L.
(Snow Bunting)

sbsp. *insulae* Salom. Icel., Faeroes.	*f. typ.* N Eur., N Asia; Alas.–N Queb.	sbsp. *townsendi* Ridgw. Both sides of Bering Str.	sbsp. *subnivalis* Brehm Greenl.

RIPARIA RIPARIA L.[1]
(Bank Swallow; Sand-Martin)

f. typ. Eur.–Sib. (E limit?); Alas.–Queb., S to Tex.	sbsp. *ijimae* Lönnb. Kamch.–Japan; Alas.(?).	sbsp. *diluta* Sharpe & Wyatt NE Sib.–India.

SITTA CANADENSIS L.
(Red-breasted Nuthatch)

f. typ. Alas.–Nfld., S to N. Mex.	sbsp. *corea* Og.–Grant Korea.	3 sbspp. China.	sbsp. *krüperi* Pelz. Cauc.–As. Minor.

sbsp. *whiteheadi* Sharpe
Corsica.

TROGLODYTES (NANNUS) TROGLODYTES L.
(Wren)

sbsp. *islandicus* Hart. Icel.	sbsp. *borealis* Fisch. Faeroes.	*f. typ.* (and related forms) Eur.–Ural.	Several sbspp. N Asia, E to Kamch., Japan, Kuril.
Several sbspp. Aleut. Isl., &c.	sbsp. *pacificus* Baird Alas.–Alberta, S to Color.	sbsp. *hiemalis* Vieill. Alberta–Nfld.	

Reptiles and Amphibians

No species in common.

Pisces—Fishes

Main literature: Jordan, Evermann & Clark (1930), Berg (1933, 1948–49), Wynne-Edwards (1952).

---

[1] The differentiation of sbspp. in *R. riparia* is uncertain.

? COTTUS GOBIO L.[1]
(Bullhead)

f. typ.	sbsp. *sibiricus* Kessl.	sbsp. *cognatus* Rich.	sbsp. *ricei* Nels.
Eur., E to Petchora.	Sib.: Ob–Lena.	Alas.–Marit. Prov. of Canada.	SE Alas.–Ontario.

ESOX LUCIUS L. (*estor* LeS.)
(Pike)

Irel. & Scand.–Anadyr (extreme NE Sib.), S to Italy, Asia Minor, W Turcestan.　　　Alas.–Labr., S to Ohio & New York.

LOTA LOTA L.
(Burbot)

f. typ.	sbsp. *leptura* Hbs. & Schtz.	sbsp. *maculosa* LeS.
Palaearct., E to Lena R.	NE Sib. (Kolyma & Anadyr); NW N. Amer. (Alas. & Mackenzie R.).	Rest of N. Amer.

Insecta—Insects

The insect fauna, when properly worked out in a remote future, will no doubt provide the best foundation for a comparative analysis of the Europe—North-America relations. At the present time only a small fraction of this, the largest class in the animal kingdom, has been the subject of modern revisions and is thus suitable for our purpose. It was difficult to find, among other things, reliable data on the distribution of most species in northern Asia, a matter of great significance for classifying the geographical type and the history of the species.

The list of insects here given could possibly have been extended to include other groups but the selection has been made in such a way that the main biological types, above all the types of dispersal, should be represented, which was considered more important than taxonomic completeness.

---

[1] Berg (1933, p. 169; 1949, p. 1148) regards *sibiricus* as distinct from *gobio*. Wynne-Edwards (1952, p. 22) says that *cognatus* is "scarcely distinguishable from *C. gobio*" but regards *ricei* as the North American representative of *sibiricus*. The taxonomic difficulties in this group are also pointed out by Jordan, Evermann & Clark (1930).

Coleoptera—Beetles

The standard sources have been Junk & Schenkling, Catalogus (1928–33), and Leng, Catalogue (1920), with five supplements (1927–48). Special references are given below. It is very much to be regretted that no catalogue of the Coleoptera of Siberia has appeared after Heyden (1880–98).

Carabidae—Ground-Beetles

A review of the species common to Europe and North America has already been published (Lindroth, 1954). Only three species are here added: *Bradycellus harpalinus* (Hatch, 1955), *Harpalobrachys leiroides* (previously overlooked), and *Somotrichus elevatus* F. (Hatch, 1953, p. 153).

ACUPALPUS MERIDIANUS L.

Brit. Isl., Eur.–Iran, Cauc., S to   † Wash., Oreg. (Hatch, 1953).
Mediterr.

AGONUM BOGEMANNI Gyll.

N Eur., mts. of C Eur., Corsica, Sib.   Alas.–Labr., Nfld., S to Color.

AGONUM CONSIMILE Gyll.

Scand.–Ural; Kamch.   Alas.–Nova Scot., Labr., Nfld.

AGONUM EXARATUM Mnh. (*aldanicum* Popp.)

Kola and Kanin Penins., E Sib.   Alas., Mackenzie Delta.

AGONUM MANNERHEIMI Dej.

f. typ.   (Transitional)   sbsp. *stygicum* Lec.
Scand., N Russ., W Sib.   E Sib.   Alas.–Labr., Nfld., S to
                                                          New York.

AGONUM MÜLLERI Hbst.

Brit. Isl., Eur., Cauc., W Sib.   † New Engl., E Can., Nfld.; Oreg., Wash.,
                                          Brit. Col.

AGONUM QUADRIPUNCTATUM DeG.

Brit. Isl., Eur.–Kamch.   Alas.–Labr., Nfld.
India, Philipp.

AGONUM RUFICORNE Gze.

Brit. Isl., Eur., Mediterr., Macaron.   † Maine, N. Brunsw., Nova Scot., Nfld.

AGONUM THOREYI Dej.

Brit. Isl., Eur.–E Sib.: Amur.   Alas.–Nova Scot., Nfld., S to Calif.

AMARA AENEA DeG.

Brit. Isl., Eur., N Afr., Hither & C   † NE U.S.A., E Can., Nfld.
Asia, W Sib.

AMARA ALPINA Payk. (fig. 40)

f. typ.	(Transitional)	sbsp. *brunnipennis* Dej.
Scotl., Scand.–W Sib.	E Sib.	Alas.–Labr., Nfld., Baffins L., S to Color., mts. of New Engl.

AMARA ANTHOBIA Villa

Brit. Isl., W, C & S Eur., Asia Minor,   † Wash., Oreg. (Hatch, 1953).
Cauc.

AMARA APRICARIA Payk.

Brit. Isl., (1 loc.), Eur.– Sib.: Amur.   (†) NE U.S.A., Can.: Nfld., Labr.–E
Brit. Col.

AMARA AULICA Panz.

Brit. Isl., Eur., Cauc., W Sib., W.   † Nova Scot. (Cape Bret. Isl.), Nfld.
Turcestan.

AMARA BIFRONS Gyll.

Brit. Isl., Eur., Cauc., W. Turcestan.   † Nova Scot., Nfld.

AMARA ERRATICA Dft.

Eur. (boreo-alpine), Cauc., Sib. E to   Alas.–Labr., Nfld., S to Color.
Kamch.

AMARA FAMILIARIS Dft.

Brit. Isl., Eur., Cauc., W Sib., N Afr.   † NE U.S.A., E Can.–Nfld.; Oreg.–
Brit. Col.

AMARA FULVA DeG.

Brit. Isl., Eur., Asia Minor, Cauc., W   † E Can., Nfld.
Sib.

AMARA HYPERBOREA Dej.

N Finl.–E Sib.   Alas.–Labr., Nfld., S to Lake Sup.

AMARA INTERSTITIALIS Dej.

Scand.–Kamch., Cauc.   Alas., Yukon Terr.

AMARA LUNICOLLIS Schiø.

Brit. Isl., Eur.–Kamch., S to Iran.   (†) NE U.S.A., E Can.–Nfld. (probably
                                        introduced); C & N Can. (probably native)

AMARA QUENSELI Schnh. (*remotestriata* Dej.)

Brit. Isl., Eur. (boreo-alpine), Cauc.,   Alas.–Labr., Nfld., S to N. Mex.
Sib. E to Kamch.

AMARA TORRIDA Ill. (*cylindrica* Lec., &c.)

N Scand.–Kamch.   Alas.–Labr., Nfld., S to Color.

ANISODACTYLUS BINOTATUS F.

Brit. Isl., Eur.–W Sib., N Afr.   † Oreg., Wash., Brit. Col. (Hatch, 1953).

ASAPHIDION FLAVIPES L.

Brit. Isl., Eur., Cauc., W Sib., N Afr.   † New York.

BEMBIDION BRUXELLENSE Wesm. (*rupestre* auctt.)

Brit. Isl., Eur.–Sib.: Lena R.   † E Can., Nfld.

BEMBIDION CRENULATUM F. Sahlb.

sbsp. *ponojense* J. Sahlb.   *f. typ.*   sbsp. *farrarae* Hatch
Kola Peninsula.   E Sib.   Oreg., Wash.

BEMBIDION DAURICUM Mtsch.

N Scand., Sib. E to Ochotsk.   Alas., N. W. Terr., N Manit.

BEMBIDION GRAPEI Gyll.

Icel., N Eur.–Kamch. (figs. 45–47)   Alas.–Labr., Nfld., S to Sierra Nevada;
                                        Greenl.

BEMBIDION HASTI C. R. Sahlb.

Scand.–N. Zeml., Sib. E at least to   Brit. Col. & N. W. Terr.–N Labr.
Baikal.

BEMBIDION HYPERBORAEORUM Munst.

N Scand., Kanin Penins., Sib. (Yenisei   Alas., N. W. Terr.
& Lena).

BEMBIDION LAMPROS Hbst.

Brit. Isl., Eur., Cauc., Sib.: E to R.   † Brit. Col.; Nfld.
Lena.

BEMBIDION LAPPONICUM Zett. (*bryanti* Carr)

f. typ.   sbsp. *latiusculum* Mtsch.   sbsp.(?)
N Scand., N Russ., Sib.   E Sib., Kamch.   Alas., N. W. Terr.
E at least to Yenisei.

BEMBIDION MCKINLEYI Fall (*scandicum* Lth.)

N Scand.   Alas.: Mt. McKinley.

BEMBIDION OBSCURELLUM Mtsch. (*fuscicrus* Mtsch.)

Denm.: Jutland; NE Eur., N & C Asia,   NW N. Amer., S to N. Mex.
E to Kamch.

BEMBIDION PETROSUM Gebl.

sbsp. *siebkei* J. Müll.   *f. typ.*   sbsp.(?)
Scand., W. Sib.   C Sib.   Alas.–Labr., Nfld., S to
                                                   N. Mex.

BEMBIDION PROPERANS Steph.

Brit. Isl., Eur., Cauc., Sib. E to Amur.   † Nova Scot.

BEMBIDION QUADRIMACULATUM L.

f. typ.   sbsp. *oppositum* Say
Brit. Isl., Eur., Cauc., Sib. E to   Brit. Col.–Nova Scot., Nfld., S to Tex.
Ussuri.   & N. Mex.

BEMBIDION STEPHENSI Crotch

Brit. Isl., Eur., E to Poland & Slovakia.   † Mass., E Can., Nfld.

BEMBIDION TETRACOLUM Say (*ustulatum* auctt.)

Brit. Isl., Eur., Cauc., Hither Asia, W   † Oreg.–Brit. Col.; E U.S.A., E Can.,
Sib., N Afr.   Nfld. (fig. 12)

BEMBIDION TRANSPARENS Gebl.

N & E Eur., Sib. E at least to R. Lena.   Alas.–Labr., Nfld., S to Indiana. (fig. 58)

BEMBIDION YUKONUM Fall (*grapeioides* Munst.)

N Scand., Sib.: Jakutsk.   Alas., Yukon Terr., N. W. Terr.

BLETHISA ESCHSCHOLTZI Fisch. (fig. 56)

SE Russ., SW Sib.   Texas.

BLETHISA MULTIPUNCTATA L. (fig. 56)

f. typ.   sbsp. *aurata* Fisch.
Brit. Isl., Eur.–W & C Sib.   E Sib.; Brit. Col. & Yukon Terr.–Labr.,
                                                     Nfld.

BRADYCELLUS HARPALINUS Serv.

Brit. Isl., Eur. E to C Russ., Cauc., N   † Vancouver, B. C. (Hatch, 1955).
Afr., Madeira.

CALATHUS FUSCIPES Gze.

Brit. Isl., Eur., W Asia E to Iran,   † Vancouver, B. C.
Cauc., N Afr.

CALATHUS MICROPTERUS Dft.

f. typ.   sbsp. *ingratus* Dej.
Brit. Isl., Eur., Cauc., W, C & (?) E Sib. Alas.–Labr., Nfld., S to Color.

CARABUS AURATUS L.

Brit. Isl. (not established), Europe   † New Engl.: Mass., Vermont, Maine.
(excl. the N & E).

CARABUS CANCELLATUS Ill.

Brit. Isl. (not established), Eur., Sib.   † Wisc., N. Carol. (doubtfully established).
E to Lena R. (Numerous sbspp.)

CARABUS GRANULATUS L. (fig. 8)

sbsp. *hibernicus* Lth.   *f. typ.*
Brit. Isl. (espec. Ireland).   Brit. Isl., N, W & C Eur. E to Ural.
† Nova Scot., N. Brunsw.   † New Engl., Wash., Brit. Col., occas. in
                                                     E Can. and N. W. Terr.
            Other sbspp. in S Eur. & Asia, E to Amur, Sakhalin, & Japan.

CARABUS NEMORALIS Müll. (fig. 7)

Brit. Isl., Eur., E to C Russ.   † Oreg.–Brit. Col.; NE U.S.A., E to Wisc.,
                                                     E Can., Nfld.

CARABUS TRUNCATICOLLIS Eschz.

sbsp. *polaris* Popp.
NE Russ. (Petchora), N. Zeml., N Sib.
E to Anadyr.

f. typ.
Alas. W to Bering Str., E to Mackenzie
Delta.

CLIVINA COLLARIS Hbst.

Brit. Isl., Eur., Cauc., W Asia E to W
Turcestan.

† Wash.; Mass., E Can.

CLIVINA FOSSOR L.

Brit. Isl., Eur.–Kamch.

† Wash.; E Can., Nfld. (fig. 13)

DIACHILA ARCTICA Gyll.

f. typ.
N Eur.,? NW Asia.

sbsp. *amoena* Fald.
S & E Sib.; Alas., NW Can., Labr.

DIACHILA POLITA Fald.

NE Eur.–Kamch., S to Baikal region.
Alas., N. W. Terr. (Mackenzie Delta).

DYSCHIRIUS HELLÉNI J. Müll.

Scand., Sib.: Yenisei.
Alas., N Manit., Labr.

DYSCHIRIUS POLITUS Dej.

Brit. Isl., Eur., Iran, Sib. E to
R. Lena.

New York, New Hampsh., Nfld. (probably overlooked).

ELAPHRUS LAPPONICUS Gyll.

Brit. Isl., Scand., Sib. E to Kamch.
Alas.–Labr.

ELAPHRUS RIPARIUS L.

Brit. Isl., Eur., N & C Asia E to
Kamch.

Alas.–Labr., Nfld., S to Calif.

HARPALOBRACHYS LEIROIDES Mtsch.

NE Russ., Sib. E to Ussuri.
N. W. Terr. (Fort Smith).

HARPALUS AFFINIS Schrk. (*aeneus* F.)

Brit. Isl., Eur., N Asia, E at least to R.
Lena and Transbaik.

† Wash., Brit. Col.; E U.S.A. (S. to Flor.,
W to Kansas), E Can.–Labr., Nfld.

HARPALUS FULIGINOSUS Dft.

Eur. (*not* Brit. Isl.), N Asia–Kamch.,
Japan.

Alas.–Labr., Nfld., S to Mich.

HARPALUS NIGRITARSIS C. R. Sahlb.

f. typ.   sbsp. *proximus* Lec.
N Fennoscand., Sib. (?).   Alas.–Labr., Nfld., S to N. Hampsh.

HARPALUS RUFIPES DeG. (*pubescens* O. F. Müll.)

Brit. Isl., Eur., N Afr., N Asia E at   † E Can., Nfld.
least to R. Lena, Japan.

LICINUS PUNCTATULUS F. (*silphoides* F.)[1]

S Engl., W & S Eur. N to W Germ.,   † Mass., Maine (temporarily established).
N. Afr., Hither Asia.

MISCODERA ARCTICA Payk.

f. typ.   sbsp. *americana* Mnh.
                                                 (little pronounced)
Brit. Isl., N & C Eur., Sib. E at least   Alas.–Labr., Nfld., S to New Engl.
to R. Lena.

NEBRIA GYLLENHALI Schnh. (*rufescens* Ström)

f. typ.   sbsp. *besseri* Fisch.   sbsp. *castanipes* Kby.
                             (transitional)
Greenl., Icel., Brit. Isl., E Sib.   Alas.–Labr., Nfld., S to New
Eur. (boreo-alpine), N   Engl.
Asia (E limit uncertain).

NEBRIA NIVALIS Payk.

f. typ.   sbsp. *femorata* Mtsch.   sbsp. *bifaria* Mnh.
                             (transitional)
Scotl., Scand., W Sib., E   E Sib.   Kamch., Alas.–Baffins L.,
at least to R. Ob.   Queb. (Gaspé), Maine
                                                           (Mt. Katahdin), Nfld.

NOMIUS PYGMAEUS Dej.

S Eur. N to Paris, N Afr., W Asia.   Brit. Col.–Lake Sup., S to Georgia &
                                                 Calif.

NOTIOPHILUS AQUATICUS L.

Icel., Brit. Isl., Eur., N Asia E to   Alas.–Labr., Nfld., S to New Mex.
Kamch.

---

[1] *L. silphoides* Rossi 1790 is a different species (*vide* Jeannel, 1942, p. 994–996) but the American specimens belong to *silphoides* Fabricius 1792, the right name of which is *punctatulus* Fabricius 1792.

NOTIOPHILUS BIGUTTATUS F.

Icel., Brit. Isl., Eur. E to Ural., Cauc.   † Nfld. (fig. 14)

PATROBUS SEPTENTRIONIS Dej.

f. typ.

Greenl., Icel., Brit. Isl., Eur. (boreo-alpine), Sib. E to Amur & Kamch.

sbsp. *labradorinus* Csy. (validity uncertain)

Alas.–Labr. (in part transitional), Nfld., S to Color.

In Eurasia two more southern sbspp.

PELOPHILA BOREALIS Payk.

f. typ.

Brit. Isl., N Eur., Sib. E at least to R Lena.

sbsp. *eschscholtzi* Mnh. (transitional)

Kamch., Alas.

sbsp. *ulkei* Horn

NW Can.–Labr., Nfld.

PERIGONA NIGRICEPS Dej.

Cosmopolitan.

† Eur. (rapidly dispersing).   † U.S.A. (widely distributed).

PLOCHIONUS PALLENS F.

Cosmopolitan

† W & S Eur.   † U.S.A. (both coasts).

PRISTONYCHUS (LAEMOSTHENES) COMPLANATUS Dej.

Almost cosmopolitan.

† Brit. Isl., W & S Eur.   Native of N. Africa.   †Pacific coast (Calif.–Brit. Col.)

PRISTONYCHUS TERRICOLA Hbst.

Icel., Brit. Isl., Eur., Cauc.   † E Can., Nfld.

PTEROSTICHUS ADSTRICTUS Eschz.

Icel., Brit. Isl., N Eur.–Kamch.   Alas.–Labr., Nfld., S to Ariz.

PTEROSTICHUS (CRYOBIUS) BREVICORNIS Kby.
(*fastidiosus* Mnh., *mandibularis* auctt.)

Kola Penins., N Russ.–Kamch.   Alas.–Labr., Nfld.; mts. of New Engl.[1]

PTEROSTICHUS MELANARIUS Ill. (*vulgaris* auctt.)

Brit. Isl., Eur., Cauc., Sib. E to Amur.   † Oreg.–Brit. Col.; E Can., Nfld.

---

[1] The form from E of Hudson Bay is probably subspecifically distinct.

PTEROSTICHIUS STRENUUS Panz.

Brit. Isl., Eur., Cauc., Sib. E to Amur.   † Nfld.

PTEROSTICHUS VERMICULOSUS Mén. (*innuitorum* Bwn.)

NE Russ. (Petchora), Sib. E at least   N. W. Terr.
to R. Lena.

SOMOTRICHUS ELEVATUS F.

                        Cosmopolitan.
† W Eur.   † Wash.

STOMIS PUMICATUS Panz.

Brit. Isl., Eur. E to Ural, Cauc., Asia   † Queb.
Minor.

TACHYS PARVULUS Dej.

S Engl., C & S Eur.   † Wash.

TACHYTA NANA Gyll.

  f. typ.   sbsp. *inornata* Say
Eur. (*not* Brit. Isl.), N Afr., Hither   Wash.–New York, S to Flor.
Asia, Sib. E to Amur.

TRECHUS DISCUS F.

Brit. Isl., Eur., Asia E to Japan.   † E Can.

TRECHUS OBTUSUS Er.

Icel., Brit. Isl., W, C & S Eur., N Afr.   † Oreg., Wash.

TRECHUS RUBENS F.

Icel., Brit. Isl., N, W & C Eur., Sib.   † E Can., Nfld.
E to Lena R.

TRICHOCELLUS COGNATUS Gyll.

Icel., Brit. Isl., N, W & C Eur., Sib.   Alas.–Labr., Nfld., Greenl.
E at least to Lena R.

Elateridae—Click-Beetles

Dr. E. C. Becker, Department of Agriculture, Ottawa, kindly gave information
on this family as a supplement to the records in Leng's Catalogue. For Asia,
besides Heyden (1880–98), Jacobson (1905–15) has been used.

AGRIOTES LINEATUS L.

Brit. Isl., Eur., N Afr., W & NW Asia.
† N. Zeal.

† Brit. Col.; Nova Scot., Nfld.

† C & S Amer.

AGRIOTES OBSCURUS L.

Brit. Isl., Eur., N Asia E to Baikal & Amur.

† Brit. Col.; Nova Scot., Nfld.

AGRIOTES SPUTATOR L.

Brit. Isl., Eur., N Afr., W, NW & C Asia.

† N. Brunsw., Nova Scot.

CORYMBITES (CTENICERA) CRUCIATUS L.

f. typ.	sbsp. *festivus* Lec.	sbsp. *pulcher* Lec.
Eur. (*not* Brit. Isl.), N Asia.	Brit. Col.–Manit.	Ontar.–Nova Scot.

CORYMBITES (CTENICERA) SJAELANDICUS O. F. Müll.

Brit. Isl., N & C Eur., N Asia S to Amur, Korea.

(†) NE U.S.A., W to Mich., N Ontar.–Gaspé.

EANUS (CORYMBITES) COSTALIS Payk.

f. typ.
N Eur., N Asia E to Amur.

sbsp. *decoratus* Mnh.[1]
N. W. Terr.–Labr., N Nfld., New Hampsh.

ELATER (AMPEDUS) NIGRINUS Hbst.

Brit. Isl., Eur., N Asia E to Amur.

Alas.–Labr., S to NE U.S.A.

HARMINIUS (ATHOUS) UNDULATUS DeG.

f. typ.
Brit. Isl., N & C Eur., N Asia E to Amur & Kamch.

sbsp.?
Queb., Ont. (certainly wider distr.)

HYPNOIDUS (HYPOLITHUS) HYPERBOREUS Gyll.

Eur. (boreo-alpine), N Asia E to Kamch.

Alas., NW Can.

HYPNOIDUS (HYPOLITHUS) RIVULARIUS Gyll.

Eur. (boreo-alpine), Altai, Sib. E at least to Lena R.

Alas.–Labr., Nfld.; N. Hampsh.

---

[1] Fall (1934, p. 35) was unable to make a definite separation between *decoratus* and the European *costalis;* Brown (1936, p. 247) regards them as different species.

MELANOTUS CASTANIPES Payk.

Brit. Isl., Eur., Cauc., W & N Asia   (†) NE U.S.A. W to Mich. & Indiana;
E to Amur.   E Canada, Nfld.

SERICUS BRUNNEUS L. (*incongruus* Lec.)

Brit. Isl., Eur., Sib. E to Amur.   B. C.–E Can., S Labr., Nfld.[1]

Coccinellidae—Ladybirds

For the Palaearctic fauna, Dobrzhanskij (1926) and Mader (1926–37) have been
consulted. Valuable supplementary informations have been received from Dr. E.
A. Chapin, West Medway, Mass.

ADALIA BIPUNCTATA L.

Brit. Isl., Eur., N Afr., Asia E to   † Wash., Idaho (Hatch, 1953); NE
Baikal and N China.   U.S.A., E Can., Nfld.

ADALIA FRIGIDA Schn.

N Eur., Sib. E to Amur & Kamch.   Brit. Col., Wash.–Maine, Nfld., S to
                                              Ariz.

ANATIS OCELLATA L.

Brit. Isl., Eur., N Asia E to Amur,   † Wash.; NE U.S.A. W to Lake Sup.,
Kamch. & Japan.   Nfld.

ANISOCALVIA 14-GUTTATA L.

f. typ.   sbsp. *12-maculata* Gebl.[2]
Brit. Isl., Eur.–Sakhalin, Kuril.; Brit.   E Sib.; N. Amer.: Wash.–Nfld.
Col.–Maine, Nfld.

ANISOSTICTA STRIGATA Thunb.

f. typ.   sbsp. *bitriangularis* Say[3]
N & C Eur., Sib. E at least to Baikal.   Wash., Oreg.–Nova Scot., S Labr.

BULAEA LICHATSCHOVI Humm.

Hung., S Russ., N Afr. Hither Asia,   † New Jersey (probably accidental).
S & W Sib., Tien-shan.

---

[1] The *Sericus* of N. America may be subspecifically distinct.
[2] By Chapin (*in litt.*) regarded as a colour aberration only.
[3] Often regarded as distinct species.

COCCINELLA HIEROGLYPHICA L.

f. typ.	sbsp. *mannerheimi* Muls.	sbsp. *humboldtiensis* Nun.	sbsp. *tricuspis* Kby.
Brit. Isl., Eur., W Sib.	E Sib.–Amur, Sakhalin.	Wash., N Calif.	C Can.–Mich.

COCCINELLA TRIFASCIATA L.

Eur. (boreo-alpine), N & C Asia E to Pacific coast.

Wash., Oreg.–Nova Scot., Nfld.

COCCINELLA 11-PUNCTATA L.

f. typ.	sbsp. *ainu* Lew.	(?) sbsp. *menetriesi* Muls.
Icel., Brit. Isl., Eur.–C Asia, N Afr. † NE U.S.A., E Can., Nfld.	Japan.	Alas.–N Calif.

HIPPODAMIA 13-PUNCTATA L.

f. typ.	sbsp. *tibialis* Say.
Brit. Isl., Eur., Asia (incl. Sib.) E to Amur, Kamch. & China.	Alas.–Maine, S Labr., Nfld., S to Calif.

NEOMYSIA OBLONGOGUTTATA L.

f. typ.	4 sbspp.
Brit. Isl., Eur., Asia E to Amur; (?) Oreg.	(sbsp. *pullata* Say, &c.) Oreg.–Labr.

STETHORUS (SCYMNUS) PUNCTILLUM Wse.

Brit. Isl., Eur., Asia E to Japan.	† Mass., Ontar.

Scarabaeidae—Dung-Beetles

The main source was Schmidt (1922). Valuable information was also obtained from Mr. B.-O. Landin of the Zool. Inst., Lund.

AEGIALIA ARENARIA F.

Brit. Isl, Baltic coasts, W & C Eur.	† Massach. (Darlington, 1927).

AEGIALIA RUFA F.

Brit. Isl., Baltic coast, W & C Eur.	† Miquelon (S of Nfld.).

APHODIUS BOREALIS Gyll.

Brit. Isl., N & C Eur., Sib. (*i.a.*   Nfld. (probably indigenous in N. Amer.
Baikal).   and overlooked).

APHODIUS DEPRESSUS Kug.

Brit. Isl., N & C Eur., N & C Asia E   † New York.
to Amur.

APHODIUS DISTINCTUS O. F. Müll. (*inquinatus* Hbst.)

Brit. Isl., Eur., N Asia (at least W Sib.).   † Wash.; Atl. States of U.S.A.

APHODIUS ERRATICUS L.

Brit. Isl., Eur., N Afr., N & C Asia E   † NE U.S.A., E Can., Nov. Scot.
at least to Baikal.

APHODIUS FASCIATUS Ol. (*putridus* Hbst., *foetidus* F. nec Hbst., *tenellus* Say)

Brit. Isl., Eur. (widely), Cauc., Sib.   † Wash.; E U.S.A. S to New Mex. &
E to Kamch.   Color., N to S Labr.

APHODIUS FIMETARIUS L.

Brit. Isl., Eur., N Afr., N & C Asia to   † Brit. Col., N.W. Terr., Wash.; Tex.–
E Sib.   Nov. Scot., Nfld.

APHODIUS FOSSOR L.

Brit. Isl., Eur., N Afr., Asia to E Sib.   † Brit. Col.; N. Carol.–Nov. Scot. & S
                                            Labr., W to Mich. & Ont., Nfld.

APHODIUS GRANARIUS L.
Almost cosmopolitan.

Brit. Isl., Eur. (generally), N & C Asia   † N. Amer. (widely distr.), N to Wash.
to E Sib.   & Nov. Scot.

APHODIUS HAEMORRHOIDALIS L.

Brit. Isl., Eur., Sib., N & C Asia.   † NE U.S.A., E Can.–Nov. Scot., Nfld.

APHODIUS LIVIDUS Ol.
Almost cosmopolitan.

Brit. Isl., Eur. (except the North), N &   † S U.S.A., N to Indiana & Calif.
C Asia.   W. Ind.

APHODIUS PRODROMUS Brahm

Brit. Isl., Eur., N & C Asia.   † E U.S.A., S to Kent., E Can.

APHODIUS RECTUS Mtsch.

(†) Greece.   Native of E Asia.   † Wash.

APHODIUS RUFIPES L.

Almost cosmopolitan.

Brit. Isl., Eur. (generally), Asia E to   † E U.S.A.
Amur, China.

APHODIUS SCROFA F.

Brit. Isl., Eur., W Asia.   † Maine, Queb., N. Brunsw.

APHODIUS SUBTERRANEUS L.

Brit. Isl., Eur., W & C Asia E at least   † NE U.S.A., E Can.–Nov. Scot.
to SW Mongol.

GEOTRUPES STERCORARIUS L.

Brit. Isl., Eur., N Asia to E Sib. &   † N. Brunsw., Pr. Edw. Isl.
Japan.

GEOTRUPES STERCOROSUS Scriba (*sylvaticus* Panz.)

Brit. Isl., Eur., W Asia.   † Rhode Isl. (1 ex.).

HYBOSORUS ILLIGERI Rche.

S Eur., Afr., W Asia.   † S U.S.A.

ONTHOPHAGUS NUCHICORNIS L.

Brit. Isl., Eur., W Asia.   † Brit. Col.; NE U.S.A., E Can.–Nov.
                                   Scot., Nfld.

OXYOMUS SILVESTRIS Scop.

Brit. Isl., Eur., W Asia.   † Wash.; NE U.S.A., Nov. Scot. (Hatch,
                                   1946).

PLEUROPHORUS CAESUS Crtz.

Almost cosmopolitan.

Brit. Isl., Eur., N Afr., Asia Minor,   † Wash., Oreg.; NE U.S.A., W to
W. Turcest.   Indiana.

RHYSSEMUS GERMANUS L. (*puncticollis* Bwn.)

Brit. Isl., Eur., Afr., N & C Asia E to   † Ontario.
N China.

TROX SCABER L.

Cosmopolitan.

Brit. Isl., Eur. (generally).   † Flor., Indiana.

Cerambycidae—Longhorn Beetles

Records of the occurrence in Asia were taken from Plavilstshikov (1936, 1940).

ACMAEOPS PRATENSIS Laich

N & C Eur. (*not* Brit. Isl.), Sib. E to   Alas.–Labr., Nfld., S to New Mex. &
Amur., Kamch., Korea, & Sakhal.   NE U.S.A.

CALLIDIUM VIOLACEUM L.

Brit. Isl., Eur., Sib. E to Amur, Sakhal.   † NE U.S.A., E Can., Nfld.
& Japan.

GRACILIA MINUTA F.

Brit. Isl., Eur., N Afr., Hither Asia.   † Wash.; E U.S.A.
                    † Japan.

HYLOTRUPES BAJULUS L.

Brit. Isl., Eur., N Afr., Hither Asia.   † E U.S.A.
"Siberia" (probably W).
                    † China.

JUDOLIA SEXMACULATA L.

Brit. Isl., N & C Eur., Sib. E to Amur,   Wash., Huds. Bay Terr.–S Labr. & New
Sakhal. & Japan.   Engl., S to Calif.

LEPTIDEA BREVIPENNIS Muls.

Brit. Isl., S & C Eur., E to S Russ.,   † Calif.
N. Afr., Cauc., Hither Asia.

LEPTURA RUBRA L. (*planata* Sw. & Hopp.)

Brit. Isl., Eur., N. Afr., Sib. E to Baikal.   † Iowa.

NEOCLYTUS ACUMINATUS F. (*erythrocephalus* F.)

† Trieste, NW Jugosl., Austria, S   Can.; Wash.–New Engl., S to Flor.
Germ.; Gr. Brit. (accidental). (G. Mül-
ler, 1949–53, p. 148–149).

PACHYTA LAMED L.

N & C Eur., Sib. S to Altai, E to　　　Alas.–Queb. & Penns., S to Calif.
Sakhal.

PHYMATODES LIVIDUS Rossi

Brit. Isl., C & S Eur., Eur. Russ.,　　　† NE U.S.A., E Can.
Cauc., N. Afr.

PHYMATODES TESTACEUS L.

Brit. Isl., Eur., N. Afr., Hither Asia.　　† Calif.; E U.S.A., S to Georgia, W to
　　　　　　　　　　　　　　　　　　　Kansas.

RHAGIUM INQUISITOR L.

f. typ.	sbsp. *stshukini* Sem.	sbsp. *rugipenne* Rtt.	sbsp. *lineatum* Ol.
Brit. Isl., Eur., N. Afr., Sib.–Amur, Kamch., Japan.	Cauc.	E Sib., Manch., Korea, Kamch., Sakhal.	Alas.–Queb. & New Engl.

SAPERDA POPULNEA L.

f. typ.		sbsp. *moesta* Lec.
Brit. Isl., Eur.–E Sib.	Wash.–Calif.	E Can.–Wyom., Penns.

TRAGOSOMA DEPSARIUM L.

N Eur., C Eur. mts., Sib. E to Amur.　　Brit. Col.–Nfld.

Chrysomelidae—Leaf Beetles

Apart from current literature, valuable information has been obtained from Mr.
W. J. Brown, Ottawa, and Dr. Ernst Palmén, Helsingfors. Records of European
species of *Phyllodecta* (*Phratora*) and of *Melasoma lapponica* L. from N. America
are false, according to Brown (1951 and *in litt.*).

ADOXUS OBSCURUS L.

f. parthenogen.[1]	*f. bisex.*
Eur. (*not* Brit. Isl.), Sib. E to Kamch., China, Japan.	Alas.–Nfld., S to New Mex.

AGELASTICA ALNI L.

Brit. Isl., Eur., W Sib., Japan.　　　　† Conn., New Jers., New York.

---

[1] Single males of *Adoxus obscurus* have been observed in S Eur. but it seems that the
species is constantly parthenogenetic in the whole of Europe.

CASSIDA FLAVEOLA Thunb.

Brit. Isl., N & C Eur.

† E U.S.A. W to Minnes., Can. W to Alberta, N to Churchill, Man., & Norman Wells, N. W. Terr.

CASSIDA RUBIGINOSA O. F. Müll.

Brit. Isl., Eur., Asia E to Japan.

† E Can., New Brunsw. to Lake Huron; Maine, New York.

CHRYSOMELA (CHRYSOLINA) STAPHYLEA L.

Icel., Brit. Isl., N & C Eur., Sib. E to Kamch. (sbsp. *daurica* Gebl.)

† Nov. Scot., Nfld.

CRIOCERIS ASPARAGI L.

Brit. Isl., Eur. (except the north), N. Afr., N Asia.

† Wash.–Calif.; E U.S.A.

CRIOCERIS 12-PUNCTATA L.

Eur. (*not* Brit. Isl.), Sib. E to Amur.

† Wash.; E U.S.A.

GALERUCELLA LUTEOLA O. F. Müll. (*xanthomelaena* Schrk.)

Eur. (*not* Brit. Isl.), Hither Asia, C Asia.

† Wash.–Calif.; NE U.S.A., E Can.

GALERUCELLA NYMPHAEAE L.

Brit. Isl., Eur., Sib. E to Amur, Kamch. & Japan.

Alas.–S Labr. & Nfld., S to Texas.

GASTROIDEA POLYGONI L.

Brit. Isl., Eur., N Asia to E Sib.

† Canada, Nov. Scot. to Sask.; U.S.A. W to Mississ.

LEPTINOTARSA DECEMLINEATA Say (fig. 3)

† W & C Eur., N to S Denm., E to Polon. & Rouman.

Native of Rocky Mts. (Color., New Mex.), now generally distributed in U.S.A. & S Can.

LILIOCERIS LILII Scop.

Brit. Isl., Eur. (except the north), Sib. E at least to Baical.

† Montreal (Brown, 1946, p. 47).

LONGITARSUS SUCCINEUS Foudr. (*ovalis* Gent.)

Brit. Isl., Eur., Sib. E to Vladiv.

† Nfld.

LONGITARSUS WATERHOUSEI Ktsch.

Brit. Isl., W, C & S Eur., Asia Minor.   † Oreg.; Mich., Indiana.

MANTURA CHRYSANTHEMI Koch

Brit. Isl., Eur., N. Afr.   † Massach.

PHAEDON ARMORACIAE L.[1]

Brit. Isl., Eur., Sib. E to Kamch. &   (†) Brit. Col.–Maine, S to Color.
Japan.

PHAEDON COCHLEARIAE F.[1]

Brit. Isl., Eur., Asia Minor.   (†) NE U.S.A., E Can., W to Utah &
                                         Alberta.

PHYLLOTRETA AEREA Allard

Brit. Isl., C & S Eur., Asia Minor.   † NE U.S.A.

PHYLLOTRETA ARMORACIAE Koch

Eur. (except the north & Brit. Isl.),   † NE U.S.A., E Can., W to Nebr.
Sib.

PHYLLOTRETA UNDULATA Ktsch.

Brit. Isl., Eur., N. Afr., Asia E to   † Maryland.
Amur.

PHYLLOTRETA VITTATA F. (*striolata* F., *sinuata* Redtb., nec auctt. americ.)

Brit. Isl., Eur., Asia E to Amur,   Alas.–Nov. Scot., Nfld., S to Calif. &
Corea, Japan & Sakhal.   the Gulf of Mex.

PHYLLOTRETA ZIMMERMANNI Crotch (*sinuata* auctt. americ.)

NE Eur. (Finl.); E Sib. (Ussuri).   New Engl.–Georgia, W to Manit.
                                         (probably wider distr.).

PHYTODECTA AFFINIS Gyll. (*arctica* Mnh.)[2]

Eur. (boreoalpine), Sib., Altai.   Alas.–Huds. Bay., Color. (Holdhaus &
                                         Lindroth, 1939).

PLAGIODERA VERSICOLORA Laich

Brit. Isl., Eur., N. Afr., Sib. E to   † NE U.S.A., E Can.
Amur, China & Japan.

---

[1] Fall's identification of *Phaedon* is possibly in need of confirmation.
[2] Brown (1942, p. 100) questions this synonymy.

PRASOCURIS PHELLANDRII L.

Brit. Isl., Eur., W Sib.   Brit. Col.–Queb., S to Color.

PSYLLIODES CHRYSOCEPHALA L.

Brit. Isl., Eur., Hither Asia, Sib.   † Nfld.

PSYLLIODES CUCULLATA Ill.

Eur. (*not* Brit. Isl.), N Asia E to Pacif.   † E Canada.: New Brunsw. & Gaspé.
coast.

ZEUGOPHORA SCUTELLARIS Suffr.[1]

N & C Eur. (*not* Brit. Isl.), W Sib.   † Wash., Oreg.; Mich., Indiana, New
                                              Mex.

Rhynchophora (*Anthribidae & Curculionidae*)—Weevils

The number of known species common to Europe and North America is larger in
this group of beetles than in any other, but a close and modern comparison of the
species in question has actually been made only for those of European origin introduced into the Maritime Provinces of Canada, including Newfoundland (Brown,
1940, 1950; Palmén, *in litt.*). Therefore several of the earlier records must be regarded with some doubt and, pending further evidence, it seems safe to omit the
following species still listed by Leng (1920): — *Anthonomus pomorum* L., *Brachy-
deres incanus* L., *Cionus scrophulariae* L., *Grypus brunnirostris* F., *Lepyrus capu-
cinus* Schall., *Phyllobius glaucus* Scop., *Phytobius velutus* Beck (*velatus* auctt.),
Sitona lineellus Bonsd. and *S. tibialis* Hbst.—Blatchley & Leng (1916) has been
very useful. Invaluable information has been given by Mr. W. J. Brown and Dr.
E. Palmén.

ACALYPTUS CARPINI Hbst.

Brit. Isl., Eur., Asia E to Amur &   † NE & C U.S.A., E Can., Nfld.
Kamch.

AMALUS HAEMORRHOUS Hbst.

Brit. Isl., Eur., Asia E to Amur.   (†) Wash.; E Can. & NE U.S.A., W to
                                              Manit. & Iowa.

APION LONGIROSTRE Ol.

S & C Eur., N. Afr., W Asia.   † C U.S.A., S Ontario.

---

[1] Brown (*in litt.*) suggests that this identification is in need of confirmation.

APION SIMILE Kby.

Brit. Isl., Eur., N. Afr., Hither Asia,   (†) Nfld.
W Sib.

ARAECERUS FASCICULATUS DeG.

Cosmopolitan.

† Brit. Isl., Eur. (widely).   † Oreg.; E U.S.A.
Probably native of India.

AULEUTES EPILOBII Payk.

N & C Eur. (*not* Brit. Isl.), Sib. E at   Alberta–Nov. Scot., Nfld., S to Texas.
least to Baical.

BARYNOTUS MOERENS F.

Brit. Isl., N, C & SW Eur.   † Nova Scotia.

BARYNOTUS OBSCURUS F.

Brit. Isl., N & C Eur.   † New Brunsw., Nov. Scot., Nfld.

BARYNOTUS SQUAMOSUS Germ. (*schönherri* Zett.)

Icel., Brit. Isl., NW & W Eur.   † NE U.S.A., New Brunsw., Nov. Scot.,
Nfld.

BARYPITHES PELLUCIDUS Boh.

Brit. Isl., NW & W Eur.   † Brit. Col.–Calif.; NE U.S.A., Nfld.

BRACHYSOMUS ECHINATUS Bonsd.

Brit. Isl., N & C Eur., Cauc.   † Queb., Nfld.

CEUTHORRHYNCHUS ASSIMILIS Payk.

Brit. Isl., Eur., N. Afr., Cauc.   † Brit. Col.–Calif.

CEUTHORRHYNCHUS ERYSIMI F.

Brit. Isl., Eur., N. Afr., W & N Asia   † New York, Ontario.
E to Amur.

CEUTHORRHYNCHUS FLORALIS Payk.

Brit. Isl., Eur. only.   † Nov. Scot., Nfld.

CEUTHORRHYNCHUS PUNCTIGER Gyll. (*marginatus* auctt. americ.)[1]

Brit. Isl., Eur. only.   † Wash.; E U.S.A., W to Missouri, E Can.

CEUTHORRHYNCHUS QUADRIDENS Panz.

Brit. Isl., Eur., N. Afr., Cauc.   † NE U.S.A.

CEUTHORRHYNCHUS RAPAE Gyll.

Brit. Isl., N & C Eur., W Asia.   † Wash.–Calif.; New Engl., E Can., Nfld.

CEUTHORRHYNCHUS SULCICOLLIS Payk.

Brit. Isl., N & C Eur., N. Afr., Cauc., Sib.   † Maryland.

CLEONUS PIGER Scop.

Brit. Isl., Eur., N. Afr., Asia E to Amur.   † New York, Queb., Ont.

CRYPTORRHYNCHIDIUS LAPATHI L.

Brit. Isl., Eur., Sib. E to Amur & Japan.   (†) Wash.; E U.S.A., W to Dakota.

ELLESCHUS BIPUNCTATUS L.

Brit. Isl., N & C Eur., Asia E to Kamch.   † NE U.S.A., W to Mich., E Can., S Labr., Nfld.

ELLESCHUS SCANICUS Payk.

Eur. (*not* Brit. Isl.), ? W Sib.   † Penns., New Jers.

GRYPUS (GRYPIDIUS) EQUISETI F.

Brit. Isl., Eur., Sib. E to Amur.   Alas.–Labr., S to Color.

GYMNETRON ANTHIRRINI Payk.

Brit. Isl., Eur., N. Afr., Syria.   † E U.S.A. W to Ohio, E Can.

GYMNETRON NETUM Germ.

C & S Eur. (*not* Brit. Isl.), N. Afr., W Asia.   † NE U.S.A. W to Iowa.

---

[1] Hatch (1953, p. 27) repeats records of *C. marginatus* Payk. and *cyanipennis* Germ. from N. America though these species were cancelled already in Leng (IV. suppl., 1939).

GYMNETRON PASCUORUM Gyll.

Brit. Isl., Eur., N. Afr., Syria.   † E. U.S.A.: New Jers.–Virg.

GYMNETRON TETRUM F. (*teter* auctt.)

Eur. (*not* Brit. Isl.), N. Afr., Asia E to   † Brit. Col.–Oreg.; E U.S.A. W to
Baical.   Iowa & Color., E Can.

LIOPHLOEUS TESSULATUS O. F. Müll.

Brit. Isl., Eur., Sib.   † New York (1 ex.).

MAGDALIS BARBICORNIS Latr.

Brit. Isl., Eur., Madeira.   † NE U.S.A.

MECINUS PYRASTER Hbst.

Brit. Isl., Eur., N. Afr., W Asia.   † Maryland.

MIARUS HISPIDULUS Lec.

(†) S Spain? (*Vide* Franz, 1947, p. 241–   Ont., Massach.–Florida.
243).

MIARUS MERIDIONALIS Bris. (*consuetus* Csy.)

S Eur., N. Afr.   † Kansas.

MIARUS MICROS Germ.

Brit. Isl., Eur., N. Afr.   † Manitoba.

NOTARIS AETHIOPS F.

Brit. Isl., Eur., Sib. E to Amur.   Alas.–Labr., Nfld., S to Color.

NOTARIS BIMACULATUS F. (*wyomingensis* Chitt.)

Brit. Isl., Eur., Asia E to Amur &   Oreg.–Color., S Labr., Nfld.
Kamch.

OTIORRHYNCHUS CRIBRICOLLIS Gyll.

S Eur., N. Afr.   † California.
       † Australia.

OTIORRHYNCHUS DESERTUS Rosenh.

Brit. Isl., NW, W & C Eur.   † Nfld.

OTIORRHYNCHUS LIGNEUS Ol.

Brit. Isl., W Eur.: Scand.–Italy.   † Maine, New Brunsw., Nov. Scot., Nfld.

OTIORRHYNCHUS LIGUSTICI L.

Brit. Isl., Eur. (except the south), Cauc. † N New York.

OTIORRHYNCHUS MERIDIONALIS Gyll.

France, Spain, Sizily; N. Afr.   † California.

OTIORRHYNCHUS OVATUS L.

Brit. Isl., Eur., Asia E to Baical.   † Brit. Col.–Calif., Utah; E Can.–New Mex., W to Wyom.; Nfld.

OTIORRHYNCHUS PORCATUS Hbst.

Brit. Isl., W & C Eur., N to Norway.   † Montreal.

OTIORRHYNCHUS RAUCUS F.

Brit. Isl., Eur. (generally), W Sib.   † Ontario.

OTIORRHYNCHUS RUGIFRONS Gyll.

Icel., Brit. Isl., N, W & C Eur.   † Nov. Scot., Nfld.

OTIORRHYNCHUS RUGOSOSTRIATUS Gze.

Faeroes, Brit. Isl., W & S Eur., N. Afr., † Brit. Col.–Calif., Utah, Color.; E & C Cauc.   U.S.A., Queb.

OTIORRHYNCHUS SCABER L.

Brit. Isl., N & C Eur.   † Nov. Scot.

OTIORRHYNCHUS SINGULARIS L.

Brit. Isl., Eur. (widely).   † Brit. Col., Wash.; New Engl., E Can., Nfld.

OTIORRHYNCHUS SULCATUS F.

Brit. Isl., N & C Eur.   † Brit. Col.–Calif.; NE U.S.A., E Can., Nfld.
                                          † Australia.

PANTOMORUS GODMANI Crotch

† SW Eur.   † S. Afr., Austral.   † U.S.A. (widely), E Can. Native of S. Amer. or Hawaii.

PENTARTHRUM HUTTONI Woll.

Brit. Isl., W Eur.   † Montreal.

PHILOPEDON PLAGIATUS Boh.

Brit. Isl., Eur., N. Afr.   † New Brunsw., Pr. Edw. Isl., Magdal. Isl., Nfld.

PHYLLOBIUS OBLONGUS L.

Brit. Isl., Eur. (except the north), W Asia.   † New York, Ontario, New Brunsw.

PHYTONOMUS (HYPERA) ARATOR L. (*polygoni* L.)

Brit. Isl., Eur., ?W Asia.   † Illinois.

PHYTONOMUS (HYPERA) MELES F.

Brit. Isl., Eur., N. Afr., Asia Minor.   † NE U.S.A., E Can., Nfld.

PHYTONOMUS (HYPERA) NIGRIROSTRIS F.

Brit. Isl., Eur., N. Afr., Asia Minor.   † Brit. Col.–Oreg.; E & C U.S.A., E Can., Nfld.

PHYTONOMUS (HYPERA) POSTICUS Gyll. (*variabilis* Hbst., *murinus* auctt. americ.)[1]

Brit. Isl., Eur., N. Afr., Sib. E to Yenisei, C Asia.   † C U.S.A., Calif. (fig. 6); since 1952 also in the East.
                                      † India.

PHYTONOMUS (HYPERA) PUNCTATUS F.

Brit. Isl., Eur., C Asia.   † Brit. Col.–Calif.; NE & C U.S.A., E Can., Nfld.

PHYTONOMUS (HYPERA) RUMICIS L.

Brit. Isl., Eur., N. Afr., Cauc.   † Iowa, N. Dak., Alberta.

POLYDROSUS IMPRESSIFRONS Gyll.

S & C Eur. (*not* Brit. Isl.).   † NE U.S.A.

POLYDROSUS SERICEUS Schall.

Brit. Isl., Eur., N. Afr., ?Sib.   † Indiana; Queb.

---

[1] There seems to be no reason for the opinion of Lehmann & Klinkowski (1942, p. 28) that *posticus* Gyll. and the true *murinus* F. should have been confused by North American authors.

PSELACTUS (PHLOEOPHAGIA) SPADIX Hbst.

Brit. Isl., Eur., N. Afr.   † NE U.S.A.
                                             † Australia.

RHINONCUS CASTOR F.

Brit. Isl., Eur., Asia E to Japan.   † Brit. Col., Oreg.; NE U.S.A. W to
                                             Illin., E Can., Nfld.

RHINONCUS PERICARPIUS F.

Icel., Brit. Isl., Eur., N. Afr., Sib.,   † New York, Nfld.
Japan.

RHYNCHAENUS (ORCHESTES) SALICIS L.

Brit. Isl., Eur., Sib. E to Kamch.,   Wash., Calif.; E U.S.A. W to Wisc.,
Japan.   Nfld. (Probably transamerican.)

SCIAPHILUS ASPERATUS Bonsd.

Icel., Brit. Isl., Eur., Casp. region   † Brit. Col.; NE U.S.A., E Can., Nfld.

SITONA CRINITUS Hbst.[1]

Brit. Isl., Eur. E to Ural.   † Wash.–Calif.; Nfld. (Certainly wider
                                             distr.)

SITONA CYLINDRICOLLIS Fåhr.

Brit. Isl., C & S Eur., W & C Asia.   † NE U.S.A. & E Can., W to Alberta.

SITONA DISCOIDEUS Gyll. (*humeralis* Steph.)[2]

Brit. Isl., Eur., Mediterr., W & C Asia.   † Rhode Isl.

SITONA HISPIDULUS F.

Brit. Isl., Eur., Cauc., Syria.   † Wash.–Calif.; NE U.S.A. & E Can.,
                                             W to Nebr., Nfld.

SITONA LEPIDUS Gyll. (*flavescens* Mrsh.)

Brit. Isl., Eur., Mediterr., Hither   † Wash.; E U.S.A. & E Can., W to
Asia, W Sib.   Kans., Nfld.

SITONA LINEATUS L.

Brit. Isl., Eur. (generally).   † Brit. Col.

---

[1] Also other European species of the *crinitus* group have been reported from N. America but the identifications require confirmation.

[2] According to Brown (*in litt.*) this record requires confirmation.

SITOPHILUS (CALANDRA) GRANARIUS L.

Cosmopolitan.

(†) Brit. Isl., Eur.; Asia.   † U.S.A., Canada.

SITOPHILUS (CALANDRA) ORYZAE L.

Cosmopolitan.

† Brit. Isl., Eur.; Asia.   † U.S.A.

STENOPELMUS RUFINASUS Gyll.

†Brit. Isl., Holl., Belg., Germ., France.   S U.S.A. N to Indiana.

STOMODES GYROSICOLLIS Boh.

C & S Eur.   † Maine.

STROPHOSOMUS MELANOGRAMMUS Forst.

Icel., Brit. Isl., C & W Eur., Madeira.   † Brit. Col.; NE U.S.A., E Can., Nfld.

TANYSPHYRUS LEMNAE F.

Brit. Isl., Eur., ?N Asia.   Manit.–Ontar., S to Flor. (probably
Japan.   wider distr.).

TRACHODES HISPIDUS L.

Brit. Isl., Eur. (except the north).   † St. Pierre (S of Nfld.; probably acci-
          dental).

TRACHYPHLOEUS BIFOVEOLATUS Beck

Brit. Isl., Eur., Cauc., Macaron. isl.   † Brit. Col.; New York, E Can., Nfld.

TROPIDERES (GONOTROPIS) DORSALIS Thunb. (*gibbosus* Lec.)

N & C Eur., Sib. E to Amur.   Color., Huds. Bay, Maine, Nfld.

TROPIPHORUS CARINATUS O. F. Müll.

Brit. Isl., N & C Eur., E to C Russ.   † Nfld.

TROPIPHORUS OBTUSUS Bonsd.

Icel., Brit. Isl., N & C Eur. E to the   † Nov. Scot.
White Sea.

TROPIPHORUS TOMENTOSUS Mrsh.

Brit. Isl., W & C Eur.   † Queb., Pr. Edw. Isl., Nov. Scot.

TYCHIUS (MICCOTROGUS) PICIROSTRIS F.

Brit. Isl., Eur. only.   † Brit. Col. & Wash.–Nov. Scot. (prob-
                                          ably transamerican).

TYCHIUS STEPHENSI Schnh. (*tomentosus* Hbst.)

Brit. Isl., Eur. only.   † E U.S.A., E Can.

Macro-Lepidoptera—Butterflies and Moths

Lepidoptera, especially the "Macros", are the most collected of all insects and the
literature dealing with them is excessively rich. In spite of this, the attempts to
get a tolerably complete picture of Eur-American species met with greater difficulties than in any other group of animals here treated. Lepidopterists generally
seem too interested in local faunas and description of new aberrations (often termed
"subspecies"). Furthermore, the perpetual change of nomenclature, in names of
all categories, and the unfortunate splitting-up of the old genera, often on small
or obscure characters, have made the modern literature on Macrolepidoptera
almost unsurveyable to the non-specialist.

Seitz' "Gross-Schmetterlinge "(1909–24) has been very useful but, of course, is
not up to date. Djakonov (1931), Valle (1933), Kozhantshikov (1937, 1950), have
given supplements for the Palaearctis. For North America, McDunnough's Check
List (1938) provided excellent service though, unfortunately, it does not give the
distribution. Many Palaearctic species are by him marked as doubtful in North
America; these I have omitted, unless the occurrence was later confirmed. For
Butterflies, Klots (1951) has been used, for some of the other groups Forbes
(1923, 1948, 1954). Krogerus (1954) and Ferguson (1955) published excellent
local faunas, of Newfoundland and Nova Scotia respectively. For additional
papers the reader is referred to the bibliography of Chapter I (p. 126 a. f.).

The difficulties mentioned above induced me to send the preliminary list of
Eur-American Macrolepidoptera to Mr. D. C. Ferguson, Halifax, and Dr. E. G.
Munroe, Ottawa. The latter co-operated, on my behalf, with Dr. T. N. Freeman
concerning the Diurna and with Dr. D. F. Hardwick concerning the Noctuids.
Mr. Ferguson also consulted Dr. J. G. Franclemont. I am highly indebted to these
gentlemen for the additions and corrections made, and also to Dr. H. Krogerus,
Helsingfors, for valuable suggestions.

Among possible Eur-American species, the following have been omitted in
await of further evidence: *Chrysophanes* (*Heodes, Lycaena*) *phlaeas* L. (*americana*

Harris, *hypophlaeas* Bdv.), *Plebeius* (*Lycaena, Lycaenopsis*) *argiolus* L. (*pseudargiolus* Bdv. & Lec.), *P.* (*Lycaena*) *glandon* Prun. (*aquilo* Bdv., and races), *Plusia* (*Caloplusia*) *hochenwarthi* Hoch., and *Schrankia turfosalis* Wocke.

Diurna[1]

ADOPAEA (THYMELICUS) LINEOLA Ochs.

Brit. Isl., Eur. (generally), N. Afr., N Asia E to Amur. † Ontario (since about 1910); Mich., Ohio.

ARGYNNIS[2] CHARICLEA Schn.

f. typ.	sbsp.?	Several sbspp.
N Scand., Kola Penins., N. Zeml.	Sib. E to Kamch.	Alas.–N Queb., Nfld., Greenl. (N to 78°17′).[3]

ARGYNNIS EUNOMIA Esp. (*aphiraphe* Hbn.)

f. typ.
N & C Eur., Asia E to Amur.

Several sbspp.
Alas.–Labr., S to Maine and, in Rocky Mts., to Color.

ARGYNNIS FREIJA Thunb.

N Eur., Sib. E to Amur, N Japan.   Alas.–Labr., Nfld., S to New Mex.

ARGYNNIS FRIGGA Thunb.

f. typ.
N Eur., Sib. E to Amur.

Several sbspp.
Alas.–Labr., Baffin Isl., S to Color.

ARGYNNIS IMPROBA Butl.

N Scand., N. Zeml., NW & NE Sib.   Alas. & Brit. Col.–Baffin Isl.

ARGYNNIS PALES Schiff.[4]

Eur. (boreoalpine), C & N Asia E to Kamch.

Alas., Brit. Col., N. W. Terr. E to Baker Lake.

ARGYNNIS POLARIS Bsd.

N Eur., W & NE Sib.

Alas.–Labr., S to Manit.; Ellesm. Isl., Greenl. (N to 81°50′).

---

[1] The famous Monarch (*Danaus plexippus* L.), native of America, is not listed here. It has been observed repeatedly in western Europe, above all in Britain, but the occurrence is accidental since the food-plant of the larva, Milkweeds (*Asclepias*, and related genera), is not indigenous in Europe. *Vide* Ford (1946, p. 152 a. f.) and Klots (1951, p. 78).

[2] Included in *Argynnis* are here: *Boloria, Brenthis, Clossiana*, &c.

[3] The Greenland form transgredes into *f. typ.* (Petersen, 1954, p. 245).

[4] The division into sbspp. is very confused (*vide* Petersen, 1954, p. 237).

ARGYNNIS SELENE Schiff. (*myrina* Cram.)

f. typ.
Brit. Isl., Eur., Asia E to Kamch.,
Kuril., Japan.

Several sbspp.
Alas.–Labr., Nov. Scot., Nfld., S to N.
Carol.

ARGYNNIS TITANIA Esp. (*amathusia* Esp.)

sbsp. *rossica* Hemm.
S Finl., Balticum, Eur.
Russ.

Several sbspp.
C & S Eur. mts.

2 sbspp.
Sib. E to Amur.

Several sbspp.
Wash.–Nov. Scot., Labr., S along the mts. to New Mex., isolated in White Mts.
(New Hampsh.).

CARTEROCEPHALUS (PAMPHILA) PALAEMON Pall.

Brit. Isl., Eur., N Asia E to Amur,
Kamch., & Kuril.

Alas.–Labr., Nfld., S to NE U.S.A.

COENONYMPHA TULLIA O. F. Müll. (*tiphon* Rott.) (fig. 55)
Many sbspp.

Brit. Isl., Eur. (widely), Asia E to
Kamch.

Alas., NW Can., S to Ariz. & New Mex.,
E to Manit., as sbsp. *inornata* Edw. to
Labr. & Nfld.

COLIAS HECLA Lef.

N Scand., W & NE Sib.

Alas.–N Labr., Baffin & Ellesm. Isl., S to
Churchill, Man., in Rocky Mts. to 54°;
Greenl. (N to 81°30').

COLIAS NASTES Bdv.

N Scand., N Zeml., E Sib.

Alas.–Labr., N to Victoria & Baffin Isl.,
S to S Brit. Col.

COLIAS PALAENO L.

f. typ.
N & C Eur., Sib. E to Amur & Kamch.

sbsp. *chippewa* Kby. (*pelidneïdes* Stgr.)
Alas.–Labr.

EREBIA DISA Thunb.

f. typ.
N Scand., N Russ., Sib. (in the East
transgreding into the N. American
sbspp.).

sbsp. *mancina* Dbl. & *steckeri* Holl.
Alas.–Labr.

EREBIA DISCOIDALIS Kby.

Petchora tundra (Kusnezov, 1925); Yenisei–E Sib., S to Altai.

Alas.–Huds. Bay, S to Minnes.

EREBIA FASCIATA Butl.

Petchora tundra (Kusnezov, 1925); N Ural., Yenisei–Anadyr.

Arct. N. Amer.: N. W. Terr. to Huds. Bay, Victoria Isl.

HESPERIA (ERYNNIS, AUGIADES) COMMA L.

f. typ.
Brit. Isl., Eur. (generally), Asia E to Amur & China.

Several sbspp.[1]
Alas.–Labr., Nfld., S to Color.

OENEIS JUTTA Hbn.

f. typ.
N Eur. S to E. Pruss., Sib. E to Amur & Kamch.

Several sbspp.
Alas.–Nov. Scot., Nfld., S to New Engl.

PAPILIO MACHAON L.

Several sbspp.

Brit. Isl., Eur. (generally), N. Afr., Asia E to Kamch., China & Japan.

sbsp. *aliaska* Scudd. (*joannisi* Ver.) & *hudsonianus* Clark[2].
Alas.–Huds. Bay & Lake Sup.

PIERIS NAPI L.

Several sbspp.
Brit. Isl., Eur. (generally), N. Afr., Asia E to Amur, China, Kamch. & Kuril.

Several sbspp.
Alas.–Labr., Nfld., S to New York & Calif.

PIERIS RAPAE L.

Brit. Isl., Eur. (generally), Asia E to Amur, Japan, Kuril.

† Transamerican (except N Can.), Nfld., S to Mexico.
† Hawaii, Austral.

PLEBEIUS (LYCAENA, LYCAEIDES) IDAS L. (*argyrognomon* auctt., nec Bergstr.)

Several forms
Eur. (except Brit. Isl.), N & C Asia E to China & Kamch.

3 sbspp.
Alas.–Nov. Scot., Labr., Nfld., S along the mts. to Color.

---

[1] Often, in part at least, kept as separate species.
[2] Forms from NE N. America (*brevicauda* Saund., &c.) are regarded as specifically distinct.

PLEBEIUS (LYCAENA) OPTILETE Knoch

f. typ. (incl. several forms)
N & C Eur., N Asia E to Amur, Kamch. & Kuril.

sbsp. *yukona* Holl.
NW N. Amer. E to Alberta.

PYRGUS (HESPERIA, SYRICHTUS) CENTAUREAE Ramb.[1]

Scand., N Russ., W & S Sib. (probably farther east).

Brit. Col.–Labr., Nfld., S to Color.

VANESSA (NYMPHALIS) ANTIOPA L.

Brit. Isl. (immigr.), Eur. (generally), N. Afr., N & C Asia E to Amur & Japan.

Alas.–Nfld., S to Venez.

VANESSA (PYRAMEIS) CARDUI L.

Cosmopolitan.

Brit. Isl., Eur. (generally, but immigr. in the north & west), Afr., Asia E to

Japan & Kuril., Austral.

Entire N. Amer. (except the Arctic, immigr. in the north).
C Amer.

VANESSA (PYRAMEIS) ATALANTA L.

Brit. Isl., Eur. (generally, but immigr. in the north & west), N. Afr., W & C Asia E at least to Altai.

Transamerican in U.S.A. & S Can. (immigr. in the north).
C Amer.

Sphinges

CELERIO GALII Rott. (*gallii* auctt.)

f. typ.
Eur. (generally), N & C Asia E to Japan, Kuril.

sbsp. *intermedia* Kby.
Brit. Col.–Labr., Nfld., S to Calif. & Georgia. Mexico.

CELERIO LINEATA F.

sbsp. *livornica* Esp.
Eur. (immigr. only), Afr., S & E Asia.

f. typ.
S Can.–U.S.A.–C & S Amer. (as an immigr. N to Brit. Col., Montr. & Nov. Scot.).

SPHINX (HYLOICUS) PINASTRI L.

Brit. Isl., Eur. (generally), Sib. E to Japan.

† NE U.S.A., Alberta (doubtfully established).

---

[1] In the East of N. Amer., Manit.-Labr., is *freija* Warr., usually regarded as distinct species and doubtfully recorded also from the Scandinavian mountains.

Bombycimorpha

ARCTIA (HYPHORAIA, PLATYPREPIA) ALPINA Quens.

N Fennoscand., Sib. S to Altai, E at least to Baikal.   N Alaska, NW N. W. Terr.

ARCTIA CAJA L.

f. typ.
(incl. several forms)
Eur. (generally), Asia E to Pamir, S to N India.

sbsp. *phaeosoma* Btlr.
E Asia, to Amur, Japan, Kuril.

5–6 sbspp.
Alas. & Brit. Col.–Labr. & Nov. Scot., S to Color. & Utah.

Transgreding forms in E Asia.

ARCTIA (HYPHORAIA, PARASEMIA) LAPPONICA Thunb. (*festiva* Bkh.)

f. typ.
N Eur., Sib. E at least to Lena R.

sbsp. *gibsoni* B. H. & *hyperborea* Curt.
N. W. Terr., NE U.S.A.

ARCTIA (ORODEMNIAS, APANTESIS) QUENSELI Payk.

f. typ.
C Eur. mts.

sbsp. *norvegica* Strd.
N Fennoscand.

2–3 sbspp.
N Mong., Lena R. –Amur, N Japan.

sbsp. *gelida* Moeschl.
Alas., Yukon Terr. & Brit. Col.–Labr., New Hampsh.; Greenl.

EUPROCTIS (PORTHESIA) CHRYSORRHOEA L. (*similis* Fuessl.)

Brit. Isl., Eur. (except the north), N & C Asia E to Amur, Japan, Sakhal. & Kuril.

† U.S.A. (not established), Ont. (greenhouse).

EUPROCTIS (NYGMIA) PHAEORRHOEA Don. (*chrysorrhoea* auctt., nec L.)

Brit. Isl., Eur. E to Ural, N. Afr., Cauc., Hither Asia.

† E Can., Nov. Scot., NE U.S.A.

GLUPHISIA CRENATA Esp.

f. typ.
N & C Eur., Sib. E to Amur.

sbsp. *septentrionis* Wlk.
Pacif. coast–Nov. Scot., Nfld., S to Georgia.

HYPHANTRIA CUNEA Drury

† Hungar., Yugosl., Austria.

S Can., U.S.A. (generally), S to Texas.
† Japan.

ORGYIA (NOTOLOPHUS) ANTIQUA L.

Icel., Eur. (generally), N. Afr., Cauc.,   Brit. Col.–Nov. Scot., Nfld., S to New
N Asia E to Amur, Corea & Japan.   York.
† Sumatra, S S. Amer.

PARASEMIA (NEMEOPHILA) PLANTAGINIS L.

Many sbspp.   Many forms (? sbspp.)
Brit. Isl., Eur. (widely), Asia E to   Yukon Terr. & Brit. Col.–Ont., S to
Kamch., Japan & Kuril.   Color.

PHRAGMATOBIA FULIGINOSA L.

f. typ.	sbsp. *borealis* Stgr.	Several sbspp.	sbsp. *rubricosa* Harr.
W & C Eur.	N Fennoscand.	Asia E to Amur & Kamch.	Brit. Col.–Nov. Scot. & Nfld., S to S. Carol.

STILPNOTIA (LEUCOMA) SALICIS L.

Brit. Isl., Eur. (generally), N. Afr.,   † Brit. Col.–Oreg.; E Can., Nov. Scot.,
Asia E to Lena R. & N China.   NE U.S.A.

UTETHEISA BELLA L.

(†) Wales (Skokholm Isl., 1 ex.;   E Can., Nov. Scot., E U.S.A. (widely).
Williams, 1950).

Noctuae (Phalaenae)

ACRONYCTA (APATELA) LEPORINA L.

f. typ.   4 sbspp.
Eur. (generally), N & C Asia E to   Brit. Col.–Nov. Scot., N U.S.A. S to
Amur, Sakhal. & N Japan.   Color.

AMPHIPYRA (PYROPHILA) TRAGOPOGONIS L.

Brit. Isl., Eur. (generally), N. Afr., Asia (†) S Can., Nov. Scot., Nfld., N U.S.A.
E to W Sib. & N India.   W at least to Mississ.; Brit. Col. Pos-
                                              sibly transamerican.

ANARTA CORDIGERA Thunb.

N & C Eur., Sib. (at least Amur).   Alas.– Labr., Nov. Scot., S to Mass. &
                                              Color.

ANARTA (SYMPISTIS) FUNEBRIS Hbn. (*funesta* Payk.)

N Fennoscand., Alps; NE Sib., N
Japan.

Alas.–Labr. & Nov. Scot., S to New
Hampsh. & Wyom.

ANARTA (SYMPISTIS) LAPPONICA Thunb. (fig. 30)

N Fennoscandia, N. Zeml.

N. W. Terr., Labr., Baff. Isl., Greenl.

ANARTA (LASIESTRA) LEUCOCYCLA Strg. (incl. *staudingeri* Aur.)

N Fennoscandia.

Brit. Col., N. W. Terr. & Victoria Isl.–
Labr., Nfld., Baff. & Ellesm. Isl., S to
Color., isolated in White Mts. (New
Hampsh.); Greenl.

ANARTA (SYMPISTIS) MELALEUCA Thunb.

Fennoscandia; NE Sib.

Mackenzie Delta–Labr., S to Gaspé.

ANARTA MELANOPA Thunb.

Shetl., Brit. Isl., Eur. (boreoalpine), E
to Kola Penins.

Brit. Col.–Nfld., New Hampsh., S along
the mts. to New Mex.

ANARTA RICHARDSONI Curt.

sbsp. *dovrensis* Stgr.	sbsp.?	sbsp. *asiatica* Stgr.	*f. typ.* & 3 sbspp.
N Fennoscand., N. Zeml.	W Sib.	E Sib.	Alas.–Labr., Grinnell L., Greenl. (N to 81°30′).

ANARTA (SYMPISTIS) ZETTERSTEDTI Stgr.

N. Fennoscandia; Mongol. (sbsp.?).

N. W. Terr. & Brit. Col.–Labr., Baff.
Isl., Greenl.

ANOMOGYNA (GRAPHIPHORA) LAETABILIS Zett.

N Fennoscandia; NE Sib., Sakhal.

Brit. Col. & Yukon–Labr.

ANOMOGYNA RHAETICA Stgr.

f. typ.	sbsp. *fennica* Brdt.	sbsp. *homogena* McD. & sbsp. *conditoides* Benj.
Alps.	N Fennoscandia.	Brit. Col.–Labr., Nfld., New Hampsh.

ANOMOGYNA SINCERA H.–S.

Fennoscandia, C Eur. mts.; Sib.: Amur. Alberta–Labr., Nfld., NE U.S.A.

ANOMOGYNA (APLECTOIDES) SPECIOSA Hbn.

f. typ.
Eur. (boreoalpine), N & C Asia E to
Kamch.

sbsp. *mixta* Walk.
N. W. Terr.–Labr., Nfld., NE U.S.A.

CHLOANTHA (LITHOMOIA, CALOCAMPA) SOLIDAGINIS Hbn.

f. typ.
Brit. Isl., N & C Eur., Sib. E to Amur.

3 sbspp.
Alas. & Brit. Col.–Queb.

CRYMODES (HADENA, APAMEA) EXULIS Lef. (fig. 38)

Icel., Faeroes, Shetl., Scotl., Spitzb.

N. W. Terr.–Labr., Nfld., Ellesm.
Isl., Greenl.

CUCULLIA LUCIFUGA Schiff.

f. typ.
N & C Eur., N & C Asia to E Sib.

sbsp. *intermedia* Speyer
N U.S.A., S Can. W at least to Alberta,
Nfld., S to Virg.

HELIOTHIS (MELICLEPTRIA, CANTHYLIDIA) SCUTOSA Schiff.

C & S Eur., N. Afr., W & C Asia E
to China & Corea.

W U.S.A., W Can., E at least to Alberta
& Kansas, S to Color.

HILLIA (ORTHOSIA, CRASIA) IRIS Zett. (*crasis* H.-S.)

N Fennoscandia, N Russia; E Sib.:
Amur.

Brit. Col.–Labr. & Nov. Scot., S to
Color. & NE U.S.A.

HYDROECIA MICACEA Esp.

Brit. Isl., N & C Eur., N Asia E to
Amur & Japan.

† NE U.S.A., E Can., Nov. Scot., Nfld.

LAPHYGMA (CARADRINA) EXIGUA Hbn. (*flavimaculata* Harv.)

S Eur., Afr., W & C Asia E to Manchur. & Japan; S Asia.

† Florida–Calif.; straggling E to Wisc. &
Kans.
† C Amer., Hawaii.

LEUCANIA (SIDERIDIS, HELIOPHILA) PALLENS L.

f. typ.
Eur. (generally), N. & C Asia E to
Amur & Kamch.

sbsp. *luteopallens* Sm.
Alas.–Nfld., S to the Gulf of Mexico.

LEUCANIA (SIDERIDIS, HELIOPHILA, PSEUDALETIA, CIRPHIS) UNIPUNCTA Haw.

Almost cosmopolitan.

(†) Brit. Isl., C & S Eur., C Asia, SE Sib., Japan.
(†) S Asia, Austral., Pacif. Isl.

U.S.A. & S Can., Brit. Col.–Nov. Scot., Nfld.
3 sbspp. in C & S Amer.

MAMESTRA (SCOTOGRAMMA) TRIFOLII Rott.

Eur. (generally), N. Afr., N & C Asia, Japan.

Transamerican in U.S.A. & Can., Nov. Scot., Nfld., S to Mexico. S. Amer.

PARASTICHTIS (HADENA, SEPTIS) BASILINEA F. (*finitima* Gn.)

Eur. (generally), N & C Asia E to Amur & Japan.

Brit. Col.–Nfld., S to Color. & NE U.S.A.

PARASTICHTIS (HADENA, AGROPERINA, SEPTIS) LATERITIA Hfn.

Eur. (generally), N & C Asia E to Amur, Japan & Kuril.

Yukon Terr. & Brit. Col.–Nfld., N U.S.A. (generally).

PLUSIA (SYNGRAPHA, AUTOGRAPHA) DIASEMA Bsd.

Fennoscandia; NE Asia: Amur & Kamch.

Yukon, N. W. Terr. & Alberta–Labr., Greenl.

PLUSIA (PHYTOMETRA, AUTOGRAPHA, SYNGRAPHA) INTERROGATIONIS L.

Icel., N & C Eur., Asia E to Kamch. & Kuril.

Alas. & Yukon–Labr., Greenl. NE U.S.A.

PLUSIA (SYNGRAPHA, AUTOGRAPHA) MICROGAMMA Hbn.

N & C Eur.; Kamch.

Brit. Col.–Nov. Scot.

PLUSIA (CHRYSOPTERA, POLYCHRYSIA) MONETA F.

Brit. Isl., Eur. (except the north), N & C Asia E to N China, Vladiv. & Kuril.

(†) Alberta, Sask., Mont.

PLUSIA (AUTOGRAPHA, SYNGRAPHA) PARILIS Hbn. (fig. 31)

N Fennoscandia.

N. W. Terr & Alberta–Labr., Baff. & Ellesm. Isl., Greenl.

PYRRHIA UMBRA Hfn.

N & C Eur., Asia E to SE Sib., Japan & Kuril.

N U.S.A. (widely) S to N. Carol., Can. W at least to Alberta, Nov. Scot., Nfld., S to Color.

RAPHIA FRATER Grote

(†) Engl. (Harpenden, 1 ex.; Williams,   Can. & U.S.A. (widely), Nov. Scot., S
1950).   to Color. & Texas.

RHYACIA (GRAPHIPHORA, NOCTUA, DIARSIA) C-NIGRUM L.

Eur. (generally), Cauc., N & C Asia E   Transamerican in U.S.A. & Can., Nfld.
to Amur, Japan, Sakhal., Kuril.; S Asia.   C Amer.

RHYACIA (ACTEBIA, OCHROPLEURA) FENNICA Tausch.

N Eur., N & C Asia E to Amur,   Alas.–Nov. Scot., Nfld., N U.S.A.
Corea, Kamch. & Sakhal.

RHYACIA (PERIDROMA, LYCOPHOTIA) MARGARITOSA Haw. (*saucia* Hbn.)

Icel., Brit. Isl., Eur. (except the north),   U.S.A. (generally), S Can., Nov. Scot.,
N Afr., Cauc., C Asia E at least to W   Nfld.
Turcest.   S Amer. (original patria?)

RHYACIA (DIARSIA) MENDICA F. (*festiva* Schiff., *dislocata* Sm.)

Icel., N & C Eur., Cauc., N & C Asia   Brit. Col.–Labr., Nfld.
E to Amur, Kamch. & Sakhal.

RHYACIA (EUROIS, PERIDROMA) OCCULTA L.

Icel., N & C Eur., N & C Asia E to   Brit. Col.–Nov. Scot., Nfld., S to Color.,
Kamch., Corea & Japan.   Greenl.

RHYACIA (OCHROPLEURA, DIARSIA, PERIDROMA) PLECTA L.

Eur. (generally), N & C Asia E to   Brit. Col.–Nov. Scot., Nfld., U.S.A.
Amur, Japan, Sakhal. & Kuril.   (widely) S to Texas.
S Asia.   † S. Afr.

RHYACIA (ANAPLECTOIDES, EUROIS, APLECTA) PRASINA Schiff.

Eur. (generally), Cauc., N & C Asia E   Brit. Col.–Nfld., N U.S.A. S to Color.
to Amur, Japan & Sakhal.

RHYACIA (PACHNOBIA) TECTA Hbn.

f. typ.   sbsp. *roosta* Sm.
N Eur., Eur. Russia; Kamch.   Alas. & Yukon–Labr.

RHYACIA (EUXOA, AGROTIS) YPSILON Rott.

Cosmopolitan.

Eur. (generally), Cauc., W, N & C Asia   Brit. Col.–Labr., U.S.A. (generally),
E to Vladiv., Corea & Sakhal.   Nfld.

S Asia, Austral., Hawaii, C & S Amer.

SCHÖYENIA (ANARTA, ARCHANARTA, GRAPHIPHORA, ANOMOGYNA) QUIETA Hbn.

N Fennoscandia; acc. to Valle (1933, p.   N. W. Terr. & Baffin Isl.
100) in N Russ. & NE Asia.

SCOLIOPTERYX LIBATRIX L.

Eur. (generally), Asia E to Kamch.   Brit. Col.–Nov. Scot., Nfld., U.S.A.
(generally).

SPAELOTIS (TRIPHAENA, AMPHITROTA) CLANDESTINA Harr. (*unicolor* Wlk.)

sbsp. *suecica* Aur.   *f. typ.*
Fennoscandia, N. Russia.   Amur & Kamch.; Brit. Col.–Nov.
Scot., Nfld., S to Color. & Missouri;
Greenl.

XANTHIA (COSMIA) LUTEA Ström *(flavago* F.)

Eur. (generally), N & C Asia   Brit. Col.–Nov. Scot., S to Penns.
E to Kamch.

Geometrae

BOARMIA (ECTROPIS) CREPUSCULARIA Hbn.

Eur. (widely), Asia E to Amur.   Brit. Col.–Nov. Scot., S to W Virg.

CALOCALPE (HYDRIA) UNDULATA L.

N & C Eur., N Asia E to Kuril.   Alas.–Nov. Scot., Nfld., S to N. Carol.
& Ariz.

CARSIA PALUDATA Thunb. (*sororiata* Hbn.)

N & C Eur., N & C Asia E to Amur   Brit. Col.–Nov. Scot., Labr., Nfld., mts.
& Kamch.   of NE U.S.A.

CHEIMATOBIA (OPEROPHTERA) BRUMATA L.

Icel., Brit. Isl., N & C Eur., Cauc.; E   † Nov. Scot. (†) Greenl.
Sib.

CIDARIA (XANTHOROE) ABRASARIA H.–S.

f. typ.   sbsp. *congregata* Wlk.
N Eur., W & NE Sib.   Pacif. coast & Yukon Terr.–Nov. Scot.,
Nfld., S to New York.

CIDARIA (PERIZOMA) ALCHEMILLATA L.

Eur. (widely), Asia E to Altai.   † Nfld. (Ferguson).

CIDARIA (EPIRRHOE) ALTERNATA O. F. Müll.

Icel., Eur. (generally), Cauc., N Asia   Alas.–Nov. Scot., Labr., Nfld., S to
E to Kamch. & Kuril.   Distr. of Col.

CIDARIA (DYSSTROMA) CITRATA L. (*immanata* Haw.)

Icel., N & C Eur., N & C Asia E to   Alas. & Brit. Col.–Nov. Scot., Labr.,
Kamch. & Kuril.   Nfld., S to New York.

CIDARIA (XANTHOROE) FERRUGATA Cl.

Eur. (generally), N & C Asia E to   Brit. Col.–Nov. Scot, Nfld., S to Penns.
Kamch.

CIDARIA (HYDRIOMENA) FURCATA Thunb. (*sordidata* F.)

Icel., N & C Eur., N & C Asia E to   Pacif. coast–Nov. Scot., Labr., N U.S.A.
China, Japan & Kamch.

CIDARIA (EULYPE, RHEUMAPTERA) HASTATA L.

Icel., N & C Eur., N & C Asia E to   Alas.–Nov. Scot., Labr., Nfld., S to
China & Kamch.   Penns.

CIDARIA (THERA) JUNIPERATA L.

Brit. Isl., Eur. (widely).   † Maine, Ontar., Nov. Scot.

CIDARIA (SPARGANIA, XANTHOROE) LUCTUATA Schiff.

f. typ.   sbsp. *obductata* Moeschl.
N & C Eur., N & C Asia E to Kamch.   Pacif. coast–Labr., Nfld., S to N. Carol.

CIDARIA (XANTHOROE) MUNITATA Hbn.

Icel., Faeroes, Eur. (boreoalpine), Sib.   Pacif. coast–Nov. Scot., Nfld.
E to Amur & Kamch.

CIDARIA (PERCNOPTILOTA) OBSTIPATA F.

Almost cosmopolitan.

Eur. (except the north), Asia (widely).   Pacif. coast–Nov. Scot., Nfld., S to the
Afr.   Gulf of Mexico. S. Amer.

CIDARIA (DASYURIS) POLATA Dup.

N Eur., W & NE Sib. to Kamch.   Alas.–Labr., Baffin & Ellesm. Isl., also
in Color.; Greenl.

CIDARIA (HYDRIOMENA) RUBERATA Frr.

Brit. Isl., N & C Eur. (Not known from Asia but possibly confused with *coerulata* F.)

Brit. Col.–Nov. Scot., Nfld., S to Color.

CIDARIA (PSYCHOPHORA) SABINI Kby. (incl. *frigidaria* Guen.)

N Fennoscandia, N. Zeml.; NE Asia to Kamch.

Alas.–NE arct. N. Amer., Greenl.

CIDARIA (DIACTINIA) SILACEATA Schiff.

N & C Eur., Asia E to Kamch., Japan.

Brit. Col. & Yukon –Nov. Scot., NE U.S.A.

CIDARIA (EULYPE) SUBHASTATA Nolck.

f. typ.
N & C Eur., Sib. E to Kamch.

2 sbspp.
Brit. Col.–Nov. Scot., Labr.

CIDARIA (DYSSTROMA) TRUNCATA Hufn.

N & C Eur., Asia E to China.

Alas. & Brit. Col.–Labr., Nfld., S to Calif. & New York.

CIDARIA (COLOSTIGIA) TURBATA Hbn.

N & C Eur., C & NE Asia E to Kamch.

Alas.–Alberta.

CIDARIA (EUPHYIA) UNANGULATA Haw.

f. typ.
N & C Eur., Sib. E to Kamch., Japan.

sbsp. *intermediata* Gn.
Pacif. coast–Nov. Scot., Nfld.

EMATURGA ATOMARIA L.

f. typ.
Eur. (generally), W, N & C Asia E to Amur & Kamch.

sbsp. *amitaria* Guen.[1]
E Can., Nov. Scot., S to Penns., W at least to Alberta.

EUPITHECIA ALBIPUNCTATA Haw. (*tripunctaria* H.–S.)

N & C Eur., Cauc., Sib. E to Amur.

Brit. Col. & Calif.–Nov. Scot. & Labr., Nfld., S to Penns.

EUPITHECIA CASTIGATA Hbn.

Eur. (widely), Asia E to Amur.

Brit. Col.–Nov. Scot., Nfld., S to N. Carol.

---

[1] Often regarded as distinct species.

EUPITHECIA GELIDATA Moeschl. (*hyperboreata* Stgr.)

N & northern C Eur.; ?Asia.   Alas.–Nov. Scot., Labr., S to New Mex.,
                                            Greenl.

EUPITHECIA INTRICATA Zett. (*helveticaria* Bsd.)[1]

f. typ.   sbsp. *gibsonata* Tayl.[1]
N & C Eur.; ?E Sib.   Alberta–Ontar., New Brunsw., NE
                                             U.S.A.

EUPITHECIA LARICIATA Frr.

f. typ.   sbsp. *bifasciata* Dyar   sbsp. *luteata* Pack.
N & C Eur., Cauc., Sib. Brit. Col.   E Can.–Nov. Scot., Nfld.,
E to Transbaic.   E U.S.A.

EUPITHECIA PALUSTRARIA Dbl. (*pygmaeata* Hbn., *obumbrata* Tayl.)

N & C Eur., Lena R., Amur.   Brit. Col.–Gaspé & Labr., S to Color.

EUPITHECIA SATYRATA Hbn.

f. typ.   3 sbspp.
Icel., N & C Eur., C Asia, ?Amur.   Alas.–Nov. Scot., Labr., S to N. Carol.

EUPITHECIA SOBRINATA Hbn.

Icel., N & C Eur.; Kamch.   ? Brit. Col.; E Can., Nov. Scot., E
                                             U.S.A. S to Texas.

EUPITHECIA UNDATA Frr. (*scriptaria* H.–S.)

N Fennoscandia, mts. of C Eur. &   Brit. Col.–Labr., S to Color.
Hither Asia, C & NE Asia.

HIMERA (COLOTOIS) PENNARIA L.

Brit. Isl., N & C Eur., Cauc., Asia   † E Canada (established?).
Minor.

ITAME FULVARIA Vill.

N & C Eur., Sib. E to Kamch., Japan.   Pacif. coast–Nov. Scot., Nfld., S to
                                             Massach.

ITAME (DYSMIGIA) LORICARIA Ev.

f. typ.   sbsp. *julia* Hulst
N Eur., Sib. E to Kamch.   Yukon Terr.–Nov. Scot., S to Wyom. &
                                             New York.

---

[1] *E. arceuthata* Frr., likewise reported from both continents, is doubtfully distinct from *intricata* Zett.

LYGRIS TESTATA L.

N & C Eur., N Asia to E Sib.   Brit. Col.–Nov. Scot., S to New Jers.

OPORINIA (EPIRRITA) AUTUMNATA Gn.

N & C Eur., Sib. E to Kamch. &   Brit. Col.–Nov. Scot., Nfld., S to Penns.
Kuril.

SCOPULA (ACIDALIA) FRIGIDARIA Moeschl.

sbsp. *schoeyeni* Sp.–Schn.   *f. typ.*
N Fennoscandia, N Eur. Russ.   Kamch.; Yukon Terr.–Labr., Nfld.

VENUSIA CAMBRICA Curt.

N & C Eur., N & C Asia E to Kamch.,   Alas.–Nov. Scot., Nfld., S to N Calif. &
Japan & Kuril.   New York.

Aegeriidae

AEGERIA (TROCHILIUM) APIFORMIS Cl.

Brit. Isl., Eur. (generally), Cauc., W   † NE U.S.A.
Asia E to Altai.

SYNANTHEDON (CONOPIA, THAMNOSPHECIA) CULICIFORMIS L.

Brit. Isl., Eur. (generally), Cauc., Sib.,   Alaska.
N China.

SYNANTHEDON (CONOPIA, RAMOSIA) TIPULIFORMIS Cl.

Brit. Isl., Eur. (generally), Cauc., Sib.   † Can. & U.S.A., W to Alberta & Wash.
       † Australia.

Cossidae

ZEUZERA PYRINA L.

Brit. Isl., Eur. (except the north);   † NE U.S.A.
N. Afr., Asia (except the north),
E to Corea & Japan. India.

       † S. Africa.

Hepialidae

HEPIALUS (HEPIOLUS) GANNA Hbn.

f. typ.   sbsp. *hyperboreus* Moeschl.[1]
       (incl. several forms)
N & C Eur., Asia to E Sib.   Alas.–Ontar.,? Labr., NE U.S.A.

---

[1] Often regarded as distinct species.

Diptera—Two-winged flies

Only two groups of blood-sucking flies, the mosquitoes (*Culicidae, Culicinae*) and the horse flies & clegs (*Tabanidae*) were considered sufficiently known for the present purpose. Information about the former was provided, for the Old World by Stackelberg (1937), Marshall (1938), Natvig (1948), and Montshadsky (1951), for North America by Dyar (1928), Matheson (1944) and Carpenter & La Casse (1955). The Tabanids were mainly treated according to Olsoufiev (1937) and Philip (1947). Mr. H. Kauri, Lund, made valuable suggestions on the synonymy of this family.

Culicidae, Culicinae—Mosquitoes

AËDES (STEGOMYIA) AEGYPTI L. (*fasciatus* F.)

Cosmopolitan in tropic & subtropic regions.

† Brit. Isl. (accidentally).   † U.S.A., S of about 40° N.
† S peninsulae of Eur.

Native of Africa.

AËDES CATAPHYLLA Dyar

N & C Eur., Cauc., W & E Sib.   Alas.–Color, E to Manit. & Wyom.

AËDES CINEREUS Meig.

f. typ.   sbsp. *fuscus* O. S.
Brit. Isl., Eur. (widely), Cauc., Sib.   Alas.–Labr., Nov. Scot., S to Color.
E to Amur.

AËDES COMMUNIS DeG.

Brit. Isl., Eur. (widely), Sib. E to   Alas.–Labr., Nov. Scot., S to Color.
Kamch.

AËDES DIANTAEUS H., D. & K.

N & C Eur., Sib. E to Ussuri.   Alas.–Labr., Nov. Scot., NE U.S.A., S
                                                    to New York & Wyom.

AËDES DORSALIS Meig.

Brit. Isl., N & C Eur., Cauc., N Asia   Brit. Col.–Queb., S to Color. & Delaw.
E to Amur & N China.

AËDES EXCRUCIANS Wlk.

N, C & SE Eur., W & N Asia E to   Alas.–Nov. Scot., Nfld., S to Color.
Ussuri.

AËDES FLAVESCENS O. F. Müll.

Brit. Isl., Eur. (widely), W & N Asia   Alas.–Labr., S to Color.
E to Kamch.

AËDES IMPIGER Wlk. (nec Dyar) (*nearcticus* Dyar)

N & C Fennoscand.; Sib.: Taimyr,   Alas.–Hudson Bay, S to Montana;
Kolyma & New Sib. Isl.   Ellesmere L.

AËDES INTRUDENS Dyar

N & C Eur., E to Ural, E Sib., Kamch.   Brit. Col.–E Can. & NE U.S.A., S to
Color.

AËDES NIGRIPES Zett.

Spitzb., N Fennoscand., N Russ., N   Alas.–N Queb.; Greenl.
Sib. E to Kamch.

AËDES PULLATUS Coq.

Eur.(boreomontane) E to Volga;   Alas.–Queb., S to Color.
Kamch. (Stackelberg, not in Mont-
shadsky).

AËDES PUNCTOR Kby.

Brit. Isl., N & C Eur., Sib. E to   Alas.–Labr., Nov Scot. S to Color.
Kamch.

AËDES RIPARIUS Dyar & Kn.

N & C Eur. E to Ural; E Sib.   Alas.–Ontar. & New York, S to Color.

AËDES STICTICUS Meig. (*hirsuteron* Theob.)

Brit. Isl., N & C Eur., W & E Sib.   Alas.–Queb. & New Engl., S to Texas.

AËDES VEXANS Meig.

Brit. Isl., Eur. (widely), W & N Asia   Yukon & Brit. Col.–Nov. Scot., S to
E to Ussuri.   Color. & Texas.
E & S Asia, Austral.

CULEX MOLESTUS Forsk.[1]

Brit. Isl., Eur. (widely), Russia (without   Calif.–New York (limits not determined).
further details)., N. Afr.

---

[1] Often regarded as a form of *pipiens* L.

CULEX PIPIENS L.

Brit. Isl., Eur. (generally), N. Afr., W & N Asia E to Amur & China.

Brit. Col.–Nov. Scot.; U.S.A. (generally).

S. Amer., E & S Afr.

CULEX TERRITANS Wlk. (*apicalis* auctt., nec Adams)

Brit. Isl., N, C & SE Eur., N. Afr., Cauc., W. Turcest.

Alas.–New Engl., S to Flor. & Texas.

CULISETA (THEOBALDIA) ALASKAENSIS Ludl.

Brit. Isl., N & C Eur., Cauc., Sib. E to Kamch.

Alas.–Queb. & Labr., S to Color.

CULISETA (THEOBALDIA) MORSITANS Theob.

Brit. Isl., N, C & SE Eur., Cauc., W Sib.

Brit. Col.–Labr., Nov. Scot. & NE U.S.A., S to Color.

Tabanidae—Horse flies & clegs

CHRYSOPS NIGRIPES Zett.

N Fennoscand., Eur. Russ. S to Leningrad, Sib. E to Kamch. & Sakhal.

Alas.–Maine.

TABANUS (HYBOMITRA, TYLOSTYPIA) AEQUETINCTUS Becker (*flavipes* Wied.)

NE Russ., Sib. E to Kamch. & Anadyr.

Wisc., Labr.

TABANUS (HYBOMITRA, TYLOSTYPIA) LAPPONICUS Wahlb. (*astutus* O. S.[1], ?*typhus* Whitn.)

N & C Eur., Sib. E to Kamch.

Brit. Col.–Labr., NE U.S.A.

TABANUS (HYBOMITRA, TYLOSTYPIA) SEXFASCIATUS Hine (*anderi* Kauri[1], *borealis* auctt., in part.)

N Fennoscand. (distr. imperfectly known).

Alas., Labr.

Hymenoptera—Wasps, &c.

Only a few groups of the *Aculeata* were considered sufficiently known for the present purpose. In all of them, the catalogue of Muesebeck, Krombein & Townes (1951) provided an excellent source of knowledge.

---

[1] This synonymy was established by Mr. H. Kauri.

Apidae, Bombinae—Bumblebees

Besides the catalogue of 1951, Lutz & Cockerell (1920) has been used for the Nearctic, Skorikov (1937), Henriksen (1937), and Pittioni (1942–43) for the Circumpolar fauna.

BOMBUS ARCTICUS Kby.[1]

N Eur., N. Zeml., Sib. E to Kamch. Alas.–Labr., Greenl. (N to 81°50′).

BOMBUS BALTEATUS Dahlb.

f. typ. (and related forms). sbsp. *kirbiellus* Curt. (and related forms)
N Eur., N. Zeml., Sib. E to Kamch. Alas.–Labr., in Rocky Mts. S to Ariz.
& Bering Strait.

BOMBUS HYPERBOREUS Schnh.

N Eur., N. Zeml., Sib. E at least to Alas.–Baffin L., Greenl. (N to 81°30′).
Lena R.

BOMBUS LAPPONICUS F.

f. typ. (and related forms) sbsp. *sylvicola* Kby.[2] (and related forms)
Brit. Isl., Eur. (boreoalpine), N Asia Aleut. Isl., Alas.–Labr., Baffin L., in
E to Kolyma & Kamch., S to Pamir. Rocky Mts. S to Ariz.

Crabronidae

Here all necessary information was gathered from Leclercq (1954, p. 126, &c.).

CROSSOCERUS (COELOCRABRO) AMBIGUUS Dahlb.

Brit. Isl., Eur. E to Ural, N China, † E Can., NE U.S.A., S to N. Carol.,
Hokkaido. W to Iowa.

ECTEMNIUS (HYPOCRABRO) CONTINUUS F.

Brit. Isl., Eur. (generally), N. Afr., Asia Alas.–E Can., U.S.A. (generally).
E to Amur & Kamch., Japan. Mexico.

ECTEMNIUS DIVES Lep. & Brull.

Brit. Isl., Eur. (widely), Sib. E to Brit. Col.–E Can., U.S.A. to Color.
Kamch., Japan.

---

[1] In the catalogue of 1951 (p. 1253) and, doubtfully, by Lutz & Cockerell (1920, p. 507) *arcticus* Kby. is regarded as a synonym of *hyperboreus* Schnh. Cf. Pittioni, 1942 (p. 182, a.f.).
[2] Often regarded as distinct species.

ECTEMNIUS (CLYTOCHRYSUS) LAPIDARIUS Panz. (*comptus* Lep. & Brull.)

Brit. Isl., Eur. (generally), Cauc., W   Alas.–Labr., Nfld., U.S.A. (generally).
Sib., Amur, Sakhal., Japan.

ECTEMNIUS (CLYTOCHRYSUS) NIGRIFRONS Cress.

Brit. Isl., Eur. (generally), W Sib.,   Wash.–E Can., Nfld., U.S.A. (generally).
Kamch., Sakhal., Japan.

ECTEMNIUS (METACRABRO) QUADRICINCTUS F.

Brit. Isl., Eur. (except the north).   † E Can., NE U.S.A. S to Maryl., W to
                                              Illin.

RHOPALUM (CRABRO, EUPLILIS) CLAVIPES L.

Brit. Isl., Eur. E to Ural.   (†) Wash.–Calif.; NE U.S.A.

RHOPALUM (CRABRO) COARCTATUM Scop.

Brit. Isl., Eur. (widely), Sib. E to   Brit. Col.–E Can., N U.S.A.
Baical.

Vespidae, Vespinae—True Wasps

The records for North America were obtained from the 1951 catalogue, those for
the Old World mainly from Berland (1928) and Weyrauch (1937).

VESPA (VESPULA) ADULTERINA Buyss.

f. typ.   sbsp. *arctica* Rohw.
Mts. of C Eur., Cauc., Mongol., Sakhal.   Alas.–N. Carol.
Brit. Col.–Color.

VESPA (VESPULA) AUSTRIACA Panz.

N & C Eur., Asia E to Kamch.   Alas.–New Jers., S to Color.

VESPA CRABRO L. (incl. several forms)

Brit. Isl., Eur. (widely), N. Afr., W &   † Atl. States of U.S.A. (sbsp. *germana*
N Asia.   Christ., of C Eur.).

VESPA (VESPULA) NORVEGICA F.

f. typ.   sbsp. *albida* Slad.   sbsp. *norvegicoides* Slad.
Eur., Sib. E to Kamch.   Alas.–Labr.   Alas.–N. Carol.
& Sakhal.

VESPA (VESPULA) RUFA L.

f. typ.	sbsp. *schrenki* Rad. (*sibirica* And.)	6 sbspp.
Eur., W & C Asia E to Kamch.	E Sib., Mong., China.	Alas.–Nov. Scot., S to Ariz.

VESPA (VESPULA) VULGARIS L.

Eur., Palaearctic Asia.   Alas.–N. Carol., S to New Mex.

Formicidae—Ants

There is a good deal of difference of opinion among North American myrmecologists concerning the taxonomic relationship of Nearctic and Palaearctic forms within such genera as *Formica, Leptothorax, Lasius, Myrmica,* &c. Marion R. Smith, in the Catalogue of 1951, represents a more liberal view in this respect. On the recommendation of Mr. I. H. H. Yarrow, British Museum, I have here followed the more restrictive position taken by Creighton (1940). Genus *Lasius* has been treated according to Wilson's monograph (1955) though with re-established subspecific names, consistently abandoned by this author.—The distribution in Eurasia was mainly compiled from Donisthorpe (1927) and Stitz (1939).

ANERGATES ATRATULUS Schenck (*friedlandi* Creighton)

Brit. Isl. (1 loc.), C Eur. N to S   (†)[1] Connect.–Virginia.
Sweden, W & E Sib.

CAMPONOTUS HERCULEANUS L.

N & C Eur., Cauc., N & C Asia E to   Alas.–Nfld., N U.S.A., S (in the mts.)
Amur, China & Sakhal.   to New Mex. & Penns.
† Brit. Isl.

CAMPONOTUS NEARCTICUS Emery (*pavidus* Wheel.)

† Brit. Isl.   Brit. Col.–Calif.; NE U.S.A., S to Tex.

CAMPONOTUS PENNSYLVANICUS DeG.[2]

† Brit. Isl.   E Can., E half of U.S.A., S to the Mex.
                    Gulf.

---

[1] *Vide* p. 234.
[2] Regarded as sbsp. of *herculeanus* L. by Smith (1951).

CREMATOGASTER LINEOLATA Say

† Brit. Isl.   E Can., E U.S.A., S to Color. & Flor.
                                    (often indoors).

FORMICA CINEREA Mayr

f. typ.   sbsp. *lepida* Wheel.[1]
Eur. (except Brit. Isl. & the north),   W Can.–Calif. & Utah, E to N. & S.
Cauc., Asia Minor.   Dakota.

FORMICA FUSCA L.

Brit. Isl., N & C Eur., N & C Asia E   Alas.–Labr., Nfld., N U.S.A. S to Ariz.
to Amur, China, Kamch. & Sakhal.

FORMICA RUFIBARBIS F.

f. typ.   sbsp. *occidua*[1] Wheel.   sbsp. *gnava* Buckl.[1]
Brit. Isl., Eur. (widely),   Wash.–Calif.   Utah–Tex., Mexico.
Cauc., N. & C Asia E to
Lena R. & Manchur.

FORMICA SANGUINEA Latr.

f. typ.   sbsp. *subnuda* Emery[2]
Brit. Isl., Eur. (generally), Cauc., N &   Alas.–Labr., Nfld., NE U.S.A., in Rocky
C Asia E to Amur, Japan.   Mts. S to Ariz.

IRIDIOMYRMEX HUMILIS Mayr

Cosmopolitan.

† Brit. Isl., W & C Eur. (indoors).   † S U.S.A., N to S. Carol.
Indigenous in S. Amer.

LASIUS ALIENUS Foerst.

f. typ.   sbsp. *americanus* Emery[3]
                                    (*pallitarsus* Prov.)
Brit. Isl., Eur. (widely), N. Afr., Cauc.,   Brit. Col. –Nov. Scot. (with gaps), S to
N & C Asia, China, Japan.   Ariz. & Flor.; Mexico.

LASIUS FLAVUS F.

f. typ.   sbsp. *brevicornis* Emery[3]
Brit. Isl., Eur. (except the   Wash.–Sask., S to   E Can. & U.S.A. E of
north), Cauc., Asia Minor,   Color.   Rocky Mts., S to N. Carol.
Sib. E to Amur, Japan.   & Tenness.

---

[1] Possibly distinct species, according to Yarrow (*in litt.*).

[2] Smith (1951) recognizes 5 North American sbspp. of *sanguinea* Latr. Wilson & Brown (1955) regard *sanguinea* Latr. as a purely Eurasian species.

[3] Wilson (1955, p. 62 a.f.) in principle does not use subspecific names in *Lasius* but the Palae- and Nearctic forms are (in part) identical in *flavus* F. only.

LASIUS NIGER L.

f. typ.
Brit. Isl., Eur. (generally), N. Afr., Cauc., Sib. E to Amur & Kamch., China, Japan.

sbsp.[1]
Wash.–New Mex. (in the mts.).

LASIUS UMBRATUS Nyl. (incl. *mixtus* Nyl.)

f. typ.
Brit. Isl., Eur. (widely), Cauc., Hither Asia. (Distr. in N & C Asia uncertain.)

sbsp.[1]
E Can., Nov. Scot., E U.S.A., W to Idaho, S to Flor. & Ariz.

MONOMORIUM DESTRUCTOR Jerd.

Cosmopolitan.

† Brit. Isl. (hothouses).
† SE U.S.A.
Indigenous in S Asia.

MONOMORIUM PHARAONIS L.

Cosmopolitan.

† Brit. Isl., Eur. (widely, indoors).
† Can. & U.S.A. (widely, indoors; fieldadaption in Flor.).
Probably indigenous in S Asia.

MYRMICA LAEVINODIS Nyl.

Brit. Isl., N & C Eur., N Asia to E Sib., Manchur., Japan.
† Queb., Mass.

MYRMICA LOBICORNIS Nyl.

f. typ. (incl. several forms)
Brit. Isl., N & C Eur., C Asia.

sbsp. *lobifrons* Perg.
Alas.–Ariz.

sbsp. *fracticornis* Emery
W Can.–Nfld., S to New Mex.

ODONTOMACHUS HAEMATODA L.

F. typ. almost cosmopolitan in the tropics.

f. typ.
† W Eur. (hothouses). *Not* introduced from N. Amer.!

4 sbspp.
Southernmost U.S.A., W Indies, Mexico.

PARATRECHINA (PRENOLEPIS) LONGICORNIS Latr.

Cosmopolitan.

† Brit. Isl., W Eur. (indoors).
† E U.S.A., N to New York (outdoors in the Gulf Coast area only).
Probably indigenous in S Asia.

---

[1] Wilson (1955, p. 62 a. f.) in principle does not use subspecific names in *Lasius* but the Palae- and Nearctic forms are (in part) identical in *flavus* F. only.

PARATRECHINA (NYLANDERIA) VIVIDULA Nyl.

Cosmopolitan.

† Brit. Isl., W Eur. (hothouses).   † SE U.S.A. (in hothouses farther north).

Indigenous in S. America.

PHEIDOLE ANASTASII Emery

† Brit. Isl., W & C Eur. (hothouses).   † E Can., E U.S.A. (fieldadaption in S
                                           Flor.).

From C America.

POLYERGUS RUFESCENS Latr.

f. typ.   3–4 sbspp.

Eur. (except Brit. Isl.), N to S Sweden,   Brit. Col.–Calif. & Ariz., E to Ontar. &
C Asia.   Mich.

PONERA COARCTATA Latr. (fig. 35)

f. typ.   sbsp. *pennsylvanica* Buckl.

Brit. Isl., S & C Eur., Cauc., N. Afr.   Queb.–Gulf of Mexico, W to S. Dak. &
                                           Kans.

Two further sbspp. are recorded from Africa & Austral.

PONERA ERGATANDRIA For.

sbsp. *bondroiti* For.   *f. typ.*
† Belgium (hothouses).   Texas, Flor.; W. Indies.
Not introduced from N. Amer.!
Probably indigenous in S. Amer.

PONERA OPACICEPS Mayr

† Brit. Isl. (hothouses).   S & SW U.S.A., C. & S. America.

TAPINOMA (TAPINOSOMA) MELANOCEPHALUM F.

Cosmopolitan in the tropics.

† Brit. Isl. (hothouses).   † Flor., Georgia.

Probably indigenous in S. America.

TETRAMORIUM CAESPITUM L.

Brit. Isl., Eur. (generally), N. Afr.,   (†)[1] Calif.; NE U.S.A., S to Tenness.,
Cauc., W, N & C Asia E to Lena R.,   W to Nebr.
China, Japan.

2–3 sbspp. in tropical Africa.

---

[1] *Vide* p. 234.

TETRAMORIUM GUINEENSE F.
Cosmopolitan in the tropics.

† Brit. Isl., C Eur. (hothouses).   † S Flor., Texas, in hothouses farther
                                          north.
              Possibly indigenous in W Africa.

TETRAMORIUM SIMILLIMUM F. Smith
Cosmopolitan in the tropics.

† Brit. Isl. (hothouses).   S Flor., in hothouses farther north.
(Intr. from N. Amer.?)

              Native country unknown.

TRIGLYPHOTRIX STRIATIDENS Emery
Almost cosmopolitan.

† Brit. Isl., W Eur. (hothouses).   † SE U.S.A. N to S. Carol.
              Indigenous in S Asia.

WASMANNIA AUROPUNCTATA Rog.

† Brit. Isl. (hothouses).   † S Flor., Calif.
              Indigenous in C & S America.

Odonata—Dragonflies

For North America the new works of Walker (1953) and Needham & Westfall (1955) have been consulted. The more scattered Old World literature is represented by Valle (1932, 1952) and Ander (1950). The almost cosmopolitan *Pantala flavescens* F. seems not to have been found with certainty in Europe as yet and was therefore omitted.

AESCHNA COERULEA Stroem

f. typ.   sbsp. *septentrionalis* Burm.
Eur. (boreo-alpine), W Sib.–Lena R.   Alas.–Nova Scot., Nfld., S to N. Hampsh.

AESCHNA JUNCEA L.

f. typ.   sbsp. *orientalis* Bart.   sbsp. ?
Eur., Asia E to Amur,   NE Sib., Sakhal., Japan.   Alas.–Labr., Nfld., S to
? Kamch.   Color.

AESCHNA SUBARCTICA Walk.

sbsp. *interlineata* Ander
W & C Eur., N to S
Sweden.

sbsp. *elisabethae* Djak.
N & E Eur., E to Ar-
chang. (Possibly confused
with *juncea* in N Asia.)

f. typ.
Brit. Col.–Nova Scot., S
to Michig.

ENALLAGMA CYATHIGERUM Charp.

Eur., entire N Asia, E to Kamch.

Alas.–Nfld., S to Calif. & Utah.

LESTES DRYAS Kby.

Eur., Sib. E to Ussuri, Japan.

Alas.–Nova Scot.

LIBELLULA QUADRIMACULATA L. (fig. 51)

Eur., Sib. E to Kamch., Sakhal.,
Japan, S to Kashmir.

Alas.–Nova Scot., Nfld., S to Ariz.

SOMATOCHLORA SAHLBERGI Tryb.

N Fennoscand. (Petsamo, Kola), N
Sib. (Yenisei, Lena R.).

Alas., N. W. Terr.

SYMPETRUM DANAE Sulz.

Eur., Sib. E to Kamch., Ussuri, Japan.

Alas.–Nfld., S to Calif. & Color.

Orthoptera Saltatoria—Grasshoppers & Crickets

The North American records were mainly compiled from Blatchley (1920), those
from the Old World from Ander (1951), Holdhaus (1954), &c.

AREOPEDELLUS (DASYHIPPUS) VARIEGATUS Fisch.

Eur. (boreoalpine), in the north from
N Finl. through Sib. E to Kamch.

Alaska.

GRYLLOTALPA GRYLLOTALPA L. (*vulgaris* Latr.)

Brit. Isl., Eur. (ecxept the north), N.
Afr., W & C Asia.

† NE U.S.A.

GRYLLUS (GRYLLULUS) DOMESTICUS L.

† Brit. Isl., Eur. (generally; indoors).
N. Afr., W & S Asia.

† E U.S.A., E Can., W to Rocky Mts.

MELANOPLUS (PODISMA) FRIGIDUS Boh.

Eur. (boreoalpine), N Asia E to Manchur., Kamch. & Sakhal.   Alas., N. W. Terr.

ROESELIANA ROESELII Hag.

Brit. Isl., C & S Eur. E to Ural, W Sib.   † Montreal (probably intr. with aircraft; Urquhart & Beaudry, 1953, p. 78).

TACHYCINES (DIESTRAMMENA) ASYNAMORUS Adel. (*marmoratus* DeH., *japanicus* Blatch.)

Cosmopolitan.

† Icel., Brit. Isl., Eur. (widely; in hothouses).   † U.S.A., E Can. (widely; in hothouses).
† Greenl.

Probably indigenous in E Asia.

TETRIX (TETTIX, ACRYDIUM) SUBULATUS L. (*granulatus* Kby.)

Eur. (generally), W, N & C Asia, E to Lena R. & Amur.   Brit. Col.–Nova Scot., S to New Jersey & Kansas.

Araneae—Spiders

The literature dealing with the taxonomy and distribution of spiders is extensive but very scattered and the list of Eur-American species here repesented is probably incomplete. Roewer's catalogue (1942, 1954) is most useful but the records of distribution are quite summary. They were supplemented, for Europe by Simon (1914–37), Reimoser (1919), Holm (1950), for northern Asia by Charitonov (1932, 1936), for North America by Chamberlin & Ivie (1947), Comstock & Gertsch (1948), Gertsch (1949), Hackman (1954), and several other papers listed in the bibliography (p. 126 a.f.).

Earlier, less complete lists of Eur-American species were published by Berland (1932, p. 379) and Gertsch (1949, p. 259). My preliminary list, compiled from the literature, was sent to Dr. W. J. Gertsch, New York, who kindly corrected and enlarged it to a great extent. I also received many valuable suggestions from Mr. H. Kauri, Lund, and Dr. Å. Holm, Uppsala. The final list here given deviates from the opinion of Dr. Gertsch only in so far that a few more species are regarded as introduced; these are marked with a cross in brackets.

Erigone arctica White and *E. atra* Bl. have been excluded from the list on the advice of Dr. Holm.

Dysderidae

DYSDERA CROCATA C. L. Koch

Cosmopolitan.

(†) Brit. Isl., S Eur. N to N France &   † U.S.A. (widely), S Can.; Bermudas.
S Russ., Cauc., N. Afr.

Scytodidae

SCYTODES THORACICA Latr.

† Brit. Isl., Eur. (widely, indoors),   † U.S.A. E of Mississippi, E Can.
E to S Russ.

S & E Asia.

Pholcidae

PHOLCUS PHALANGIOIDES Fuessl.

Cosmopolitan.

Brit. Isl., Eur. (widely, indoors),   † Entire U.S.A., S Can. (usually in-
E to Russ., Cauc.   doors).
Afr., Asia.   † S. Amer.

PHOLCUS OPILIONOIDES Schrank (*manueli* Gertsch)

C & S Eur., S Russ., Turkest., China.   † NE U.S.A.

PSILOCORUS (PSHYSOCYCLUS) SIMONI Berl. (*simplicior* Ch. & Iv.)

† France, Engl. (indoors).   Calif., Oreg.

Theridiidae

CRUSTULINA STICTA Cambr.

Brit. Isl., NW, W & S Eur.   N U.S.A., S Can.

CTENIUM (ROBERTUS) LIVIDUM Blackw.

Faeroes, Brit. Isl., Eur. (widely), N.   Alaska.
Zeml., W & N Asia E to Kamch.

DIPOENA PRONA Menge (*hamata* Tullgr.)

Brit. Isl., N & C Eur., Hung., Corfu.   (†) U.S.A. (widely).

STEATODA BIPUNCTATA L.

Icel., Brit. Isl. (mostly indoors), Eur. † Mass.; E Can., Nfld.
(widely), W & N Asia E to Kamch.

TEUTANA CASTANEA Cl.

N, C & S Eur. (*not* Brit. Isl.), Turkest.   † Ontario (hothouses).

TEUTANA GROSSA C. L. Koch
Almost cosmopolitan.

(†) Brit. Isl., Eur. (widely), W Sib.   † Brit. Col.–S Calif.; N. Carol.–Tex.

TEUTANA TRIANGULOSA Walck.

C & S Eur. (*not* Brit. Isl.), N. Afr.,   † U.S.A. (widely), S Can.
Cauc., W. Turkest.

THERIDIUM BERKELEYI Em.

Sweden.   Calif.–New Jers., Ontario.

THERIDIUM (NEOTTIURA) BIMACULATUM L.

Brit. Isl., Eur. (widely), W Sib.   † Brit. Col., Wash.

THERIDIUM IMPRESSUM L. Koch

Brit. Isl., Eur., Cauc., W & N Asia   Alaska–Alberta & N. W. Terr.
E to Kamch.

THERIDIUM MELANURUM Hahn (*denticulatum* Walck.)

Brit. Isl., Eur. (generally), N. Afr., W   Brit. Col.–Calif. & Utah.
& C Asia.

THERIDIUM OHLERTI Thor. (*umbraticum* L. Koch, *lundbecki* Sør., *simulatum* Em.)

N & C Eur. (boreoalpine), Sib.   Alas., Can., Calif. & New Mex. (moun-
(Yenisei).   tains); Greenl.

THERIDIUM ORNATUM Hahn (*pictum* Walck., *zelotypum* Em.)

Brit. Isl., Eur. (generally), N. Afr., Sib.   N. W. Terr., Manit., Utah.
E to Kamch.

THERIDIUM (ENOPLOGNATHA) OVATUM Cl. (*redimitum* Cl., *lineatum* L.)

Brit. Isl., Eur. (widely), N. Afr., Cauc.,   † Brit. Col.–Calif.; Nov. Scot.–New
W. Turkest.; Japan.   York.

THERIDIUM PETRAEUM L. Koch

C & S Eur., N. Afr.   (†) Wash.–Calif.; Ontario, Maine.

THERIDIUM SIMILE C. L. Koch

Brit. Isl., Eur. (widely), E to S Russ.,   † Brit. Col.–Wash.
Mediterr.

THERIDIUM (ACHAEARANEA) TEPIDARIORUM C. L. Koch
Cosmopolitan.

† Icel., Brit. Isl., Eur. (widely, hot-   † U.S.A. (widely) & S Can. (indoors in
houses); W Sib., China.   the north).

Originally tropical.

THERIDIUM (ENOPLOGNATHA) THORACICUM Hahn

Brit. Isl., Eur. (widely), N. Afr.   † Oregon.

THERIDIUM TINCTUM Walck.

Brit. Isl., Eur. (generally), Cauc.;   † Wash., Oregon.
Japan.

THERIDIUM VARIANS Hahn

Icel., Brit. Isl., Eur. (generally), N.   † Brit. Col.–Wash.
Afr., W & N Asia E at least to Yenisei.

THERIDULA GONYGASTER SIM. (*opulenta* auctt. eur., nec Walck.)
Almost cosmopolitan in the tropics.

† France, Corsica (probably not in-   Florida.
troduced from America).

Afr., Madag.; Japan.   W. Ind., C. & S. Amer.

Nesticidae

NESTICUS CELLULANUS Cl. (*terrestris* Em.)

Brit. Isl., Eur. E to C Russ.   † NE U.S.A.

NESTICUS (EIDMANELLA) PALLIDUS Em.

† England.   Brit. Col., entire U.S.A., Nov. Scot.,
                                            Nfld.

† Hawaii.   C & S Amer.

Linyphiidae

AGYNETA CAUTA Cambr.

Brit. Isl., Eur. (boreoalpine).   NE U.S.A., E Can., Nfld.

BATHYPHANTES (STYLOPHORA) CONCOLOR Wid.

Brit. Isl., Eur. (generally), E to S Russ.,   (†) NE U.S.A., W at least to Wisc., E
Madeira, W Sib.   Can., Nfld.

BATHYPHANTES GRACILIS Blackw.

Brit. Isl., Eur. (except the south), Sib.   (†) Nfld.
E to Kamch. & Sakhal.

BATHYPHANTES (STYLOPHORA) NIGRINUS Westr.

Brit. Isl., Eur. (widely), E to S Russ.,   N U.S.A., W to Oreg., E Can.
W Sib.

BATHYPHANTES PULLATUS Cambr. (*kuratai* Ch. & Iv.)

Brit. Isl., N & W Eur., Eur. Russ.;   Alas., Wyom., Queb., Nfld.
Kamch.

BATHYPHANTES SETIGER F. Cambr. (*hyperboreus* Holm, *josephus* Ch. & Iv.)

Brit. Isl., N & C Eur.   Alaska.

CENTROMERUS (CENTROMERITA, CENTROMERINUS) BICOLOR Blackw.

Faeroes, Brit. Isl., N & C Eur. E to   (†) Nfld.
Moscow.

CENTROMERUS SYLVATICUS Blackw.

Brit. Isl., N & C Eur., Sib. E to   (†) NE U.S.A., E Can., Nfld.
Kamch.

ESTRANDIA (LINYPHIA) GRANDAEVA Keys. (*tridens* Schenk., *nearctica* Banks)

N Fennoscand.; Kamch.   Alas.–Nova Scot., Labr., Nfld., S to N.
                                       Carol.

HELOPHORA (LINYPHIA) INSIGNIS Blackw.

Brit. Isl., N & C Eur., Sib. E to   Alas.–Nova Scot., Nfld., S to Penns. &
Kamch.   Wisc.

LEPTHYPHANTES COMPLICATUS Em. (*umbraticola* Keys., *audax* Sør.)

Icel., Scotl., Eur. (boreoalpine), Spitzb.   Alas., Labr., Nfld.; Greenl.

LEPTHYPHANTES LEPROSUS Ohl.

Icel., Faeroes, Brit. Isl., Eur. (generally),   (†) N U.S.A., Nova Scot., Nfld.
Hither Asia; Kamch.

LEPTHYPHANTES MINUTUS Blackw.

Brit. Isl., N & C Eur. E to Eur. Russ.   E U.S.A. W to Mich.

LEPTHYPHANTES NEBULOSUS Sund.

Brit. Isl., Eur. (widely), Sib. E to   (†) U.S.A. (widely), W at least to Mon-
Kamch.   tana & Utah; Nov. Scot.

LINYPHIA MARGINATA C. L. Koch (*triangularis* Walck.)

Brit. Isl., Eur. (widely), Hither Asia,   Alas.; Nov. Scot., Nfld., S to Texas.
W Sib.; China, Japan.

MACRARGUS (MICRONETA) MULTESIMUS Cambr.

N Scand., Sib.   NE U.S.A.

MICROLINYPHIA (LINYPHIA, PUSILLIA) IMPIGRA Cambr. (*cayuga* Em.)

Brit. Isl., C Eur., W Sib.   Alas.; Ont., New York.

MICRONETA (MICRONETARIA) VIARIA Blackw.

Brit. Isl., Eur. (generally) E to Volga,   Alas.–E Can., S at least to Illin. & New
N. Afr., Hither Asia.   York.

OREONETIDES VAGINATUS Thor. (*adipatus* L. Koch)

Brit. Isl., Eur. (boreoalpine), N. Zeml.,   Alas., Labr., NE U.S.A., Nfld.; Greenl.
Sib. E to Kamch.

Erigonidae (Micryphantidae)

AULACOCYBA SUBITANEA Cambr.

Icel., Brit. Isl., W Eur. N to Sweden,   (†) Mass.
N. Afr.

COLLINSIA (CORYPHAEOLANA) HOLMGRENI Thor. (*mendica* L. Koch)

Spitzb., Jan Mayen, Icel., Faeroes,   Alas.; Labr., Baffin L., Greenl.
Scotl., Eur. (boreoalpine), N. Zeml.,
Sib. E to Kamch.

COLLINSIA (MICROERIGONE, TYPHOCHRAESTUS) SPETSBERGENSIS Thor. (*oxycephala*
L. Koch)

Spitzb., Icel., N Scand., N. Zeml., Sib.   Alaska; Greenl.
E to Lena R.

CORNICULARIA CUSPIDATA Blackw. (*brevicula* Cby. & Bish.)

Icel., Faeroes, Brit. Isl., N & C Eur.;   (†) New York, Nfld.
Kamch.

CORNICULARIA KARPINSKII Cambr.

Spitzb., Icel., Brit. Isl., Eur. (boreo-   Labr., Nfld., Greenl.
alpine), Sib. E to Kamch.

CORNICULARIA UNICORNIS Cambr.

Brit. Isl., N & C Eur. E to Moscow.   (†) Nfld.

DIPLOCENTRIA (SCOTOUSSA) BIDENTATA Em. (*rivalis* Cambr.)

Icel., Brit. Isl., Eur. (boreoalpine),   Alas.–Labr., Nfld., S to Color.
E to Czechosl.

DIPLOCEPHALUS CRISTATUS Blackw.

Icel., Faeroes, Brit. Isl., Eur. (generally),   (†) NE U.S.A. W to Wisc., E Can.,
N. Afr., Sib. E to Kamch.   Nfld.
                              † New Zeal.

DISMODICUS BIFRONS Blackw.

f. typ.   sbsp. *decemoculatus* Em.
Icel., Brit. Isl., N & C Eur., Sib. E to   Alas.–Nfld., N U.S.A.
Transbaic.

ENTELECARA (MYTHOPLASTOIDES) MEDIA Kulcz. (*sombra* Ch. & Iv.)

Eur. (boreoalpine), Sib. E to Kamch.   Alaska.

EPERIGONE MACULATA Banks

† Switzerl. (hothouse).   E U.S.A. W to Kansas, Nfld.

ERIGONE PSYCHROPHILA Thor.

Spitzb., Fr. Jos. L., Icel., Faeroes, N   Alas., Grant L., Ellesm. L., Greenl.
Scand., N. Zeml., Sib. E to Kamch.

ERIGONE TIROLENSIS L. Koch

Spitzb., Jan Mayen, Icel., Scotl., Eur.   Alas.; Labr., Baffin L., Ellesm. I..,
(boreoalpine), N. Zeml., Sib. E to   Greenl.
Kamch.

GONATIUM RUBENS Blackw.

Icel., Faeroes, Brit. Isl., Eur. (widely),   (†) Ontar., E U.S.A., S to Flor., W at
W Sib.   least to Wisc.

HILAIRA FRIGIDA Thor.

Jan Mayen, Icel., Faeroes, Brit. Isl., N   Labr., Baffin L., Greenl.
Eur.; Kamch.

HILAIRA (UTOPIELLUM) HERNIOSA Thor. (*mirabilis* L. Koch, *consimilis* Cambr.)

Eur. (boreoalpine), W Sib.   Arct. Can., Nfld.

HYPSELISTES FLORENS Cambr.

Brit. Isl., W Sib.   Alas., S Can., N U.S.A.

ISLANDIANA (ADUVA) ALATA Em.

N Scand.   Alas.–NE U.S.A. (mts.), S to Wyom.;
                                             Nfld.

MASO (CASEOLA) SUNDEVALLI Westr. (*herbicola* Em.)

Icel., Brit. Isl., Eur. (widely), Sib.   Alas., NE U.S.A., E Can., Nfld.
E to Kamch.

MONOCEPHALUS (THYREOSTHENIUS, HORMATHION) PARASITICUS Westr. (*becki* Cambr.,
                          limnatus Cby. & Bish.)

Icel., Brit. Isl., N & C Eur.   NE U.S.A., W to Wisc., Nfld.

MINYRIOLOIDES TRIFRONS Cambr.

f. typ.   sbsp. *aquatilis* Cby. & Bish. (*affinis*
                                             Schenk.)
Brit. Isl., N & W Eur.; Kamch.   New York.

POCADICNEMIS PUMILA Blackw.

Brit. Isl., Eur. (generally), E to Moscow.   Alas.–E Can., N U.S.A.

RHAEBOTHORAX (TYPHOCHRAESTUS) BOREALIS Jacks. (incl. *thori* Jacks.)

Spitzb., Icel., N Scand.   Labr., Greenl.

RHAEBOTHORAX PAETULUS Cambr.

Eur. (boreoalpine).   Alas.; Greenl.

SISICUS APERTUS Holm (*longitarsi* Ch. & Iv.)

N Scand., Switzerl.   Alaska.

TIBIOPLUS NEARCTICUS Ch. & Iv.

N Sweden.   Alaska.

TRACHYNELLA (TRACHYNOTUS) NUDIPALPIS Westr.

Icel., Faeroes, Brit. Isl., Eur. E to   (†) Nfld.
Moscow.

TRICHOPTERNA (PELECOPSIS, LOPHOCARENUM) MENGEI Sim. (*excavata* Em.)

Brit. Isl., N & C Eur. (not in Russ.).   (†) NE U.S.A., E Can., Nfld.

WALCKENAERA (SPIROPALPUS, CORNICULARIA) VIGILAX Blackw. (*spiralis* Em.)

Brit. Isl., Eur. (widely), E to Volga and   E U.S.A., W to Wyom. & Missouri, S
Crimea.   to Louis. & Georg.

ZORNELLA (LINYPHIA) CULTRIGERA L. Koch

Fennoscand., W Sib.   Alas. & Brit. Col.–NE U.S.A., S to
Utah; Nfld.

Araneidae (Argiopidae)

ARANEUS CORNUTUS Cl. (*foliatus* Fourc.)

Icel., Brit. Isl., Eur. (generally), N & C   Alas.–E Can., N U.S.A., Nfld.; Greenl.
Asia E to Kamch., China.

ARANEUS DIADEMATUS Cl. (*diadema* L.)

Icel., Brit. Isl., Eur. (generally), N & C   † Brit. Col. & Wash.–New Engl., Nov.
Asia E to Kamch.   Scot., Nfld.; Greenl.

ARANEUS DISPLICATUS Hentz

sbsp. *westringi* Thor.   *f. typ.*
Brit. Isl., Eur. (widely but local), Sib.   Alas.–Nfld., S to Georgia.
E to Lena R.

ARANEUS MARMOREUS Cl. (*raji* Scop.)

Brit. Isl., Eur. (generally), Cauc., Sib.   Alas., N U.S.A., E Can.
E to Amur & Kamch.

ARANEUS NORDMANNI Thor.

N, C & E Eur. (*not* Brit. Isl.); Trans-   Alas. & Oreg.–E Can., NE U.S.A.
baic.

ARANEUS PATAGIATUS Cl. (*ocellatus* Cl., *dumetorum* Vill.)

Icel., Brit. Isl., Eur. (generally), N.   Alas.–Labr., Nfld., N & NE U.S.A.;
Afr., W & N Asia E to Kamch.   Greenl.

ARANEUS QUADRATUS Cl.

Brit. Isl., Eur. (generally), Sib. E to   Alaska, Yukon; Greenl.
Kamch.

ARANEUS SCLOPETARIUS Cl. (*sericatus* Cl., *oviger* Panz.)

Icel., Brit. Isl., Eur. (widely) E to   E U.S.A. (generally) W at least to Wisc.,
Volga & S Russ., C Asia, China, Japan.   E Can., Nfld.

CERCIDIA PROMINENS Westr.

Brit. Isl., Eur. (widely) E to Volga;   E Can., NE U.S.A. W at least to Wisc.
Kamch.

CYCLOSA CONICA Pall.

Brit. Isl., Eur. (generally), N. Afr.,   Alas.–Nfld., N U.S.A.
W & N Asia E to Transbaic.

META MENARDI Latr.

f. typ.   sbsp. *ovalis* Gertsch
Brit. Isl., Eur. (except the east), N.   NE U.S.A. W to Wisc., E Can., Nfld.
Afr., W & C Asia.
† Madagascar.

ZYGIELLA (ZILLA) CALOPHYLLA Walck. (*atrica* C. L. Koch)

Brit. Isl., Eur. E to S Russ.; Sakhal.   † E U.S.A., E Can.

ZYGIELLA (ZILLA) MONTANA C. L. Koch (nec auctt. americ.)

Mts. of C Eur., Cauc., W. Turcest.;   Brit. Col.–Calif.
Kamch.

ZYGIELLA (ZILLA) X-NOTATA Cl. (*litterata* Ol.)

Brit. Isl., Eur. (generally) E to S Russ.,   † Alaska–Calif.; E Can.–New Engl.
C Asia, Sakhal.   † S. Amer.

Tetragnathidae

PACHYGNATHA CLERCKI Sundev. (*sewardi* Ch. & Iv.)

Brit. Isl., Eur. (generally), Sib. E to   Alaska.
Kamch., Japan

TETRAGNATHA EXTENSA L. (*groenlandica* Thor., *manitoba* Ch. & Iv.)

Icel., Brit. Isl., Eur. (generally), N.   Alas.–Nov. Scot., Labr., Nfld., N U.S.A.;
Afr., W & N Asia E to Kamch., China,   Greenl.
Japan.

Agelenidae

TEGENARIA AGRESTIS Walck. (*magnacava* Exl.)

Brit. Isl., Eur. E to C Russ. † Wash.

TEGENARIA ATRICA C. L. Koch (*saeva* Blackw., *gigantea* Ch. & Iv.)

Brit. Isl., Eur. (widely) E to S Russ. † Brit. Col.

TEGENARIA DOMESTICA Cl. (*derhami* Scop.)
Almost cosmopolitan.

Icel., Faeroes, Brit. Isl., Eur. (generally), † U.S.A. & S Can. (widely).
N. Afr., N. Zeml., Sib. E to Kamch.,
Japan. † C & S Amer.
India, Austral., Hawaii.

TEGENARIA LARVA Sim. (*praegrandis* Fox)

Brit. Isl., C & S Eur. (probably over- † Distr. of Columbia.
looked).

TEGENARIA PAGANA C. L. Koch (*simplex* Bryant, *antrias* Ch. & Iv.)

Brit. Isl., Eur., N. Afr., Hither Asia. † Calif., Tex., Alab.

Lycosidae

ALOPECOSA (TARENTULA) ACULEATA Cl. (*beani* Em.)

N & C Eur. (*not* Brit. Isl.), N & Alas. & Oreg.–Maine, Nfld.
C Asia E to Kamch.

ARCTOSA (LYCOSA) ALPIGENA Dol.

Icel., Brit. Isl., Eur. (boreomontane), Alas.–Labr., Nfld., S to Ariz.; Greenl.
W Sib.

PARDOSA (LYCOSA) PALUSTRIS L. (*tarsalis* Thor., *andersoni* Gertsch)

Icel., Faeroes, Brit. Isl., Eur. (gener- Alaska.
ally), N. Zeml., N & C Asia E to Kamch.
& Kuril.

PARDOSA (LYCOSA) SALTUARIA L. Koch (incl. *hyperborea* Thor.)

Icel., Eur. (boreoalpine), E to E. Prussia Alas.–Maine, Labr., Nfld.; Greenl.
& Kola Penins.

PIRATA INSULARIS Em. (*piccolo* Dahl)

N & C Eur. (*not* Brit. Isl.), E to C   E U.S.A., W at least to Wyom., Utah &
Russ. (possibly overlooked).   Color.; Nfld.

PIRATA PIRATICUS Cl.

Icel., Faeroes, Brit. Isl., Eur.   Alas.–Nfld., N U.S.A.; Greenl.
(generally), N. Afr., W Sib.

TROCHOSA (LYCOSA) TERRICOLA Thor.

f. typ.	sbsp. *orophila* Ch. & Gertsch	sbsp. *pratensis* Em.
Faeroes, Brit. Isl., Eur. (generally), Sib. E to Kamch.	Alas., W Can., Rocky Mts.	E Can., N & NE U.S.A., Nfld.

Gnaphosidae

GNAPHOSA MUSCORUM L. Koch (*conspersa* Thor.)

N & C Eur. (*not* Brit. Isl.), W Sib.   Alas.–Nfld., N U.S.A.

GNAPHOSA ORITES Chamb. (*humilis* Holm, *holmi* Tullgr., *labradorensis* Fox)

N Scandinavia.   Alas.; New Engl., Queb., Labr.

HAPLODRASSUS (DRASSODES) SIGNIFER C. L. Koch

Icel., Faeroes, Brit. Isl., Eur.   Alas.–Nfld., S to Ariz.; Greenl.
(generally), Hither Asia, W. Sib.

HERPYLLUS (SCOTOPHAEUS) BLACKWALLI Thor. (*pius* Chamb.)

Brit. Isl., W & C Eur. (mostly indoors), † Wash.–Calif., Louisiana.
Macaron.

SOSTOGEUS (SCOTOPHAEUS) LORICATUS L. Koch (*zygethus* Ch. & Gertsch)

C & E Eur. (*not* Brit. Isl.), Turcest., † Conn., Illin., Wisc., Utah.
Sib. E to Yenisei.

ZELOTES (DRASSYLLUS) RUSTICUS L. Koch (*femoralis* Banks, *razumowskii* Pav.)

Brit. Isl., C & S Eur., N. Afr., Cauc., † Wash.–Calif., Ariz.; Conn., Illin.,
W Sib.; Tongking.   Kans.

ZELOTES SUBTERRANEUS C. L. Koch

Eur. (widely, but *not* Brit. Isl.), W & N   Alas.–Nfld., S to Ariz.
Asia E to Kamch.

Clubionidae

CHEIRACANTHIUM MILDEI L. Koch

C & S Eur., Mediterr., Cauc.   † NE U.S.A., Utah.

CLUBIONA KULCZINSKII De Less. (*intermontana* Gertsch)

Eur. (boreoalpine); Kamch.   Brit. Col.–New Engl., S to Wyom.

CLUBIONA LUTESCENS Westr.

Brit. Isl., Eur. (widely), W Sib.; Japan.   † Wash.

CLUBIONA NORVEGICA E. Str. (*humida* Jacks., *californica* Fox)

Brit. Isl., N Scand.   Alas.–Calif., Nfld.

CLUBIONA PALLIDULA Cl. (*holosericea* L.)

Brit. Isl., Eur. (widely), Cauc., W Sib.   † Brit. Col.–Wash.

CLUBIONA TRIVIALIS C. L. Koch (*obtusa* Em.)

Faeroes, Brit. Isl., Eur. (boreoalpine).   Alas.–Maine, S to Utah.

MICARIA PULICARIA Sund. (*montana* Em.)

Brit. Isl., Eur. (widely), Sib. E to   (†) N U.S.A., W to Oreg., S to Ariz.,
Kamch.   Can. (widely), Nfld.

Xysticidae

CORIARACHNE VERSICOLOR Keys.

† SW France (1 ex.).   E U.S.A. & E Can., W to Manit. &
                                        Rocky Mts., Nov. Scot., Nfld.

MISUMENA VATIA Cl. (*calycina* L.)

Brit. Isl., Eur. (generally), Cauc., Sib.   Alas.–Nov. Scot., Nfld., S to Flor. &
E to Amur, Sakhal., Japan.   Texas.

OXYPTILA GERTSCHI Kurata

Sweden.   Alberta, Ontario.

OXYPTILA PRATICOLA C. L. Koch

Brit. Isl., Eur. (except the east).   † Wash.

XYSTICUS LABRADORENSIS Keys. (*deichmanni* Sør., *albidus* Grese)

N Fennoscand., N Russ., NW Sib.   Alas.–Labr., S to Calif. & Color.;
                                         Greenl.

Philodromidae

PHILODROMUS CAESPITICOLIS Walck. (*aureolus* Cl. in part, *canadensis* Em.)

Brit. Isl., Eur. (widely), Cauc., Sib. E   N U.S.A. & Can. (widely).
at least to Yenisei.

PHILODROMUS DISPAR Walck.

Brit. Isl., Eur. (widely), Cauc.   † Wash.

PHILODROMUS RUFUS Walck. (*pictus* Em.)

Brit. Isl., Eur. (except the north), N.   Alas.–Nfld., U.S.A. (widely).
Afr., W Sib.; Japan.

THANATUS COLORADENSIS Keys. (*alpinus* Kulcz.)

C Eur.   Rocky Mts. of U.S.A. & Can.

THANATUS FORMICINUS Cl. (*canadensis* Gertsch)

Brit. Isl., Eur. (generally), N. Afr., Sib. Can. & N U.S.A. (widely), Nfld.
E to Kamch.

THANATUS STRIATUS C. L. Koch (*walteri* Gertsch)

Brit. Isl., Eur. (except the east).   Alas., Idah.–Utah., NE U.S.A.

TIBELLUS MARITIMUS Menge

Brit. Isl., Eur. (widely), N. Afr., Sib.   Alas.–Nfld., U.S.A. (widely).
E to Kamch.

TIBELLUS OBLONGUS Walck. (*parallelus* Sim.)

Brit. Isl., Eur. (generally), N. Afr.,   Alas.–E Can., U.S.A. (widely).
Cauc., Sib. E to Kamch.

Salticidae

HASARIUS ADANSONI Aud.

Cosmopolitan in warm regions.

† Brit. Isl., Finl., France, S Eur. (hot-   † U.S.A. N to Wisc. & New York.
houses).

MENEMERUS (MARPISSA) BIVITTATUS Duf.

Almost cosmopolitan in warm regions.

† S Engl., France † Flor.–Texas.

NEON RETICULATUS Blackw.

Brit. Isl., Eur. (generally); Baical. Alas.–Oreg., Rocky Mts. S to Ariz.

PELLENES (EVARCHA) FALCATA Cl. (*flammata* Cl., *hoyi* Peckh.)

Brit. Isl., Eur. (widely), N. Afr., Sib. Alas.–Nfld., N U.S.A.
E to Amur & Kamch.

PHLEGRA FASCIATA Hahn (*leopardus* Peckh.)

Brit. Isl., N, C & S Eur., W Sib. E U.S.A., S to Texas, W to Kansas.

PLEXIPPUS PAYKULLI Aud.

Cosmopolitan in the tropics.

† S Eur. (accidentally). † Southern-most U.S.A.

SALTICUS SCENICUS L.

Brit. Isl., Eur. (generally), N. Afr., W † Wash.–Nfld., S to Calif.; Greenl.
Sib.
† Iceland.

SITTICUS TRUNCORUM L. (*pubescens* F.)

Brit. Isl., Eur. (generally, usually in- † New Engl.
doors), C Asia, Amur.

Amaurobiidae

AMAUROBIUS FEROX Walck.

Eur. (except Brit. Isl., the east & † E Can. & E U.S.A. (widely).
north).

Dictynidae

DICTYNA ANNULIPES Blackw. (*muraria* Em., *mitis* Thor.)

Scandinavia. Alas., Can. & N U.S.A. (widely).

DICTYNA ARUNDINACEA L. (*voluta* Gertsch & Iv.)

Brit. Isl., Eur. (generally), W & N Color., Ontario.
Asia E to Amur & Kamch.

DICTYNA MAJOR Menge (*hamifera* Thor., *vincens* Chamb.)

Brit. Isl., N & C Eur.; Kamch.   Alas.–Calif., E at least to Mont.; Greenl.

TITANOECA NIVALIS Sim. (*silvicola* Ch. & Iv.)

Eur. (boreoalpine).   Alas., Rocky Mts. of Can. & U.S.A.

Oecobiidae

OECOBIUS ANNULIPES Luc. (*parietalis* Hentz)

Cosmopolitan in the tropics.

† S Eur., Mediterr., Cauc.   † Calif.–Flor., N to New York.
                                           † Hawaii.

Chilopoda—Centipedes

The distribution in North America was derived mainly from Chamberlin (1925, &c.), Bailey (1928), and Palmén (1954). For Europe, Attems (1926, 1929–40), Brolemann (1932), Verhoeff (1937), Brade-Birks (1939), and others, were consulted. The distribution of Centipedes (as well as of Millipedes and Woodlice) in northern Asia, unfortunately, is quite imperfectly known. Mr. H. Lohmander, Göteborg, has kindly looked through the lists of Chilopoda, Diplopoda, and Isopoda. Valuable information on the two first-named groups were obtained from Dr. O. Schubart (*in litt.*).

CRYPTOPS HORTENSIS Leach

Brit. Isl., Eur. (generally), Macarones.   † Utah, New York.
Isl.

CRYPTOPS PARISI Brol.

Brit. Isl., Eur. (widely; in the north   † Nfld. (greenhouse).
restricted to greenhouses).

GEOPHILUS ELECTRICUS L.

Brit. Isl., N & C Eur., N to C Scand.,   † Nfld.
E to Rouman.

GEOPHILUS (NECROPHLOEOPHAGUS) LONGICORNIS Leach

Brit. Isl., Eur. (generally), N. Afr.,   † Mass., Ontar., Nfld.
Hither Asia.

HAPLOPHILUS (STIGMATOGASTER) SUBTERRANEUS LEACH

Brit. Isl., Eur. (widely); of Mediterr.   † Nfld.
origin, in the north usually restricted to
greenhouses.

LAMYCTES FULVICORNIS Mein.

Almost cosmopolitan.

Icel., Faeroes, Brit. Isl., Eur. (widely),   † Alas.–NE U.S.A., Nfld.
N to C Scand., N. Afr., Macarones.
Isl., Cauc.

† E Afr., Austral.

LITHOBIUS FORFICATUS L.

Brit. Isl., Eur. (generally), Cauc., N.   † Canada & U.S.A., W to Rocky Mts.,
Afr.   Nfld.[1]
                    † S. Amer., St. Helena, Austral.

LITHOBIUS MELANOPS Newp.

Icel., Faeroes, Brit. Isl., Eur. (widely),   † Nfld.
N Scand.

LITHOBIUS (MONOTARSOBIUS) MICROPS Mein. (*dubosqui* Brol.)

Brit. Isl., N & C Eur. (in the north   † Nfld.
synanthropic).

PACHYMERIUM FERRUGINEUM C. L. Koch

Almost cosmopolitan.

Faeroes, Eur. (except Brit. Isl. & the   † Alas.; E U.S.A., S to Flor., W to
north), N. Afr., Cauc., W & C Asia.   Minnes.
                                         Mexico.
                    † Pacific islands.

SCHENDYLA NEMORENSIS C. L. Koch

Brit. Isl., Eur. (generally), N. Afr.   † E Can., NE U.S.A., Utah; Nfld.

SCOLIOPLANES (LINOTAENIA) ACUMINATUS Leach (*chionophilus* Wood)[2]

Brit. Isl., W & S Eur., N. Afr., Cauc.   (†) Alas., & N. W. Terr.–Queb., N U.S.A.
(†) Bering Isl.

---

[1] *Vide* map by Chamberlin (1922, fig. 3, p. 451; by mistake exchanged with fig. 4, p. 453).
[2] According to Lohmander (*in litt.*), *acuminatus* Leach and *crassipes* C. L. Koch have been largely confused and the distribution here given may need revision.

THEATOPS ERYTHROCEPHALUS C. L. Koch

S Eur.   † W U.S.A.

Diplopoda—Millipedes

Records for North America were mainly obtained from Chamberlin (1921) and
Palmén (1952), for Europe from Attems (1929–40), Schubart (1934), Blower
(1952), and other papers mentioned among the references (p. 126 a.f.).

BLANIULUS GUTTULATUS Bosc.

Brit. Isl., N & C Eur., E to S Russ.   † NE U.S.A., E Can., Nov. Scot., Nfld.
(synanthropic in the north).
                                    † St. Helena.

BRACHYDESMUS SUPERUS Latz.

Faeroes, Brit. Isl., Eur. (widely), E to   † Ohio, Nov. Scot., Nfld.
SW Russ., N. Afr.

BRACHYIULUS LITTORALIS Verh. (*pusillus* Chamb.)

Brit. Isl., N & C Eur. E to Polon., S   † Calif.; E U.S.A., S to N. Carol., W
to Alban.   to Mississ.; Nov. Scot., Nfld.

CHONEIULUS PALMATUS Němec

Brit. Isl., N & C Eur. E to Russ.   † Nov. Scot., Nfld.

CYLINDROIULUS BRITANNICUS Verh.
Almost cosmopolitan.

Faeroes, Brit. Isl., Eur. (widely), E to   † Nfld.
S Russ.
                        † S. Amer., S. Afr., S Asia.

CYLINDROIULUS FRISIUS Verh. (*oweni* Bollm., *luscus* Mein.)
Almost cosmopolitan.

Faeroes, Brit. Isl., Eur. (S Scand.–N   † Calif.; C & E U.S.A., Nov. Scot.,
France), E to S Russ.   Nfld.
        † C & S Amer., Juan Fern., S. Afr., St. Paul (S Ind. Ocean).

CYLINDROIULUS SILVARUM Mein

Brit. Isl., N & C Eur., E to NW Polon.   † Nfld.

CYLINDROIULUS TEUTONICUS Poc. (*londinensis* C. L. Koch)

Brit. Isl., N & C Eur., E to W Russ.   † U.S.A. (widely), E Can., Nov. Scot., Nfld.

CYLINDROIULUS TRUNCORUM Silv.

† Brit. Isl.[1], Eur. (widely; mainly in greenhouses), E to S Russ.   † Wash., Color. (greenhouses), Nfld.

N. Afr.

NOPOIULUS VENUSTUS Mein. (*pulchellus* & *minutus* Chamb.)

Brit. Isl., Eur. (widely), E to S Russ., Asia Minor.   † E U.S.A., Nfld.

† C & S Amer., Juan Fern., St. Helena.

OPHIODESMUS ALBONANUS Latz.

Brit. Isl., W Eur., Sweden.   † Nfld.

OPHYIULUS FALLAX Mein. (*pilosus* auctt., *longabo* Chamb.)

Brit. Isl., N & C Eur. E to Polon.   † NE U.S.A. W to Ohio, E Can., Nov. Scot., Nfld.

† Austral.

ORTHOMORPHA GRACILIS C. L. Koch

Cosmopolitan.

† Brit. Isl., Eur. (widely; mainly in greenhouses), E to Russ.   † U.S.A. (widely, greenhouses), Nfld. (greenhouse); Bermudas.

† S. Afr., S & E Asia, Austral., Pacific Islands.   S. Amer. (probably indigenous).

POLYDESMUS DENTICULATUS C. L. Koch

Brit. Isl., N & C Eur. E to Ural.   † Nfld.

POLYDESMUS INCONSTANS Latz. (*coriaceus* auctt., nec Porat, *testi* Bollm.)

Brit. Isl., N & C Eur., E to Volga.   † Indiana, Ohio, Illin.; Nfld.

POLYDESMUS RACOVITZAI Brol.

Pyrenées Orientales.   † Wash.

PROTEROIULUS FUSCUS a. St.

Icel., Brit. Isl., N & C Eur., E to W Russ.   † E U.S.A., Nov. Scot., Nfld.

---

[1] Not published from the British Isles but recorded by Palmén (*in litt.*) from Bristol.

Isopoda Terrestria—Woodlice

Van Name's excellent monograph (1936, 1940) of the American fauna was supplemented by Hatch (1947) and Palmén (1951). European records were obtained from Wächtler (1937), Collinge (1943), Palmén (1946), &c.

ANDRONISCUS DENTIGER Verh.

Brit. Isl., S, C & W Eur.   † Ontar., Nfld. (greenhouses).

ARMADILLIDIUM NASATUM B.-Lund

Brit. Isl., Eur. (except the north), E to   † Brit. Col., E Can., U.S.A. (widely; in
Polon. (in Scand. usually in green-   the north in greenhouses).
houses).

ARMADILLIDIUM VULGARE Latr.
Almost cosmopolitan.

Brit. Isl., Eur. (widely), N. Afr.,   † Brit. Col., U.S.A. (generally), Bermu-
W Asia.   das.

† C & S Amer., Austral., Pacific Isl.

CYLISTICUS CONVEXUS DeG.

Brit. Isl., Eur. (generally), Hither Asia.   † Brit. Col.–New Brunsw., Nfld.,
                                             U.S.A. (widely), S to N. Carol. & Color.
                           † C & S Amer.

HAPLOPHTHALMUS DANICUS B.-Lund

Brit. Isl., Eur. (except the north);   † E U.S.A., W to Utah, E Can., Nfld.
originally Mediterranean (regularly in
greenhouses).

HYLONISCUS RIPARIUS C. L. Koch (*vividus* C. L. Koch)

Brit. Isl., Eur. (except the north), E   † Nfld.
to Polon.

ONISCUS ASELLUS L.

Faeroes, Brit. Isl., Eur. (generally).   † Brit. Col.–Oreg.; E U.S.A., E Can.,
                                             Nov. Scot., Nfld.
                           † W. Indies.

PHILOSCIA MUSCORUM Scop.

Brit. Isl., Eur. (except the east), N.   †Wash.
Afr.

                           † C Amer.

PLATYARTHRUS HOFFMANSEGGI Brandt

Brit. Isl., S, W & C Eur., SE to Dal-   † Connect. (myrmecophilous).
matia.

PORCELLIO DILATATUS Brandt

Icel., Brit. Isl., S & W Eur.   † Brit. Col.–Ariz.; Nfld.
                          † Australia.

PORCELLIO LAEVIS Latr.

Brit. Isl., Eur. (generally), N. Afr., W   † U.S.A. (widely) W to Calif., E Can.
Asia.
                 † C & S Amer., Pacific isl.

PORCELLIO (PROPORCELLIO) QUADRISERIATUS Verh.

S Eur., Hither Asia.   † Texas (greenhouse).

PORCELLIO SCABER Latr.
Cosmopolitan.

Icel., Faeroes, Brit. Isl., Eur. (generally).   † Alas.–Labr., Nfld., U.S.A. (generally).
   † C & S Amer., S. Afr., New Zeal., Pacific isl., Japan, Kamch.

PORCELLIO SPINICORNIS Say (*pictus* Brandt)
Almost cosmopolitan.

Brit. Isl., N & C Eur. E to Russ.   † E Can., E U.S.A. W to Mich.

PORCELLIONIDES (METOPONORTHUS) PRUINOSUS Brandt
Cosmopolitan.

Brit. Isl., Eur. (widely), E to C Russ.,   † Brit. Col.–E Can., U.S.A. (generally).
N. Afr.
        † C & S Amer., Madag., S Asia, Pacif. isl., Japan.

TRACHELIPUS (TRACHEONISCUS) RATHKEI Brandt
Almost cosmopolitan.

Icel., Brit. Isl., Eur. (except the east),   † Brit. Col., NW U.S.A.; E U.S.A., E
Cauc.   Can., Nov. Scot., Pr. Edw. Isl., Nfld.
                   † C & S Amer.

TRICHONISCOIDES SARSI Pat.

Brit. Isl., W & C Eur., N to Norway.   † Nfld.

8 – 565597 *Lindroth*

TRICHONISCUS PROVISORIUS Racov.

Brit. Isl., C Eur., N Eur. (in green-   † Nfld.
houses).

TRICHONISCUS PUSILLUS Brandt, *f. parthenog.* (? *demivirgo* Blake)

Icel., Faeroes, Brit. Isl., N & C Eur.   † Wash.; NE U.S.A., E Can., Nov.
                                             Scot., Nfld.

TRICHONISCUS PYGMAEUS G. O. Sars

Brit. Isl., N & C Eur. (in the north in   † New York, Illin., Nfld.
greenhouses).

TRICHONISCUS (CORDIONISCUS) STEBBINGI Pat.

Brit. Isl., W Eur. to S Swed. (Loh-   † Oreg., Mass. (in greenhouses).
mander, *in litt.*).

TYLOS LATREILLI Ad. & Sav.

Coasts of S Eur., N to C France, Asia   (†) Florida; Bermudas.
Minor, N. Afr., Macaron. Isl.   C Amer., W. Indies.

Mollusca, Gastropoda—Land- and freshwater Molluscs

The main sources of information on Mollusca were Ehrmann (1937), Taylor (1902–21), Ellis (1926), and Licharev & Rammelmayer (1952), for Eurasia, Pilsbry (1939–48) and La Rocque (1953), for North America. Other references may be found in the bibliography (p. 126 a.f.). The nomenclature follows Pilsbry (l.c.). Valuable information was obtained from Mr. H. W. Waldén, Stockholm.

Terrestrial or amphibious species closely connected with the seashore are not considered.

CEPAEA (HELIX) HORTENSIS O. F. Müll. (fig. 29)

Icel., Faeroes, Brit. Isl., Eur. (except the   (†)Mass.–Queb., N. S., Nfld., ?Labr.;
southern peninsulae), E to Leningrad   ? Greenl.
& Vitebsk.
                        † New Zeal.

CEPAEA (HELIX) NEMORALIS L.

Brit. Isl., Eur. (widely), E to Balticum,   † NE U.S.A. S to Tenn., E Can., An-
E. Pruss., Bohem., & Bosnia.   ticosti.

HELICELLA (THEBA, EUPARYPHA) PISANA O. F. Müll.

Brit. Isl., W & S Eur. N to N France,   † Calif.
E to Bulg.; N. Afr., Hither Asia.

† S. Afr.

HELICOGONA (ARIANTA) ARBUSTORUM L.

Icel., Faeroes, Brit. Isl., Eur. (except the   † Nfld. (old record).
southern peninsulae), E to Balticum &
Kiew.

HELIX ASPERSA O. F. Müll.

Brit. Isl., S & W Eur. N to Holl.,   † Calif. (generally); Louis., S. Carol.
isolated on Crimea; N. Afr., Asia Minor.

† C & S Amer., S Afr., Austral.

Jacostidae

COCHLICELLA VENTROSA Fér.

S Eur., N. Afr.   † Calif.; S. Carol.
† Bermudas.

HYGROMIA (TRICHIA, TROCHULUS) HISPIDA L.

Brit. Isl., Eur. (except the extreme   † NE U.S.A., E Can., Nov. Scot., Pr. Edw.
south), E to Volga; Cauc., N. Afr.   Isl.

HYGROMIA (TRICHIA, TROCHULUS) STRIOLATA Pfeiff.

Brit. Isl., W & C Eur. N to S Swed.,   † NE U.S.A., E Can., Labr., Nov. Scot.,
E to Czechosl.   Nfld.

JACOSTA (HELICELLA, TROCHOIDEA, XEROCLIVIA) ELEGANS Gmel.

Mediterr.: S Eur., N. Afr.   † S. Carol.
† Brit. Isl.

MONACHA (THEBA) CANTIANA Mont.

Brit. Isl., C & W Eur., S Russ., Hither   † E Can. (Ont., Queb.).
Asia.

Achatinidae

CECILIOIDES ACICULA O. F. Müll.

Brit. Isl., Eur. (widely) E to Ucraina &   † Florida, Penns.
Crimea; Cauc., W. Turcest.

† Bermudas, New Zeal.

LAMELLAXIS (OPEAS) CLAVULINUS Pot. & Mich.

† Brit. Isl. (greenhouses).   † Penns.
                              Islands of Ind. Ocean.
                              † Hawaii, Japan.

LAMELLAXIS (OPEAS) MAURITIANUS Pfeiff.

† Irel., Holl., Germ. (greenhouses).   † E U.S.A. (greenhouses).
                              Mauritius.

OPEAS PUMILUM Pfeiff.

† Brit. Isl., W Eur.   Florida.   † E U.S.A.
(greenhouses).   C & S Am.   (greenhouses).

RUMINA (STENOGYRA, BULIMUS) DECOLLATA L.

S Eur., N. Afr., Hither Asia.   † Texas–N. Carol.
† Brit. Isl. (greenhouses).   † W. Indies.

SUBULINA OCTONA Brug.

† Brit. Isl., W. Eur. (greenhouses).   S & C Amer. N to Florida.
                        † Afr., S Asia, &c.

Testacellidae

TESTACELLA EUROPAEA Roissy (*haliotidea* Drap.)

Brit. Isl., S & W Eur. N to Belg., E   † Calif.; NE U.S.A., Nov. Scot.
to Dalmat.; N. Afr.   (greenhouses).

Zonitidae

EUCONULUS FULVUS O. F. Müll. (*trochiformis* Mont.)

Icel., Brit. Isl., Eur. (generally), N.   Alas.–Labr., S to Middle Atl. States;
Afr., N Asia E to Kamch.   Nfld., Greenl.
                        † S Asia, Austral.

HAWAIIA MINUSCULA Binn.

† Brit. Isl., Holl. (greenhouses).   Alas.–E Can., Nfld.; U.S.A. (generally)
E Sib. (S parts of Marit. Prov.,   S to C Amer.; Bermudas.
probably indigenous).
                        † Corea, Japan, Formosa, Pacific islands.

OXYCHILUS (HYALINIA) ALLIARIUS Mill.

Icel., Faeroes, Brit. Isl., W & C Eur.   †Brit. Col.–Calif.; Ont.–N. Y.
E to Leningrad; N. Afr.   † Greenl.
                        † S. Afr., Austral.

OXYCHILUS (HYALINIA) CELLARIUS O. F. Müll.

Brit. Isl., W & C Eur. E to Leningrad; † Oreg., Calif.; E U.S.A., E Can.,
N. Afr., Cauc., Hither Asia.   Nov. Scot.

† S. Amer., S. Afr., Austral.

OXYCHILUS (HYALINIA) DRAPARNALDI Beck (*lucidus* Drap.)

Brit. Isl., Eur. (not indig. N of Holl.) † Wash.–Calif.; E U.S.A., E Can., Nfld.
E to C Russia; N. Afr., Hither Asia.

OXYCHILUS (HYALINIA) HELVETICUS Blum

Brit. Isl., W & C Eur. N to Belg.   † Calif.

RETINELLA (PERPOLITA, HYALINIA) HAMMONIS Stroem (*radiatula* Ald.)

f. typ.   sbsp. *electrina* Gould[1]
Icel., Faeroes, Brit. Isl., Eur. (except   Alas.–Labr., S to New Mex. & Ariz.,
the south), N Asia E to Kamch.,   Nov. Scot., Nfld.
Japan.

ZONITOIDES ARBOREUS Say

† Brit. Isl., C & W Eur. E to C Russ.   Brit. Col.–Labr., Nfld., entire U.S.A.
                                  C Amer., W. Ind.

Kamch. (probably indig.).

† Japan, S. Afr., Austral.

ZONITOIDES NITIDUS O. F. Müll.

Brit. Isl., Eur. (generally), N. Afr.,   Alas.–E Can., Nfld., S to Maryl. &
Cauc., C & N Asia, Japan.   Utah.

† Austral.

Limacidae

DEROCERAS CARUANAE Poll.

S & W Eur., N. Afr.   † Calif.
(Original patria?)

DEROCERAS (AGRIOLIMAX) LAEVE O. F. Müll., *sensu lato* (*campestre* Binn.)

Icel., Faeroes, Brit. Isl., Eur. E to C   Alas.–Nfld.–S Baffin L.; S to S U.S.A.
Russia, Hither Asia (forms from N
Asia possibly conspecific).

† C & S. Amer., S. Afr., Austral.

---

[1] Often regarded as distinct species (*vide* Pilsbry, 1946, p. 258).

118

CHAPTER I

DEROCERAS (AGRIOLIMAX) RETICULATUM O. F. Müll. (*agrestis* auctt. nec L.)

Icel., Faeroes, Brit. Isl., Eur. E to C   † Brit. Col., Calif.; E Can., Labr.,
Russia.   Nfld.; U.S.A. (disjunct but widely).
        † S. Amer., S. Afr., E Asia, Austral.

LIMAX FLAVUS L.

Brit. Isl., Eur. E to S Russia (origi-   † U.S.A. (generally).
nal patria).
N. Afr., Hither Asia, Cauc.
        † S. Amer., S. Afr., Austral., E Asia.

LIMAX (LEHMANNIA) MARGINATUS O. F. Müll. (*arborum* Bourch. & Chant.)

Icel., Faeroes, Brit. Isl., Eur. E to W   † U.S.A. (disjunct)[1], Nfld.
Russia and Greece, N. Afr.
        † S. Amer., Austral., Atl. & Pacif. islands.

LIMAX MAXIMUS L.

Brit. Isl., Eur. E to S Russia, Cauc.;   † Brit. Col., Calif.; E Can., Nfld.; U.S.A.
N. Afr., Asia Minor.   (widely but disjunct).
        † S. Amer., S. Afr., Austral., Hawaii.

MILAX GAGATES Drap.

Brit. Isl., S & W Eur. N to Belg.;   † Wash.–Calif.; E U.S.A. (usually in
N. Afr.   greenhouses).
        † S. Afr., Austral., Juan Fern.

Endodontidae

DISCUS (GONIODISCUS) ROTUNDATUS O. F. Müll.

Brit. Isl., W & C Eur. E to S Russ.;   † Mass., Nfld.
N. Afr.

HELICODISCUS PARALLELUS Say (*lineatus* Say)

† Brit. Isl., Holl.   Can. W to Manit., Nova Scot., Nfld.,
                                        E & C U.S.A.

Arionidae

ARION ATER L. coll. (*empiricorum* Fér.)

Icel., Faeroes, Brit. Isl., C, W & N Eur.   † Brit. Col.–Oreg.; E Can., Nfld.; NE
E to Latvia & Hungaria.   U.S.A.
        † New Zeal.

---

[1] The mainland form of North America, according to information from H. W. Waldén, Stockholm, belongs to the European-Mediterranean *L. poirieri* Mab.

ARION CIRCUMSCRIPTUS Johnst. (incl. *fasciatus* Nilss.)

Icel., Faeroes, Brit. Isl., W, C & N Eur. E to C Russia.

† Brit. Col.–Calif.; NE U.S.A. W to Wisc.; E Can., Nfld.

ARION HORTENSIS Fér.

Icel., Faeroes, Brit. Isl., S, W & C Eur., E to W & NW Russia.

† Wash.–Calif.; E U.S.A., E Can., Nov. Scot., Nfld.

ARION INTERMEDIUS Norm.

Icel., Faeroes, Brit. Isl., W, C & N Eur. E to C Russia.

† Calif.

† S. Afr., New Zeal.

ARION SUBFUSCUS Drap.

f. typ.

Icel., Faeroes, Brit. Isl., C & N Eur. E to Ural.

† NE U.S.A., E Can., Nov. Scot., Nfld.
† New Zeal.

sbsp. *sibiricus* Simr.
Altai, E Sib.

Pupillidae

COLUMELLA (SPHYRADIUM) EDENTULA Drap. (*simplex* Gould)

Icel., Faeroes, Brit. Isl., Eur. (generally), N Asia E to Kamch., Sakhal., Kuril., Japan.

Alas.–Labr., Nfld., S to Iowa & Penns.

PUPILLA MUSCORUM L.

Icel., Brit. Isl., Eur. (generally), N. Afr., W, C & N Asia E to Amur & Sakhal.

Alas.–E Can., Nfld., S to New Mex.

VERTIGO ALPESTRIS Alder

f. typ.
Brit. Isl., W, N. & C Eur., Sib. E to Amur.

† Nfld.

sbsp. *oughtoni* Pilsb.
Huds. Bay (W Ontario), Baffin L.

VERTIGO MODESTA Say

(incl. *arctica* Wallenb., *borealis* Morel., *kraussena* Reinh., &c.)

Icel., Eur. (boreomontane), Siberia, Commander Isl.

Alas.–Labr., Nfld., NE U.S.A., Baffin L., Greenl.

VERTIGO PYGMAEA Drap.

Brit. Isl., Eur. (generally), Cauc., N. Afr., N & C Asia.

(†) E Can., Nov. Scot., NE U.S.A. S to Virg., W to Ohio.

Valloniidae

VALLONIA COSTATA O. F. Müll.

Brit. Isl., Eur. (generally), N. Afr.,   Alberta–Queb., NE U.S.A. S to Virg.
Sib. E to Amur.

† Austral.

VALLONIA EXCENTRICA Sterki

Brit. Isl., Eur. (excl. the north).   (†) E Can., Nov. Scot., Nfld.; NE
                                             U.S.A., locally elsewhere (for inst.
                                             Oreg. & Calif.).
                                  † Mexico, S. Afr.

VALLONIA PULCHELLA O. F. Müll.

Brit. Isl., Eur. (generally), N. Afr.,   N. Amer. E of Rocky Mts., N to Nov.
Sib. E to Amur.   Scot., S to Kentucky.
                                             † Calif., Texas.
                         † Makarones., Austral., &c.

ZOOGENETES (ACANTHINULA) HARPA Say

Eur. (boreoalpine), Cauc., N Asia E to   Alas.–Labr., Nfld., S to Color. & New
Amur, Kamch., Sakhal. & Bering Isl.   Hampsh.

Cionellidae

CIONELLA (COCHLICOPA) LUBRICA O. F. Müll.

Icel., Faeroes, Brit. Isl., Eur. (gener-   Alas.–Labr., Nfld., S to Ariz. & north.
ally), N. Afr., N & C Asia E to Kamch.   Mexico.
& Japan.

† New Zeal.

Carychiidae

CARYCHIUM MINIMUM O. F. Müll.

Brit. Isl., NW & C Eur., entire Russia,   † Massach. (greenhouse).
Cauc., Sib.

Lymnaeidae

(Vide Hubendick, 1951)

LYMNAEA (RADIX) AURICULARIA L. (*s. str.*)

Brit. Isl., Eur., N. Afr., N & C Asia   S Alaska (probably indigenous).
E to Amur, Kamch., Japan.   † U.S.A.

LYMNAEA (STAGNICOLA) CATASCOPIUM Say

(†) Scotl. (Kevan, 1943).   Great Slave Lake–Nov. Scot.; NE
                                         U.S.A.

LYMNAEA (PSEUDOSUCCINEA) COLUMELLA Say (*peregrina* Cless.)

† Brit. Isl., W & C Eur.   E U.S.A., SE Can.
(mainly in hothouses).   † Oreg.–Calif.
                    † C & S Amer.; S. Afr.

LYMNAEA (GALBA) CUBENSIS Pfeiff.

† Irel., Germ. (hothouses).   SE U.S.A., C & S Amer.

LYMNAEA (STAGNICOLA) PALUSTRIS O. F. Müll.

Brit. Isl., Eur., N. Afr., C & N Asia   Alas.–Queb., Nfld., S to Arizona.
E to Amur & Kamch.

LYMNAEA (RADIX) PEREGRA O. F. Müll.

Icel., Faeroes, Brit. Isl., Eur. (gener- Nfld.
ally), N. Afr., Asia E to Baikal.

LYMNAEA STAGNALIS L.

Brit. Isl., Eur., N. Afr., Asia E to   Alas.–Nov. Scot., S to Arizona.
Amur & Kamch.

LYMNAEA (FOSSARIA) TRUNCATULA O. F. Müll.

Icel., Faeroes, Brit. Isl., Eur., Afr.   Aleut. Isl., S Alas., C Canada.
(widely), C & N Asia E to Amur &
Kamch.

Physidae

APLEXA (APLECTA) HYPNORUM L.

Brit. Isl., Eur. (generally), W & N   Alas.–E Can., S to Color.
Asia E to Kamch.

PHYSA ANCILLARIA Say

† Germany (hothouses).   NE U.S.A., E Can. W to Manitoba.

PHYSA GYRINA Say

† Brit. Isl. (Cardiff).   Alas.–E Can., S to Alabama, Nfld.

PHYSA HETEROSTROPHA Say

† Germ., Czechosl., Holl., Denm.   Manit.–Nfld., U.S.A. E of Mississ.
(mainly hothouses).

Planorbidae

GYRAULUS (ARMIGER) CRISTA L.

Brit. Isl., Eur. E to C Russia, N. Afr.,   Alas.–Ont., NE U.S.A.
W Sib.

GYRAULUS GREDLERI Bielz (incl. *borealis* Lovén, syn. *arcticus* Beck)

Eur. (boreoalpine), N & C Asia E to   Alas.–Labr.; Greenl.
Kamch. (Glacial subfossils in the Brit.
Isl.)

GYRAULUS (TORQUIS) PARVUS Say[1]

† Denmark (aquarium).   Alas.–E Can., S to Florida, Nfld.

HELISOMA DURYI Weth. (incl. *eudiscus* Pilsb.)

† Engl. (aquarium).   Florida.

HELISOMA (PIEROSOMA) TENUIS Phil.

† Denmark (aquarium).   Calif., Mexico.

HELISOMA (PIEROSOMA) TRIVOLVE Say

† Moscow (aquarium).   Alas.–E Can. & Maine, S to Missouri.

Valvatidae

VALVATA PISCINALIS O. F. Müll.

Brit. Isl., Eur. (generally), Cauc.,   † NE U.S.A., E Can., Nov. Scot.
Hither Asia, W Sib.

Amnicolidae

BULIMUS (BITHYNIA) TENTACULATUS L.

Brit. Isl., Eur. (generally), N. Afr.,   (†) NE U.S.A., E Can., W to Wisc.[2]
Cauc., W Sib.

---

[1] Sometimes regarded as a sbsp. of the Palaearctic *G. laevis* Ald.
[2] Baker (1928, p. 81) described a new and possibly indigenous sbsp. of *Bulimus tentaculatus* from N. America but its state seems doubtful (La Rocque, 1953).

Oligochaeta, Lumbricidae—Earthworms

Great interest in the zoogeography of Oligochaeta was shown by the late W. Michaelsen (*vide* 1903) but only the terrestrial or amphibious members of the Lumbricid family, the true earthworms, seem suited to our purpose. Valuable information has also been obtained from Smith (1917), Ude (1929), and Cernosvitov & Evans (1947), as well as from a few additional papers listed in the bibliography (p. 126 a.f.).

ALLOLOBOPHORA (HELODRILUS) CALIGINOSA Sav.

Cosmopolitan.[1]

Icel., Brit. Isl., Eur. (generally), N.   † U.S.A. (generally), E. Can.
Afr., Hither Asia.
       † S. Amer., S. Afr., S & E Asia, Austral., Hawaii.

ALLOLOBOPHORA (HELODRILUS) CHLOROTICA Sav.

Brit. Isl., Eur. (generally), Hither Asia.   † Brit. Col., W & E U.S.A., E Can.,
                            Bermud.; Greenl.
       † C & S Amer.

ALLOLOBOPHORA (HELODRILUS) LONGA Ude

Brit. Isl., Eur. E to S Russ.   † E Can., Maine, Indiana.

BIMASTUS (HELODRILUS) BEDDARDI Mich.

† Ireland.   U.S.A. (widely).
      † Tibet, Hawaii.

BIMASTUS (HELODRILUS) TENUIS Eis. (*constrictus* Rosa)

Icel., Brit. Isl., Eur. (generally), Sib.   Alaska (probably indigenous).
                       (†) Brit. Col.–Calif.; E U.S.A.
   † C & S Amer., India, N. Zeal., Hawaii.

DENDROBAENA (HELODRILUS) OCTAEDRA Sav.

Icel., Brit. Isl., Eur. (generally), N.   † Color., Nfld., Greenl.
Zeml., Cauc., Sib. E at least to Baical.   † Mexico.

DENDROBAENA (HELODRILUS) SUBRUBICUNDA Eis.

Icel., Brit. Isl., Eur. (generally), N.   † Calif., Color., Illin.; E Can., Nfld.
Afr., S Sib.
      † S. Amer., India, Austral.

---

[1] "The commonest species of earthworm in the world "(Cernosvitov & Evans, 1947).

EISENIA CAROLINENSIS Mich.

† Germ. (Hamburg; Smith, 1917).   N. Carolina.

EISENIA FOETIDA Sav.

Almost cosmopolitan.

Icel., Brit. Isl., Eur. (generally),   † Brit. Col., U.S.A. (generally), E Can.,
Hither Asia, Sib., Japan.   Bermud.
          † C & S Amer., S. Afr., S Asia, Austral., Hawaii.

EISENIA ROSEA Sav.

Almost cosmopolitan.

Icel., Brit. Isl., Eur. (generally), N.   † Calif., Ariz., E U.S.A., E Can.
Afr., W & N Asia.
          † C & S Amer., S. Afr., Austral.

EISENIA VENETA Rosa ("var. *hortensis* Mich.")

Brit. Isl., Eur. (except the north),   † Calif.
Hither Asia (*f. typ.*).
          † S. Amer., S. Afr.

EISENIELLA TETRAEDRA Sav.

Almost cosmopolitan.

Icel., Brit. Isl., Eur. (generally),   † Wash.–Calif.; C & NE U.S.A., E Can.
Hither Asia, Cauc.
          † S. Amer., S. Afr., S Asia, Austral.

LUMBRICUS CASTANEUS Sav.

Faeroes, Brit. Isl., Eur. (widely), Sib.   † NE U.S.A., E Can.

LUMBRICUS FESTIVUS Sav.

Brit. Isl., Eur. N to S Sweden.   † E Can.

LUMBRICUS RUBELLUS Hffm.

Icel., Faeroes, Brit. Isl., Eur. (generally), † Wash.–Calif.; Mich., E Can., Nfld.
Cauc., Sib. E at least to R. Lena.
          † S Asia, Austral.

LUMBRICUS TERRESTRIS L. (*herculeus* Rosa)

Icel., Brit. Isl., Eur. (generally).   † W & E U.S.A., E Can., Nfld.
          † Mexico, Falkland Isl., Macaron. Isl.

OCTOLASIUM LACTEUM Oerl.

Brit. Isl., Eur. (except the north) E   † W & C U.S.A.
to C Russia, N. Afr., Hither Asia.
          † C & S Amer., S & E Asia, Austral.

TABLE I. Summary of species common to Europe and North America among animal groups treated above.[1]

	Diff. sbsp.	Iden-tical	Total	Introduced species				
				Eur. to N. Am.	N. Am. to Eur.	In both contin.	Total introd.	Total %
Mammalia	17	3	20	1	—	2	3	15
Aves	63	44	107	—	—	—	0	—
Pisces	3	—	3	—	—	—	0	—
Coleoptera (in part) .	27	241	267	162–170	3–4	9	174–183	65–68
Carabidae	17	74	91	37–38	—	4	41–42	45–46
Elateridae	2	10	12	3–5	—	—	3–5	25–42
Coccinellidae	5	8	12	5	—	—	5	38
Scarabaeidae	—	25	25	23	—	1	24	96
Cerambycidae . . .	2	12	14	7	1	—	8	57
Chrysomelidae . . .	1	27	28	19–21	1	—	20–22	71–79
Rhynchophora (in part)	—	85	85	68–71	1–2	4	73–77	86–91
Lepidoptera (in part)	41	94	135	15–17	1–4	—	16–21	12–16
Diurna	14	15	29	2	—	—	2	7
Sphinges	2	1	3	1	—	—	1	33
Bombycimorpha . .	6	7	13	3	1–2	—	4–5	31–38
Noctuae	8	38	46	2–4	0–2	—	2–6	4–13
Geometrae	10	29	39	4	—	—	4	10
Isolated families . . .	1	4	5	3	—	—	3	60
Diptera (in part) . .	1	24	25	—	—	1	1	4
Culicidae	1	20	21	—	—	1	1	5
Tabanidae	—	4	4	—	—	—	0	—
Hymenoptera (in part)	15	35	50	4–7	5	12	21–24	42–48
Bombinae	2	2	4	—	—	—	0	—
Crabronidae	—	8	8	2–3	—	—	2–3	25–38
Vespinae	2	4	6	1	—	—	1	17
Formicidae	11	21	32	1–3	5	12	18-20	56–63
Odonata	3	5	8	—	—	—	0	—
Orthoptera Saltatoria	—	7	7	2	—	2	4	57
Araneae	5	141	146	30–46	5	8	43–59	29–40
Chilopoda	—	13	13	12–13	—	—	12–13	93–100
Diplopoda	—	17	17	15	—	2	17	100
Isopoda Terrestria .	—	22	22	21–22	—	—	21–22	95–100
Mollusca	2	70	71	32–36	13–14	3	48–53	66–73
Lumbricidae	—	17	17	15	2	—	17	94
Total	177	733	908	309–344 =33–38%	27–34 =3–4 %	39 =4 %	375–417	41–46

[1] The following five species stated or believed to occur in North America in part as indigenous, in part introduced from Europe, are counted twice on calculating the percentage of introduced species and, for the subspecifically distinct *Coccinella* and *Vertigo*, also in the two first columns: *Amara lunicollis* (Col. Car.), *Coccinella 11-punctata* (Col. Cocc.), *Vertigo alpestris* (Moll.), *Lymnaea auricularia* (Moll.), *Bimastus tenuis* (Lumbr.).

Bibliography of Chapter I.

ANDER, K., 1950. Zur Verbreitung und Phänologie der boreoalpinen Odonaten der Westpaläarktis. — Opusc. Ent. 15. Lund, p. 53–71.

—— 1951. Västpalearktis' och Nordamerikas orthopterfauna, en jämförelse. — Ent. Medd. 26. Copenhagen, p. 155–156.

ANDERSON, R. M., 1946. Catalogue of Canadian recent Mammals. — Bull. Nation. Mus. Can. 102 (Biol. Ser. 31). Ottawa, p. 1–238.

ATTEMS, C., 1926. Chilopoda. — Handb. d. Zool. (W. Kükenthal). IV:1. Berlin & Leipzig, p. 239–402.

—— 1929–40. Myriapoda. 1–3. — Das Tierreich. 52. 54, 68–70, Berlin & Leipzig.

BACKLUND, H. O., 1949. Oligochaeta. 1. Lumbricidae. — Zool. of Icel. 2. Copenhagen, p. 1–15.

BAILEY, J. W., 1928. The Chilopoda of New York State with notes on the Diplopoda. —Bull. N.Y. State Mus. 276. Albany, N.Y., p. 1–50.

BAKER, F. C., 1928. The fresh water Mollusca of Wisconsin. I. — Bull. Wisc. Geol. & Nat. Hist. Survey. 70. Madison, Wisc., pp. I–XX, 1–507.

—— 1945. The Molluscan family Planorbidae. — Univ. Illin. Press. Urbana, Ill., pp. I–XXXVI, 1–530.

BARTENEF, A., 1935. Über die Gattung Libellula und besonders über ihre paläarktischen Arten. — Zeitschr. wissensch. Zool. (Arch. f. Naturgesch.) (N.S.) 4. Leipzig, p. 274–290.

BERG, L. S., 1933. Übersicht der Verbreitung der Süsswasserfische Europas. — Zoogeogr. 1. Jena, p. 107–208.

—— 1948–49. Ryby presnych vod SSSR i sopredelńych stran (Freshwater fishes of SSSR and adjacent countries). 1–3. — Opredel. Fauna SSSR. 27. 29. 30. Moscow & Leningrad, p. 1–1382.

BERLAND, L., 1928. Hyménoptères vespiformes. II. — Faune de France. 19. Paris, p. 1–208.

—— 1932. Les Arachnides. - Encycl. Ent. 16. Paris, p. 1–485.

BLAKE, C. H., 1931. Distribution of New England Wood Lice. — Occ. Papers Boston Soc. Nat. Hist. 5. Boston, p. 349–355.

BLATCHLEY, W. S., 1920. Orthoptera of Northeastern America. — Indianapolis, p. 1–784.

BLATCHLEY, W. S. & LENG, C. W., 1916. Rhynchophora or Weevils of North Eastern America. — Indianapolis, p. 1–682.

BLAUVELT, HELEN H., 1936. The comparative morphology of the secondary sexual organs of Linyphia and some related genera, including a revision of the group. — Festschr. f. Embr. Strand. 2. Riga, p. 81–171.

BLOWER, G., 1952. British Millipedes with special reference to Yorkshire species. — The Naturalist (Quarterly Journ. Nat. Hist. N. Engl.). London, p. 145–157.

BOETTGER, C. R., 1932. Die Besiedelung neu angelegter Warmhäuser durch Tiere. — Zeitschr. Morph. & Ökol. d. Tiere. 24. Berlin, p. 394–407.

BOWMAN, K., 1951. An annotated list of the Lepidoptera of Alberta. — Can. Journ. Zool. 29. Ottawa, p. 121–165.

BRADE–BIRKS, S. G., 1939. Notes on Myriapoda XXXVI. Sources for description and illustration of the British fauna. — Journ. S.–E. Agric. Coll., Wye. 44. London, p. 156–179.

BROLEMANN, H. W., 1930. Éléments d'une faune des Myriapodes de France. — Faune de France. 25. Paris, p. 1–405.

BROWN, W. J., 1935. American species of Ludius; the cruciatus and edwardsi groups (Coleop.). — Can. Ent. 67. Orillia, Ont., pp. 1–8, 125–135, 213–221.

—— 1936. Notes on some species of Elateridae (Coleoptera). — Ibidem. 68. p. 246–252.

—— 1940. Notes on the American distribution of some species of Coleoptera common to the European and North American continents. — Ibidem. 72. p. 65–78.

—— 1943. The American species of Phytodecta Kby. (Coleoptera, Chrysomelidae). — Ibidem. 74. p. 99–105.

—— 1946. Some new Chrysomelidae with notes on other species (Coleoptera). — Ibidem. 78. p. 47–54.

—— 1950. The extralimital distribution of some species of coleoptera. — Ibidem. 82. p. 197–205.

—— 1951. The American species of Phratora Chev. (Coleoptera: Chrysomelidae). — Ibidem. 83. p. 121–130.

BRYK, F., 1942. Zur Kenntnis der Grossschmetterlinge der Kurilen. — Deutsch. Ent. Zeitschr. "Iris". 56. Dresden, p. 3–90.

BUCHANAN, L. L., 1927. Synonymical notes on several Otiorhynchid Weevils. — Can. Ent. 59. Orillia, Ont., p. 183–184.

BURT, W. H. & GROSSENHEIDER, R. P., 1952. A field guide to the Mammals. — Boston, p. 1–200.

CARPENTER, S. J. & LA CASSE, W. J., 1955. Mosquitoes of North America. — Berkeley & Los Angeles, p. 1–360.

CERNOSVITOV, L. & EVANS, A. C., 1947. Lumbricidae (Annelida). With a key to the common species. — Synops. Brit. Fauna (Linn. Soc.). London, p. 1–36.

CHAMBERLIN, R. V., 1921. The Julidae and Isobatidae in North America. — Proc. Biol. Soc. 34. Washington, D.C., p. 81–84.

—— 1925. The genera Lithobius, Neolithobius, Gonibius, and Zinapolys in America north of Mexico. — Bull. Mus. Comp. Zool. 57. Cambridge, Mass., p. 441–504.

—— 1946. On the Chilopods of Alaska. — Ann. Ent. Soc. Amer. 39. Columbus, Ohio, p. 177–189.

CHAMBERLIN, R. V. & IVIE, W., 1947. The Spiders of Alaska. — Bull. Univ. Utah. 37. Salt Lake City, p. 1–103.

CHARITONOV, D. E., 1932. Katalog der Russischen Spinnen. — Ann. Mus. Zool. 32, Beilage (Ac. Sci. URSS). Leningrad, p. 1–206.

—— 1936. (Supplement of the Catalogue.) — Scient. Mem. Gorky State Univ. 2:1. Perm, p. 167–225.

Check-List of North American Birds, 1931. 4. ed. — Amer. Ornith. Union. Lancaster, Pa., p. 1–526. (With supplements in The Auk, 61–71, 1944–54.)

CHITTENDEN, F. H., 1923. Notes on the distribution and habits of North American Phyllotreta (Coleop.). — Proc. Ent. Soc. 25. Washington, D.C., p. 131–139.

Coleopterorum Catalogus, 1910–40. (Junk & Schenkling). 1–170. — Berlin & Haag.

COLLINGE, W. E., 1943. The distribution of the woodlice of Great Britain. — N. W. Naturalist. 18. Arbroath, p. 69–73.

COLWELL, W. E., 1943. Some common alfalfa troubles. — Cornell Extension Bull. 616. Ithaca. N.Y., p. 1–8.

COMSTOCK, J. H. & GERTSCH, W. J., 1948. The Spider Book. — Ithaca, N.Y., pp. I–XI, 1–729.

CREIGHTON, W. S., 1950. The ants of North America. — Bull. Mus. Comp. Zool. 104. Cambridge, Mass., p. 1–585.

DARLINGTON, P. J., Jr., 1927. Aegialia arenaria Muls. in New England, with local records for other species. — Psyche. 34. St. Albans, Vt., p. 98–99.

DJAKONOV, A., 1931. Die Geometridenfauna von Kamtshatka. (Russian.) — Ann. Mus. Zool. Ac. Sci. URSS. 32. Leningrad, p. 385–410.

DOBRZHANSKIJ, T., 1926. Die paläarktischen Arten der Gattung Coccinella L. — Revue Russe Ent. 20. Moscow, p. 16–32.

DONISTHORPE, H. S. J. K., 1927. British Ants. Their life-history and classification. 2. ed. — London, pp. I–XVI, 1–436.

DYAR, H. G., 1928. The Mosquitoes of the Americas. — (Carnegie Inst.) Washington, D.C., p. 1–616.

EASON, E. H., 1951. Notes on the Chilopoda (Centipedes) of Warwickshire and Worcestershire. — Ann. Mag. Nat. Hist. (12) 4. London, p. 257–268.

EHRMANN, P., 1937. Mollusca. — Tierwelt Mitteleur. II. Leipzig, p. 1–210.

ELLERMAN, J. R. & MORRISON-SCOTT, T. C. S., 1951. Checklist of Palaearctic and Indian Mammals. — (Brit. Mus.) London, p. 1–810.

ELLIS, A. E., 1926. British snails. A guide to the non-marine Gastropoda of Great Britain and Ireland, pliocene to recent. — Oxford, p. 1–275.

FALL, H. C., 1924. The blueberry leaf-beetle and some of its relatives. — Maine Agric. Exp. Stat. 319. Orono, p. 81–91.

—— 1929. On the genus Phaedon (Coleoptera). — Pan-Pac. Ent. 5. San Francisco, p. 145–152.

—— 1934. On certain North American Elateridae, new and old. — Journ. N. Y. Ent. Soc. 42. New York, p. 7–36.

FERGUSON, D. C., 1955. The Lepidoptera of Nova Scotia. 1. Macrolepidoptera. — Bull. N. S. Mus. Sci. 2. Halifax, p. 1–375.

FLEROW, C. C., 1934. On the geographical distribution and systematics of Elks or Moose (Alces Gray). — C. R. Ac. Sci. SSSR. (N. S.) 2. Leningrad, p. 141–143.

—— 1952. Mammalia. I:2. — Fauna SSSR. 55. Moscow & Leningrad, p. 1–256.

FORBES, W. T. M., 1923, 1948, 1954. The Lepidoptera of New York and neighboring, states. 1–3. — Mem. Cornell Univ. Agric. Exp. Stat. 68. 274. 329. Ithaca, N. Y., pp. 1–729, 1–263, 1–433.

FORD, E. B., 1946. Butterflies. — The New Naturalist. London, pp. I–XIV, 1–368.

FRANZ, H., 1947. Beiträge zur Curculioniden-Systematik. 1. Revision der europäischen Arten der Gattung Miarus Steph. — Ann. Naturh. Mus. 55. Wien, p.210–264.

GERTSCH, W. J., 1934. Notes on American Lycosidae. — Amer. Mus. Nov. 693. New York, p. 1–25.

—— 1939. A revision of the typical crab-spiders (Misumeninae) of America north of Mexico. — Bull. Amer. Mus. Nat. Hist. 76. New York, p. 277–442.

—— 1949. American Spiders. — (The New Illustrated Naturalist.) New York, pp. I–XIII, 1–285.

GIBSON, A., 1920. Lepidoptera. — Rep. Can. Arct. Exp. 3. Ottawa, p. 1–58.

HACKMAN, W., 1954. The spiders of Newfoundland. — Acta Zool. Fenn. 79. Helsingfors, p. 1–99.

Handbook of British birds, 1945. By H. F. Witherby, F. C. R. Jourdain, N. F. Ticehurst, and B. W. Tucker. I–V. 3. impr. London, pp. 1–326, 1–352, 1–387, 1–461, 1–381.

Handbuch der Pflanzenkrankheiten (P. Sorauer), 1949–54. IV: 1–2. V: 1–2. 5. ed. Berlin & Hamburg.

HARRINGTON, W. H., 1891. Notes on a few Canadian Rhynchophora. — Can. Ent. 23. London, Ont., p. 21–27.

HARTERT, E., 1903, 1912–21, 1921–22, 1932–38. Die Vögel der paläarktischen Fauna. I. II. III. Ergänzungsband. Berlin, pp. 1–2328, 1–602.

HATCH, M. H., 1947. The Chelifera and Isopoda of Washington and adjacent regions. — Univ. Wash., Publ. Biol. 10: 5. Seattle, Wash., p. 157–274.

—— 1953. The beetles of the Pacific Northwest. I. Introduction and Adephaga. — Ibidem. 16. p. 1–340.

—— 1955. Bradycellus harpalinus Serv. in North America. — Coleopt. Bull. 9. Rochester, N. Y., p. 10.

HENRIKSEN, K. L., 1937. Insects collected on the fifth Thule expedition. — Rep. 5th Thule Exp. 1921–24. II: 8. Copenhagen, p. 1–34.

HEYDEMANN, F., 1943. Die Bedeutung der sogenannten Dualspecies (Zwillingsarten) für unsere Kenntnis der Art- und Rassenbildung bei Lepidopteren. — Ent. Zeit. 104. Stettin, p. 116–142.

HEYDEN, L. VON, 1880–98. Catalog der Coleopteren von Sibirien. With 3 suppl. — (Deutsch. Ent. Gesellsch.) Berlin, pp. I–XXIV, 1–224, 1–217, 1–84, 1–24.

HOLDHAUS, K., 1954. Die Spuren der Eiszeit in der Tierwelt Europas. — Abh. Zool.-Bot. Gesellsch. 18. Wien, p. 1–493.

HOLDHAUS, K. & LINDROTH, C. H., 1939. Die europäischen Koleopteren mit boreoalpiner Verbreitung. — Ann. Naturh. Mus. 50. Wien, p. 123–293.

HOLLAND, W. J., 1903 (1917, 1934). The Moth Book. — New York, pp. I–XXIV, 1–479.

HOLM, Å., 1950. Studien über die Spinnenfauna des Torneträskgebietes. — Zool. Bidr. 29. Uppsala, p. 103–213.

HOLZAPFEL, MONIKA, 1932. Die Gewächshausfauna des Berner Botanischen Gartens. — Rev. Suisse Zool. 39. Genève, p. 325–374.

HOPPING, R., 1932. Anoplodera planata S. & H. — Can. Ent. 64. Orillia, Ont., p. 72.

HOVANITZ, W., 1950. The biology of Colias butterflies. 1. The distribution of the North American species. — Wasm. Journ. Biol. 8. San Francisco, p. 49–75.

HUBENDICK, B., 1951. Recent Lymnaeidae. Their variation, morphology, taxonomy, nomenclature, and distribution. — K. Vet. Ak. Handl. (4) 3. Stockholm, p. 1–223.

JACOBI, A., 1931. Das Rentier, eine zoologische Monographie der Gattung Rangifer. — Zool. Anz. 96 (Ergänzungsband). Leipzig, p. 1–264.

JACOBSON, G. G., 1905–15. Žuki Rossij. (The Beetles of Russia, &c.) 1–10. (Russian.) — Leningrad, p. 1–864.

JAWLOWSKI, H., 1930. On European Diplopoda introduced to North America. — Fragm. Faun. Mus. Zool. Pol. 1:7. Warszawa, p. 181–185.

JOHANSEN, F., 1926. On the woodlice (Oniscoidea) occurring in Canada and Alaska. — Can. Field-Natur. 40. Ottawa, p. 165–167.

JOHNSON, C. W., 1906. On the distribution of Helix hortensis Mueller, in North America. — Nautilus. 20. Philadelphia, p. 73–80.

JOHNSTON, E. C., 1950. Lepidoptera of the Pribilof Islands, Alaska. — Lep. News. 4. New Haven, Conn., p. 27–30.

JORDAN, D. S., EVERMANN, B. W., & CLARK, H. W., 1930. Check list of the fishes and fishlike vertebrates of North and Middle America, &c. — Rep. U.S. Comm. Fisheries. 1928: 2. (Dept. of Commerce.) Washington, D.C., p. 1–670.

JOURDAIN, F. C. R., 1933. On the Palaearctic element in the A. O. U. 'Check-List' (4th edit.). — The Auk. 50. Lancaster, Pa., p. 201–204.

JULIN, E., 1949. De svenska daggmaskarterna. (The Swedish Earthworms.) — Ark. f. Zool. 42 A. Stockholm, p. 1–58.

KASTON, B. J., 1948. Spiders of Connecticut. — Bull. State of Conn. Geol. & Nat. Hist. Surv. 70. Hartford, Conn., p. 1–874.

KENNARD, A. S. & WOODWARD, B. B., 1926. Synonymy of the British non-marine Mollusca. — (Brit. Mus.) London, pp. I–XXIV, 1–447.

KEVAN, D. K. McE., 1943. Study of an introduced North American freshwater Mollusc, Stagnicola catascopium (Say). — Proc. R. Soc. B 61. Edinburgh, p. 430–461.

KLOET, G. S. & HINCKS, W. D., 1945. A check list of British insects. — Arbroath, pp. I–LIX, 1–483.

KLOTS, A. B., 1951. A field guide to the Butterflies of North America, east of the Great Plains. — Cambridge, Mass., pp. I–XVI, 1–349.

KOZHANTSHIKOV, I. B., 1937. Noctuidae, Agrotinae. — Fauna SSSR. 13: 3. Moscow & Leningrad, pp. I–XVI, 1–675.

——— 1950. Orgyidae. — Ibidem. 12. p. 1–582.

KRAEPELIN, K., 1901. Über die durch den Schiffsverkehr in Hamburg eingeschleppten Tiere. — Jahrb. Hamb. Wissensch. Anst. 18 (1900). Hamburg, p. 185–209.

KROGERUS, H., 1954. Investigations on the Lepidoptera of Newfoundland. I. Macrolepidoptera. — Acta Zool. Fenn. 82. Helsingfors, p. 1–80.

KUSNEZOV, N. J., 1925. Some new Eastern and American elements in the fauna of Lepidoptera of Polar Europe. — C. R. Ac. Sci URSS (A). Leningrad, p. 119–122.

LECLERCQ, J., 1954. Monographie systématique, phylogénétique et zoogéographique des Hyménoptères Crabroniens. — Liège, p. 1–371.

LEHMANN, H. C. & KLINKOWSKI, M., 1942. Zur Pathologie der Luzerne. 1. Die schädlichen Rüsselkäfer (Curculionidae). — Ent. Beihefte. 9. Berlin-Dahlem, p. 1–78.

LENG, C. W., 1920, 1927–48. Catalogue of the Coleoptera of America, north of Mexico. With 5 suppl. — Mount Vernon, N. Y.

LEONARD, M. D., 1926. A list of the insects of New York. With a list of the spiders and certain other allied groups. — Mem. Cornell Univ. Agric. Exp. Stat. 101. Ithaca, N. Y., p. 1–1121.

Lepidopterorum Catalogus, 1911–39. (Ed. F. Bryk.) — 1–94. Berlin & Haag.

LICHAREV, I. M. & RAMMELMAYER, E. S., 1952. Terrestrial Mollusca of SSSR. (Russian.) — Opredel. Fauna SSSR. 43. Moscow & Leningrad, p. 1–512.

LINDROTH, C. H., 1954. Carabidae common to Europe and North America. — Coleopt. Bull. 8. Washington, D. C., p. 35–52.

—— 1955. The Carabid beetles of Newfoundland, including the French islands St. Pierre and Miquelon. — Opusc. Ent., Suppl. XII. Lund, p. 1–168.

LOCKET, G. H. & MILLIDGE, A. F., 1951–53. British spiders. I. II. — (Ray Soc.) London, pp. 1–310, 1–449.

LOWRIE, D. C. & GERTSCH, W. J., 1955. A list of the spiders of the Grand Teton Park Area, &c. — Amer. Mus. Nov. 1736. New York, p. 1–29.

LUTZ, F. E. & COCKERELL, T. D. A., 1920. Notes on the distribution and bibliography of North American bees, &c. — Bull. Amer. Mus. Nat. Hist. 42. New York, p. 491–641.

MADER, L., 1926–37. Evidenz der paläraktischen Coccinelliden und ihrer Aberrationen in Wort und Bild. — Zeitschr. Ver. Naturbeob. Wien; Ent. Anz. Wien; Ent. Nachr.-Blatt Troppau. pp. 1–412, I–XII.

MALKIN, B., 1953. New records of Arachnida from Alaska. — Pan-Pac. Ent. 29. San Francisco, p. 205–206.

MANDAHL-BARTH, G., 1938. Land and freshwater Mollusca. — Zool. of Icel. 4. Copenhagen, p. 1–31.

MARSHALL, J. F., 1938. The British Mosquitoes. — (Brit. Mus.) London, pp. I–XII, 1–341.

MC DUNNOUGH, J. H., 1938. Check list of the Lepidoptera of Canada and the United States of America. 1. — Mem. S. Calif. Ac. Sci. 1. Los Angeles, p. 1–272.

—— 1949. Revision of the North American species of the genus Eupithecia (Lepidoptera, Geometridae). — Bull. Amer. Mus. Nat. Hist. 93. New York, p. 537–728.

—— 1950. Species of Euxoa of eastern North America, &c. — Ibidem. 95: 6. p. 355–408.

MEEUSE, A. D. J. & HUBERT, B., 1949. The Mollusc fauna of glasshouses in the Netherlands. — Basteria. 13. Liège, p. 1–30.

MICHAELSEN, W., 1903. Die geographische Verbreitung der Oligochaeten. — Berlin, p. 1–186.

MONTSHADSKY, A., 1951. Culicid larvae. (Russian.) — Opred. Fauna SSSR. 37. Moscow & Leningrad, p. 1–290.

MOZLEY, A., 1935. The fresh-water and terrestrial Mollusca of Northern Asia. — Trans. R. Soc. 58 (1936). Edinburgh, p. 605–695.

—— 1938. The fresh-water Mollusca of sub-arctic Canada. — Can. Journ. Research. 16 D. Ottawa, p. 93–138.

MUESEBECK, C. F. W., KROMBEIN, K. V., & TOWNES, H. K., 1951. Hymenoptera of America north of Mexico. Synoptic catalog. — U.S. Dept. Agric., Agric. Monogr. 2. Washington, D. C., p. 1–1420.

MÜLLER, G., 1949–53. I Coleotteri della Venezia Giulia. II. — Publ. Centro Sperim. Agric. Forest. 4. Trieste, p. 1–685.

MUNROE, E. G., 1951. The geographic variation of Dasyuris polata (Duponchel) in North America (Lepidoptera: Geometridae). — Can. Ent. 83. Ottawa, p. 290–294.

NATVIG, L. R., 1948. Contributions to the knowledge of the Danish and Fennoscandian Mosquitoes. Culicini. — Norsk Ent. Tidsskr., Suppl. 1. Oslo, pp. I–XXIII,
1–567.

NEEDHAM, J. G. & WESTFALL, M. J., Jr., 1955. A manual of the Dragonflies of North
America (Anisoptera). — Berkeley & Los Angeles, p. 1–615.

NUNENMACHER, F. W., 1934. Studies among the Coccinellidae. 7. — Pan-Pac. Ent.
10. San Francisco, p. 113–114.

OEKLAND, F., 1925. Die Verbreitung der Landgastropoden Norwegens. — Skr.
Norske Vid.-Ak., Mat.-Naturv. Klasse. 8. Oslo, pp. I–VIII, 1–168.

OLSOUFIEV, N. G., 1937. Tabanidae. — Fauna SSSR. 7: 2. Moscow & Leningrad,
pp. I–XIII, 1–434.

OUGHTON, J., 1948. A zoogeographical study of the land snails of Ontario. — Univ.
Toronto, Biol. Ser. 57. Toronto, pp. I–XI, 1–126.

PALMÉN, E., 1946. Die Landisopoden Finnlands. — Ann. Zool. Soc. Zool. Bot.
Fenn. Vanamo. 11. Helsingfors, p. 1–35.

—— 1948. The Chilopoda of Eastern Fennoscandia. — Ibidem. 13. p. 1–45.

—— 1951. A survey of the Oniscoidea (Isopoda Terr.) of Newfoundland. — Ibidem.
14. p. 1–27.

—— 1952. Survey of the Diplopoda of Newfoundland. — Ibidem. 15. p. 1–31.

—— 1954. Survey of the Chilopoda of Newfoundland. — Arch. Soc. Zool. Bot.
Fenn. Vanamo. 8. Helsingfors, p. 131–149.

PETERS, J. L., 1931–51. Check-list of birds of the world. I–VII. Cambridge,
Mass.

PETERSEN, B., 1954. Some trends of speciation in the cold-adapted Holarctic fauna.
— Zool. Bidr. 30. Uppsala, p. 233–314.

PETERSON, R. L., 1952. A review of the living representatives of the genus Alces. —
Contr. R. Ont. Mus. Zool. & Paleont. 34. Toronto, p. 1–30.

PHILIP, C. B., 1947. A catalog of the blood-sucking fly family Tabanidae (Horseflies
and Deerflies) of the Nearctic region north of Mexico. — Amer. Midl. Nat. 37.
Notre Dame, Ind., p. 257–324.

PIERCE, W. D., 1919. Contributions to our knowledge of the weevils of the superfamily Curculionoidea. — Proc. Ent. Soc. 21. Washington, D. C., p. 21–36.

PILSBRY, H. A., 1939–48. Land Mollusca of North America (north of Mexico).
I: 1–2. II: 1–2. — Ac. Nat. Sci., Monogr. 3. Philadelphia, pp. I–XVII, 1–994;
I–VI, 1–1113.

PITTIONI, B., 1942–43. Die boreoalpinen Hummeln und Schmarotzerhummeln. —
Mitt. Kgl. Naturw. Inst. 15–16. Sofia, pp. 155–218, 1–78.

PLAVILSTSHIKOV, N. N., 1936, 1940. Cerambycidae. 1–2. — Fauna SSSR. (N. S.) 7.
22. Moscow & Leningrad, pp. 1–612, 1–784.

RAUSCH, R., 1953. On the status of some Arctic Mammals. — Arctic. 6: 2. Ottawa.
p. 91–148.

REIMOSER, E., 1919. Katalog der echten Spinnen (Araneae) des Paläarktischen Ge-
bietes. — Abh. Zool. Bot. Gesellsch. 10: 2. Wien, p. 1–280.

ROCQUE, A. LA, 1953. Catalogue of the recent Mollusca of Canada. — Bull. Nation.
Mus. Can. 129. Ottawa, pp. I–IX, 1–406.

ROEWER, C. F., 1942, (1944) 1954. Katalog der Araneae. 1–2. Bremen, pp. 1–1040,
1–160; Bruxelles, p. 1–1751.

SAHLBERG, J., 1880. Bidrag till Nordvestra Sibiriens insektfauna. Coleoptera, &c. — K. Svensk. Vet. Ak. Handl. 17. Stockholm, p. 1–115.

SCHMIDT, A., 1922. Aphodiinae. — Das Tierreich. 45. Berlin & Leipzig, p. 1–614.

SCHUBART, O., 1934. Diplopoda. — Tierwelt Deutschl. 28. Jena, p. 1–318.

SEITZ, A. (with co-operators) 1909–24. Die Gross-Schmetterlinge der Erde. 1–160. Stuttgart.

SHADIN, W. I., 1935. Über die ökologische und geographische Verbreitung der Süsswassermollusken in der USSR. — Zoogeogr. 2. Jena, p. 495–554.

—— 1952. Freshwater Mollusca. (Russian.) — Opred. Fauna SSSR. 46. Moscow & Leningrad, p. 1–376.

SIMON, E., 1914–37. Les Arachnides de France. 6: 1–5. Paris, p. 1–1298.

SIMPSON, G. G., 1945. The principles of classification and a classification of Mammals. — Bull. Amer. Mus. Nat. Hist. 85. New York, pp. I–XVI, 1–350.

SKORIKOV, A. S., 1937. Die grönländischen Hummeln im Aspekte der Zirkumpolarfauna. — Ent. Medd. 20. Copenhagen, p. 37–64.

SMITH, F., 1917. North American earthworms of the family Lumbricidae in the collection of the United States National Museum. — Proc. U. S. Nat. Mus. 52. Washington, D. C., p. 157–182.

SMITH, J. B., 1893. Catalogue of the Lepidopterous superfamily Noctuidae found in Boreal America. — Bull. Smiths. Inst. 44. Washington, D. C., p. 1–424.

SMITH, M. R., 1951, *vide* Muesebeck, Krombein, & Townes.

STACKELBERG, A. A., 1937. Culicidae, Culicinae. (Russian.) — Fauna SSSR. 3: 4. Moscow & Leningrad, pp. I–X, 1–258.

STEGMANN, B., 1938. Principes généraux des subdivisions ornithogéographiques de la région paléarctique. — Fauna SSSR (N.S.). 19. Moscow & Leningrad, p. 1–157.

STEPHENSON, J., 1930. The Oligochaeta. — Oxford, pp. I–XVI, 1–978.

STITZ, H., 1939. Ameisen oder Formicidae. — Tierwelt Deutschl. 37. Jena, p. 1–428.

TAYLOR, J. W., 1902–21. Monograph of the land & freshwater Mollusca of the British Isles. II–IV. — Leeds, pp. 1–312, 1–522, 1–160.

TITUS, E. G., 1911. The genera Hypera and Phytonomus (Coleoptera, Family Curculionidae) in America, north of Mexico. — Ann. Ent. Soc. Amer. 4. Columbus, Ohio, p. 383–473.

URQUHART, F. A. & BEAUDRY, J. R., 1953. A recently introduced species of European grasshopper. — Can. Ent. 85. Ottawa, p. 78–79.

VALLE, K. J., 1933. Die Lepidopterenfauna des Petsamogebietes. — Ann. Zool. Soc. Zool. Bot. Fenn. Vanamo. 1. Helsingfors, pp. I–VII, 1–262.

—— 1952. Die Verbreitungsverhältnisse der ostfennoskandischen Odonaten. — Acta Ent. Fenn. 10. Helsingfors, p. 1–87.

—— 1955. Odonata from Newfoundland. — Ann. Ent. Fenn. 21. Helsingfors, p. 57–60.

VANDEL, A., 1945. La répartition géographique des Oniscoidea. — Bull. Biol. France et Belg. 79. Paris, p. 221–272.

VAN NAME, W. G., 1936. The American land and fresh-water Isopod Crustacea. — Bull. Amer. Mus. Nat. Hist. 71. New York, p. 1–535.

—— 1940. A supplement to the American land and fresh-water Isopod Crustacea. — Ibidem. 77. p. 109–142.

VERHOEFF, K. W., 1937. Diplopoda u. Chilopoda. — Tierwelt Mitteleur. II. Leipzig,
  p. 1–120.
WÄCHTLER, W., 1937. Isopoda. — Tierwelt Mitteleur. II. Leipzig, p. 225–317.
WALKER, E. M., 1927. The woodlice or Oniscoidea of Canada (Crustacea, Isopoda).
  — Can. Field-Natur. 41. Ottawa, p. 173–179.
—— 1953. The Odonata of Canada and Alaska. 1. — Toronto, p. 1–292.
WARNER, ROSE E., 1952. Another European weevil, Pentarthrum huttoni Woll. in
  North America. — Coleopt. Bull. 6. Washington, D. C., p. 51–52.
WEYRAUCH, W., 1937. Zur Systematik und Biologie der Kuckuckswespen Pseudo-
  vespa, Pseudovespula und Pseudopolistes. — Zool. Jahrb., Abt. Syst. 70. Jena,
  p. 243–290.
WILCOX, J., MOTE, D. C. & CHILDS, L., 1934. The root-weevils injurious to straw-
  berries in Oregon. — Bull. Agric. Exp. Stat., Oreg. State Agric. Coll. 330. Cor-
  vallis, Oreg., p. 1–109.
WILLIAMS, C. B., 1950. American moths in Britain. — Lep. News. 4. New Haven,
  Conn., p. 62.
WILLIAMS, S. R. & HEFNER, R. A., 1928. The Millipedes and Centipedes of Ohio.
  — Ohio State Univ. Bull. 33. Columbus, Ohio, p. 91–147.
WILSON, E. O., 1955. A monographic revision of the ant genus Lasius. — Bull.
  Mus. Comp. Zool. 113. Cambridge, Mass., p. 1–205.
WILSON, E. O. & BROWN, W. L., Jr., 1955. Revisionary notes on the sanguinea and
  neogagates groups of the ant genus Formica. — Psyche. 62. Watertown, Mass., p.
  108–129.
WYNNE-EDWARDS, V. C., 1952. Freshwater vertebrates of the Arctic and Subarctic.
  — Bull. Fish. Research Board Can. 94. Ottawa, p. 1–28.
ØKLAND, vide OEKLAND.

Chapter II

THE HUMAN TRANSPORT OF ANIMALS ACROSS THE
NORTHERN ATLANTIC

The five criteria of an introduced species

Man has purposely carried several animal species, and not only domesticated ones, across the Atlantic in either direction, and many of them have become permanently established (instances, *vide* above, p. 16). By far more numerous are the animal and plant species which were carried over unintentionally by all kinds of ships. Of course only a small fraction of them were able to find and colonize suitable ground in the new continent and the successful event, with very few exceptions, was not apparent until long afterwards when it was impossible to reconstruct the procedure accurately. Consequently, in trying to sort out the foreign elements of recent introduction from the indigenous fauna of a continent, we are usually restricted to second hand evidence: certain features of distribution, abundance, ecology, &c., shown by a species in the country where it is believed to have been introduced. There are reasons to presume that such characteristics of an immigrant into North America from Europe, or vice versa, as a rule have not been completely blotted out during the comparatively short period of, at most, 460 years.

The foremost criteria of an introduced species are:

1. THE HISTORICAL CRITERION. This includes all cases in which we are able to trace by historical evidence, if not the very landing of a species, which is a rare exception, at least parts of the following *expansion*. It is true that the period open to scientific survey is too short to control the *normal* changes of a species' area, but the *recent immigrants* often show a surprising power of rapid dispersal during the interval between first establishment and balanced distribution. Thus the introduction, temporary extermination, re-introduction, and final victorious progress of the Colorado-Beetle (*Leptinotarsa decemlineata* Say) in Europe (fig. 3), as well as the history of the Gypsy Moth (*Lymantria dispar* L.) in North America, were followed in detail from year to year.

Similar instances are provided by *Passer domesticus* L. (the English sparrow) and *Sturnus sturnus* L. (the Starling; fig. 4), which are *known* to be introduced into North America, as well as the Muskrat (*Fiber* or *Ondatra zibethicus* L.) in Europe (fig. 5), and by *Pieris rapae* L. (the Cabbage Butterfly), *Phytonomus posticus* Gyll. (the

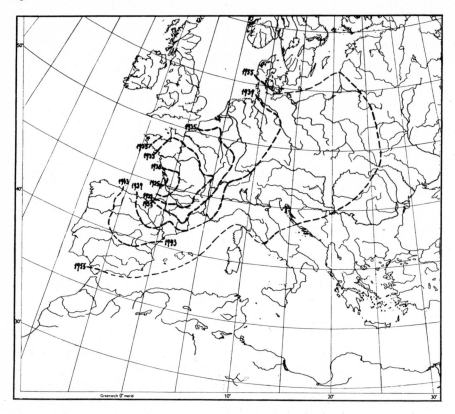

FIG. 3. Spread of the Colorado Beetle (*Leptinotarsa decem-lineata* Say) in Europe until World War II, starting from Sénéjac near Bordeaux about 1920. The present eastern limit is tentative only.

(According to ALFARO, 1941, 1943, and O. AHLBERG, *in litt.*)

(Photo P. ARDÖ.)

Alfalfa Weevil; fig. 6), the ground-beetle *Carabus nemoralis* Müll. (fig. 7)[1], and many others, which are *supposed* to be European introductions, in part just because of their rapid expansion. Another ground-beetle, *Pterostichus melanarius* Ill. (*vulgaris*

---

[1] The statement made by Evans (1952, p. 217–218), that *Carabus nemoralis* had been purposely introduced into eastern Canada as a general predator, is due to a misinterpretation of Cosens (1923, p. 10).

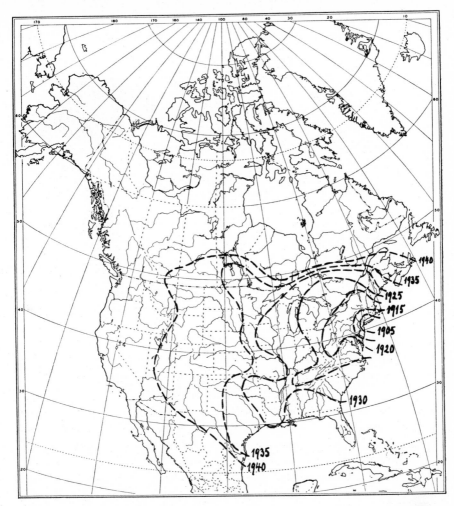

FIG. 4. Spread of the Starling (*Sturnus sturnus* L.) in North America since its introduction into New York in 1890.
(After WING, 1943.)

(From ROSENBERG, Fåglar i Sverige.)

auctt.), and a small clover-feeding weevil, *Tychius picirostris* F., are spreading fast over the northern parts of the American continent at this very time.

Other examples of recent dispersal, in Newfoundland and adjacent regions, are mentioned below (p. 151).

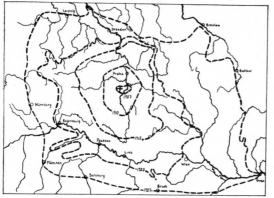

(From Burt & Grossenheider, 1952.)

FIG. 5. Spread of the Muskrat, *Ondatra* (*Fiber*) *zibethica* L., in Central Europe since its introduction 40 km. SSW of Prague, in 1905.

(After Ulbrich, 1930.)

On the other hand, introduced species may very well be conservative and remain for a long time restricted to the port of introduction or its immediate vicinity. This, as suggested by Brown (1950, p. 197), is probably due to the fact that these species are often confined to open ground, the surrounding forests forming an efficient barrier against further distribution. The click-beetle *Agriotes lineatus* L., found in Newfoundland as early as about 1840, is still restricted to the Avalon Peninsula of the southeast where it was first introduced.

There are also instances, at least in Europe, of animals showing a rapid temporary expansion of area *not* due to human influences, for example certain aquatic birds, the Carabid beetle *Amara majuscula* Chaud. (Lindroth, 1949, p. 625), and the Click-beetle *Corymbites cupreus* F. (Holdhaus & Lindroth, 1939, pp. 184, 260), in Scandinavia and Finland. In these cases, however, the migration has taken place *from* a larger continent (Asia and SE Europe) *towards* the periphery (Atlantic Europe), never in the opposite direction.

2. THE GEOGRAPHICAL CRITERION. The distribution of an introduced species is often "immature": the area is more or less restricted, usually to some coastal district, and "unnatural", in the sense that its limits can hardly be co-ordinated with any external factor (climate, soil, vegetation, &c.) which could explain this restriction. A disjunct (broken-up) area is especially suspicious; for instance if a species, otherwise not coast-bound, occurs in North America only in the Northeast and in the Pacific Northwest. Thus the ground-beetle *Bembidion lampros* Hbst. is restricted to British Columbia and the very town of St. John's, New-

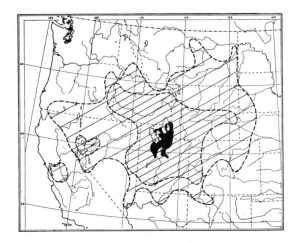

(From Essig, 1931.)

FIG. 6. Spread of the Alfalfa Weevil, *Phytonomus posticus* Gyll. (*variabilis* Hbst.) in Central and Western U.S.A. since its introduction in Utah about 1902.
Black area = before and incl. of 1910
Densely hatched area = before and incl. of 1919
Thinly hatched area = ,, ,, ,, ,, 1952.
    Since 1952 the beetle has appeared also in the eastern states.

(According to Titus, 1911, Reeves, 1927, and information from Bureau of Agriculture, Washington, D.C.)

foundland. Other Carabid beetles showing almost as wide a gap in their North American distribution are *Carabus granulatus* L. (fig. 8), *C. nemoralis* Müll. (fig. 7), *Agonum mülleri* Hbst., *Clivina fossor* L., and *Pterostichus melanarius* Ill. (for further examples, *vide* p. 144). This pattern of distribution in introduced species holds also true for terrestrial Molluscs (Pilsbry, 1948, p. 522). An "immature" distribution as a sign of introduction in Newfoundland is shown by *Bembidion tetracolum* Say (*ustulatum* auctt.), *Clivina fossor* L. (maps, figs. 12–13), and many others.

3. THE ECOLOGICAL CRITERION. The ecology of a species may indicate its character of a foreigner. It is most striking to a European biologist that in North America the "culture steppe", the open, dry (artificially drained) land in and around ports and other settlements, especially along the Atlantic coast, is inhabited by a flora and fauna of pronounced European character. Certain indigenous North American species may invade such spots too, but a plant or an animal *restricted* to this habitat is very likely to be a recent introduction.

    An instance is given by the ground-beetle genus *Amara*. With very few exceptions, its members are confined to dry, open ground, some of them inhabiting

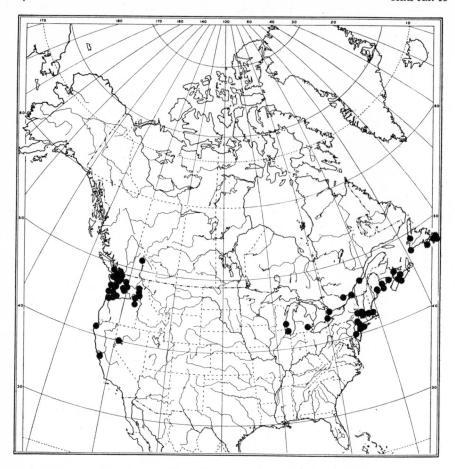

FIG. 7. Distribution of *Carabus nemoralis* O. F. Müll., introduced into North America.

(From Faune de France.)

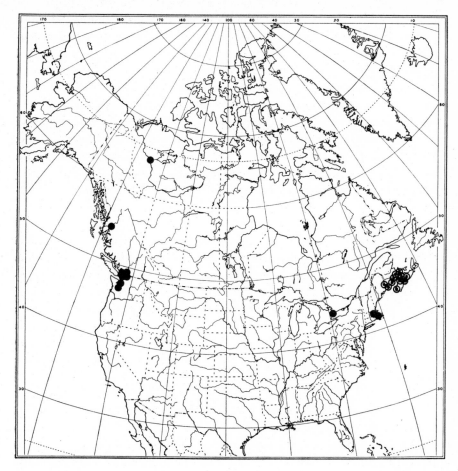

FIG. 8. Distribution of *Carabus granulatus* L., repeatedly introduced into North America. The figured specimen is of *forma typica* from Sweden.

Black dots = *forma typica*. Pointed dots = sbsp. *hibernicus* Lth.

(Photo P. ARDÖ.)

the alpine region, others moorland and sandflats at a lower altitude, or native meadows, including the epilittoral zone of lakes or the sea. In the maritime provinces of Canada, however, a notably high number of *Amara* species is restricted to cultivated ground, waste places, &c., to the "culture steppe". From Labrador, Newfoundland, and Nova Scotia, 24 species of *Amara* are known altogether; 13 of these inhabit ground more or less untouched by man, as just described, only one, *Amara fulva* DeG., being a recent introduction. The remaining 11 are bound to waste ground or arable land or at any rate are clearly favoured by human culture; of these 6 are European introductions (*A. aenea* DeG., *apricaria* Payk., *aulica* Panz., *bifrons* Gyll., *familiaris* Dft., *lunicollis* Schiø.) and only 5 indigenous to North America (*A. avida* Say, *impuncticollis* Say, *latior* Kby., *pallipes* Kby., *patruelis* Dej.).

4. THE BIOLOGICAL CRITERION. The natural history of a species may preclude any idea of regarding it as indigenous. This evidence is very strong in plant-feeders and parasites monophagously bound to a single host. The colorado beetle (*Leptinotarsa decemlineata* Say) was unable to live in Europe before the cultivation of potatoes was started in the late 16th century and the same applies to several pests of *Citrus* trees in North America before the introduction of their hosts. The weevils (*Curculionidae*) and other insects feeding on various species of clover (*Trifolium*) in eastern Canada and northern New England had no indigenous host at their disposal until the transatlantic trade started.

5. THE TAXONOMIC CRITERION. This is especially valuable in cases where a species occurs on a continent partly as indigenous, partly as a result of recent introduction. In certain cases the two forms may be taxonomically separate, even if the distinguishing characters are of less than subspecific value. The form of the lady-bird *Coccinella 11-punctata* L. occurring on the Pacific coast of North America (as far north as Alaska) has been separated as a subspecies or variety, *menetriesi* Muls., and is probably indigenous. The same species on the Atlantic coast is not distinguishable from the European *forma typica* and is no doubt a late introduction. A taxonomic separation may also be possible between one indigenous and one introduced form of the Carabid beetle *Amara lunicollis* Schiø.

Due to subspecific differences it can also be proved that *Carabus granulatus* L. (fig. 8) has been introduced at least twice into the North American continent. Nova Scotia and New Brunswick are inhabited by the sbsp. *hibernicus* Lth. which in Europe seems to occur in unmixed populations only in Ireland (Lindroth, 1955b), and it therefore certainly originated from this island. In other parts of eastern North America, as well as in the Pacific Northwest, *granulatus* is represented by its typical form which must have been brought over independently from parts of Europe other than Ireland, though possibly from Great Britain.

The distribution of long-winged (macropterous) and short-winged (brachypterous) individuals of *Notiophilus biguttatus* F. in Newfoundland, the only part of North America where it has been found, clearly demonstrates its introduction to and subsequent dispersal from the Avalon Peninsula (fig. 14).

Westward transport

From where did they come?

Most of the animal species stated or believed to be introduced into North America are widespread in Europe and great difficulties are therefore encountered in deciding on that basis alone from which country they once emigrated. As will be shown in the following chapters, it is easier to find out the possible directions of transport by studying the North Atlantic trade during the past three or four centuries. It may anyhow be worth while to analyze the distribution in western Europe, and also in North America, of the Carabid beetles in the list above (p. 40 a.f.) regarded as introduced into the latter continent.

A summary of table 2 shows that the British Isles are the only part of the European west coast where all 40 species of *Carabidae* introduced from Europe to North America occur, though two of them (*Carabus auratus* L. and *cancellatus* Ill.) are occasional only and certainly reached North America from some other European country. The same can be said about *Amara anthobia* Villa, quite recently discovered in Britian, and *Trechus obtusus* Er., occurring there in its short-winged (brachypterous) form only, whereas in North America (the Pacific Northwest) it is constantly long-winged (macropterous), a form otherwise restricted to southern Europe, north to SW France.

The remaining 36 species of table 2 may very well have been introduced from the British Isles and it is interesting to observe that all of them have been found in southwestern England, 22 species even on ballast-places or localities in the old ports where such are supposed to have been situated (besides the 20 species treated on p. 193 a.f., below, *Clivina collaris* Hbst. and *fossor* L. which, according to specimens in the Bristol Museum, have been taken on the Avon River banks).

The 23 Carabid species introduced into Newfoundland all occur in southwestern England, as do the 5 additional species found on the mainland of eastern Canada (*Bembidion properans* Steph., *Carabus granulatus* L., *Clivina collaris* Hbst., *Stomis pumicatus* Panz., and *Trechus discus* F.)

TABLE 2. Distribution of Carabid beetles regarded as European introductions in North America.[1]

Three cosmopolitan species (*Perigona nigriceps* Dej., *Plochionus pallens* F., and *Somotrichus elevatus* F.) are excluded.

	Europe					S. W. England[2]						N. America				
	Norway	Gr. Britain	Ireland	W. France	Iber. Penins.	Dorset	S. Devon	Cornwall	N. Devon	Somerset	Gloucester	Newfoundl.	N. Scotia	Atl. coast	Central N. Am.	Pacif. coast
Acupalpus meridianus L.	+	+	—	+	+	+	+	+	+	+	+	—	—	—	—	+
Agonum mülleri Hbst.	+	+	+	+	+	+	+	+	+	+	+	+	+	+	—	+
A. ruficorne Gze.	+	+	+	+	+	+	+	+	+	+	+	+	+	+	—	—
Amara aenea DeG.	+	+	+	+	+	+	+	+	+	+	+	+	+	+	—	—
A. anthobia Villa	—	+	—	+	+											+
A. apricaria Payk.	+	+	+	+	+	+	+	—	+	+	+	+	+	+	+	+
A. aulica Panz.	+	+	+	+	+	+	+	+	+	+	+	+	+			
A. bifrons Gyll.	+	+	+	+	+	+	+	+	+	+	+	+	+			
A. familiaris Dft.	+	+	+	+	+	+	+	+	+	+	+	+	+	+	—	+
A. fulva DeG.	+	+	+	+	+	+			+	+		+	+	+	—	+
A. lunicollis Schiø.[3]	+	+	+	+	+	+	+	+	+	—	+	+	+	+	+	+
Anisodactylus binotatus F.	+	+	+	+	+	+	+	+	+	+	+					+
Asaphidion flavipes L.	+	+	+	+	+	+	+		+		+		+			
Bembidion bruxellense Wesm. (*rupestre* auctt.)	+	+	+	+	—	+	+		+	+		+	+	+		
B. lampros Hbst.	+	+	+	+	+	+	+	+	+	+	+	+				+
B. properans Steph.	+	+	+	+	+	+[4]	+	—	+	+	+		+			
B. stephensi Crotch	+	+	+	+	—	+	+	+				+		+		
B. tetracolum Say (*ustulatum* auctt.)	+	+	+	+	+	+	+	+	+	+	+	+	+	+	?	+
Bradycellus harpalinus Serv.	+	+	+	+	+	+			+	+	+					+
Calathus fuscipes Gze.	+	+	+	+	+	+	+	+	+	+	+					+
Carabus auratus L.	(+)	(+)	—	+	+	—	(+)							+		
C. cancellatus Ill.	+	—	(+)	+	+	—								+	?	
C. granulatus L.	+	+	+	+	+	+	+			+	+	—	+	+	—	+
C. nemoralis Müll.	+	+	+	+	+	+	+				+	+	+	+	—	+

[1] The European records were compiled from Blair (1931), Fuente (1918–21), Jeannel (1941–42), Johnson & Halbert (1902), Lindroth (1945), Palmer (1946), Pearce (1926–27), &c. Several unpublished British records from the museums of Bristol, Exeter, Plymouth, and the British Museum, are included. Valuable information was received from Mr. G. H. Ashe, Colyton (S. Devon), and Mr. R. S. George, Gloucester.

[2] *Vide* map, fig. 16.

[3] *Amara lunicollis* is probably introduced in NE North America only.

[4] *Bembidion properans* was not kept separate from *lampros* by Pearce (1926–27) but both are doubtless widely spread in Dorset.

	Europe											N. America				
						S. W. England										
	Norway	Gr. Britain	Ireland	W. France	Iber. Penins.	Dorset	S. Devon	Cornwall	N. Devon	Somerset	Gloucester	Newfoundl.	N. Scotia	Atl. coast	Centr. N. Am.	Pacif. coast
Clivina collaris Hbst.	—	+	+	+	+	+	+	—	—	+	+	—	—	+	—	—
C. fossor L.	+	+	+	+	+	+	+	—	+	+	+	+	+	+	—	+
Harpalus affinis Schrk. (*aeneus* auctt.)	+	+	+	+	+	+	+	+	+	+	+	+	+	+	—	+
H. rufipes DeG. (*pubescens* Müll.)	+	+	+	+	+	+	+	+	+	+	+	+	+	+	—	—
Licinus punctatulus F.	—	+	—	+	+	+	—	—	—	—	+	—	—	+	—	—
Nebria brevicollis F.	+	+	+	+	+	+	+	+	+	+	+	+	—	—	—	—
Notiophilus biguttatus F.	+	+	+	+	+	+	+	+	+	+	+	+	—	—	—	—
Pristonychus complanatus Dej.	—	+	—	+	+	—	+	—	—	—	—	—	—	—	—	+
P. terricola Hbst.	+	+	+	+	+	+	+	—	+	+	+	+	+	+	—	—
Pterostichus melanarius Ill. (*vulgaris* auctt.)	+	+	+	+	+	+	+	+	+	+	+	+	+	+	—	+
Pterostichus strenuus Panz.	+	+	+	+	+	+	+	+	+	+	+	+	—	—	—	—
Stomis pumicatus Panz.	—	+	+	+	+	+	+	—	+	+	+	—	—	+	—	—
Tachys parvulus Dej.	—	+	—	+	+	—	—	+	—	—	—	—	—	—	—	+
Trechus discus F.	+	+	+	+	—	—	—	—	—	—	+	—	—	+	—	—
T. obtusus Er.	+	+	+	+	+	+	+	+	+	+	+	—	—	—	—	+
T. rubens F.	+	+	+	—	—	+	+	—	—	—	—	+	+	+	—	—

Conditions are similar as regards *weevils* (*Curculionidae*). Of 69 species regarded as European introductions in North America, 61 belong to the British fauna. The 31 Newfoundland species of the same provenience all occur there.

37 species of "*Iso-Myriapods*" (*Chilopoda, Diplopoda, Isopoda terrestria*) and 14 species of non-marine *Gastropoda* in the fauna of Newfoundland are regarded as introduced and all of them are known from the British Isles; of the other 10 European species of Iso-Myriapods found on the North American mainland, 5 are British (for explanation, *vide* p. 168 a.f.).

The fauna of Newfoundland as an illustration

The European species

It is a well-known fact that the *flora* of Newfoundland contains a notably large number of plants in common with Europe. The recent "Enumeratio" by Rouleau[1]

---

[1] Rouleau's list (1949) apparently includes species originally cultivated in Newfoundland and later escaped and naturalized.

(1949) lists 1107 species of flowering plants (Phanerogams) from the island, of which almost exactly half, 556 species, grow in Europe (incl. the British Isles, but excl. Iceland) though in some cases as a different *subspecies*. The floristic relationship is quite striking in certain families: in *Boraginaceae* all 12 Newfoundland species are "Europeans", in *Cruciferae* 35 out of 50, in *Leguminosae* 18 of 27, in *Labiatae* 12 of 19, in *Scrophulariaceae* 25 of 40.

The European introductions in the Newfoundland flora can easily be extracted from records given in "Gray's Manual" (Fernald, 1950). Of the 556 "Europeans" mentioned, 227 species are regarded as such in North America, that is no less than 21 per cent of the whole flora of the island.[1] Only 4[2] of these are lacking in the British Isles (Clapham, Tutin & Warburg, 1952).

The lower terrestrial *fauna* of Newfoundland shows similar features though, unfortunately, only a restricted number of taxonomical groups has so far been subjected to a modern revision, including a detailed comparison with European specimens. Table 3 therefore represents a rather artificial selection.

In the first place it is notable how variable is the European element within the different groups treated in table 3, consisting (next-to-last column) of from 100 per cent identical species among terrestrial Isopods, to 14 per cent among the Odonata. As demonstrated by the last column, this is mainly due to the different influence of *introduced* species. This, in its turn, is easily explained by the utterly different suitability for passive, anthropochorous transport of the selected groups of animals, as will be more closely elucidated in the following pages (p. 198 a.f.)

In spite of the unequal importance of an introduced European element in different taxonomic groups, its striking dominance in the Newfoundland fauna, as compared with that of the adjacent mainland, is quite clear (cf. maps, figs. 10–11). Against

---

[1] This figure is no doubt too low. Fernald apparently overstimated the age and the original peculiarity of the Newfoundland flora. At least the following 30 species, regarded by Fernald as indigenous, should probably be removed to the group of European introductions:

Alchemilla filicaulis	*Gnaphalium sylvaticum*	*P. sylvatica*
A. minor	*Juncus acutiflorus*	*Polygonum hydropiper*
A. pastoralis	*J. bulbosus*	*P. Raii*
Cardamine flexuosa	*Lathyrus pratensis*	*Potentilla anglica*
Cirsium palustre	*Linum catharcticum*	*P. erecta*
Cochlearia danica	*Luzula campestris*	*P. sterilis*
Festuca capillata	*L. pallescens*	*Scrophularia nodosa*
Fragaria vesca	*Montia rivularis*	*Sieglingia decumbens*
Galium aparine	*Nardus stricta*	*Spergularia rubra*
G. saxatile	*Pedicularis palustris*	*Veronica officinalis*

If these species are included, the percentage of European introductions in the flora of Newfoundland is increased to 23.

[2] *Alopecurus ventricosus* Pers., *Centaurea nigrescens* Willd., *Geranium ibericum* Cav., *Lappula echinata* Gilib., and possibly 2 or 3 micro-species of *Hieracium*. A few other species grow in the British Islands only as cultivated, escaped, or casual adventives.

(Photo the author, 4.VII. 1949.)

FIG. 9. St. Fintans, SW Newfoundland. A patch of dry meadow along the railway embankment. The vegetation is dominated by Marguerites (*Chrysanthemum leucanthemum* L.) and Red Clover (*Trifolium pratense* L.), both introduced from Europe.

the 14 per cent introduced species of Carabid beetles in the fauna of Newfoundland (23 species of 165), Nova Scotia (Lindroth, 1954c) possesses 11 per cent (20 of 186 species) and the total number of European species is there 34 (18 per cent). The European Carabids are more numerous in Labrador (Lindroth, 1954d), contributing no less than 39 per cent (32 species of 82), but of these only 4 per cent (3 species) may be regarded as introduced.

It can be stated, without any exaggeration, *that Newfoundland more than any other part of North America has received an introduced element of animals and plants from Europe.* It is an important task to explain why.

Another interesting feature is that the introduced European species show an unequal, in the individual species often disjunct, distribution within the limits of Newfoundland, with a marked concentration in the southeast, on the Avalon Peninsula, the centre of trade and population. On the eastern coast of Avalon 19 introduced species of Carabid beetles have been found, the highest number shown by any part of North America (*vide* maps, figs. 10–11).

TABLE 3. The European element in the fauna of Newfoundland as illustrated by some sufficiently known groups of terrestrial (and limnic) animals. Arrangement of groups from largest to smallest European influence.

	Total	In common with Europe			
		Total	Different sbspp.	Identical	Regarded as introduced from Europe
Isopoda (Palmén, 1951)	12	12 = 100%	0	12 = 100%	12 = 100%
Diplopoda (Palmén, 1952) . .	18	16 = 89%	0	16 = 89%	16 = 89%
Chilopoda (Palmén, 1954). . .	12	9 = 75%	0	9 = 75%	9 = 75%
Curculionidae (Leng, 1920; Brown & Palmén, in litt.) . .	66	35 = 53%	1 = 2%	34 = 52%	29 = 44%
Scarabaeidae (Landin, in litt.) .	14	6 = 43%	0	6 = 43%	5 = 36%
Mollusca (Brooks, 1936, 1940).	58[1]	33 = 57%	1 = 2%	32 = 55%	14[2] = 24%
Chrysomelidae (Brown & Palmén, in litt.).	30[3]	8 = 27%	1 = 3%	7 = 23%	6 = 20%
Coccinellidae (Chapin, in litt.) .	15	7 = 47%	1 = 7%	6 = 40%	3 = 20%
Carabidae (Lindroth, 1955) . .	165	53 = 32%	12 = 7%	41 = 25%	23 = 14%
Elateridae (Becker, in litt.) . .	25	5 = 20%	1 = 4%	4 = 16%	2 = 8%
Araneae (Hackman, 1954). . .	220	54 = 25%	0	54 = 25%	11 = 5%
Macrolepidoptera (Krogerus, 1954)	280	61 = 22%	19 = 7%	42 = 15%	4 = 1%
Odonata (Walker, 1953; Needham & Westfall, 1955; Valle, 1955)	29	5 = 17%	1 = 3%	4 = 14%	0
All groups together	944	285 = 30%	37 = 4%	259 = 28%	134 = 14%

[1] The *Lymnaeidae* of Brooks' list (1940, p. 75) have been revised according to Hubendick (1951).

[2] The Brooks' (1936, 1940) are very restrictive in regarding only 6 of the Newfoundland Molluscs (one, *Deroceras reticulatum* Müll., even doubtfully) as introduced from Europe. To my mind, at least the following 8 species should be added: *Arion circumscriptus* Johnst., *Cepaea hortensis* Müll., *Hygromia striolata* Pfeiff., *Limax marginatus* Müll., *L. maximus* L., *Oxychilus draparnaldi* Beck, *Vallonia excentrica* Sterki, *Vertigo alpestris* Ald. For *Lymnaea peregra* Müll. a transport with birds is perhaps equally probable (*vide* below, p. 251).

[3] The revision of the Newfoundland Chrysomelidae is not finished and the figures here given are preliminary only.

This is a feature of general validity. In the "Iso-Myriopods" (Palmén, 1951, 1952, 1954) 42 species have been stated in Newfoundland, 37 of which are regarded as European introductions, and of these no less than 20 are known from the Avalon Peninsula only.

In a foregoing section of this chapter (p. 135 a.f.) the criteria of an introduced species were formulated. Let us now try to test them in practice. The reader, of

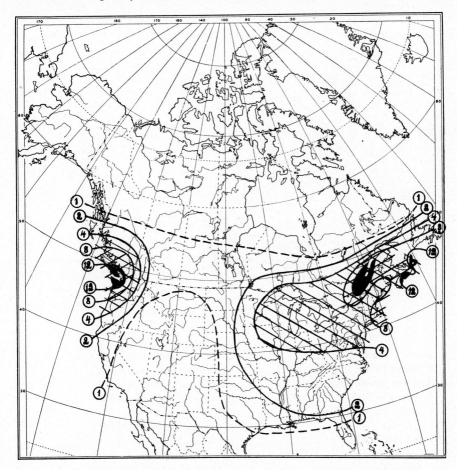

FIG. 10. "Europeization" of the North American fauna, according to the number of introduced Carabid beetles.

course, is by no means obliged to accept the verdict "introduced" for any species without hearing the arguments. Carabid beetles, as usual, may provide the material.

Carabid beetles common to Europe and Newfoundland

† = regarded as introduced from Europe

Agonum bogemanni Gyll.
A. consimile Gyll.
A. mannerheimi Dej.
(different subspecies)

† *A. mülleri* Hbst.
A. quadripunctatum DeG.
† *A. ruficorne* Gze.
A. thoreyi Dej.

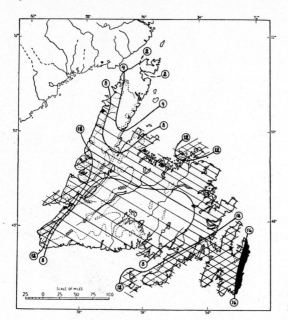

FIG. 11. "Europeization" of
the fauna of Newfoundland,
according to the number of
introduced Carabid beetles.

† *Amara aenea* DeG.
 A. alpina Payk.
 (different subspecies)
† *A. apricaria* Payk.
† *A. aulica* Panz.
† *A. bifrons* Gyll.
 A. erratica Dft.
† *A. familiaris* Dft.
† *A. fulva* DeG.
 A. hyperborea Dej.
† *A. lunicollis* Schiø.
 A. quenseli Schnh.
 A. torrida Ill.
† *Bembidion bruxellense* Wesm.
 (*rupestre* auctt.)
 B. grapei Gyll.
† *B. lampros* Hbst.
 B. petrosum Gebl.
 (different subspecies)
 B. quadrimaculatum L.
 (different subspecies)
† *B. stephensi* Crotch
† *B. tetracolum* Say (*ustulatum* auctt.)

B. transparens Gebl.
Blethisa multipunctata L.
(different subspecies)
Calathus micropterus Dft.
(different subspecies)
† *Carabus nemoralis* Müll.
† *Clivina fossor* L.
Dyschirius politus Dej.
Elaphrus riparius L.
† *Harpalus affinis* Schrk. (*aeneus* F.)
H. fuliginosus Dft.
H. nigritarsis C. R. Sahlb.
(different subspecies)
† *H. rufipes* DeG. (*pubescens* Müll.)
Loricera pilicornis F.
Miscodera arctica Payk.
(different subspecies)
† *Nebria brevicollis* F.
N. gyllenhali Schnh.
(different subspecies)
N. nivalis Payk.
(different subspecies)
Notiophilus aquaticus L.

(Photo P. ARDÖ.)

FIG. 12. *Bembidion tetracolum* Say (*ustulatum* auctt.) in Newfoundland. An introduced Carabid beetle with "immature" disjunct area, constantly fligthless on this island.

† *N. biguttatus* F.
  Patrobus septentrionis Dej.
  (different subspecies)
  Pelophila borealis Payk.
  (different subspecies)
† *Pristonychus terricola* Hbst.
  Pterostichus adstrictus Eschz.

P. brevicornis Kby.
(different subspecies)
† *P. melanarius* Ill. (*vulgaris* auctt.)
† *P. strenuus* Panz.
† *Trechus rubens* F.
Trichocellus cognatus Gyll.

Species regarded as introduced are 23 in number. This has been decided on the basis of "the five criteria" (above. p. 135 a.f.), in the following way:

1. On HISTORICAL evidence. Three species, *Amara aulica*, *A. bifrons*, and *Harpalus rufipes*, easy to collect and now common in the southwest of Newfoundland, were not captured during the intense collecting carried out in this region in the period 1905–15 by several skilled collectors (Lindroth, 1955a, p. 8). They are probably the result of later introduction. On the other hand, *Amara fulva* and *Bembidion bruxellense* were taken there by P. G. Bolster in 1905 and 1907, respectively, the first North American records. Other first-records were made outside the area: *Carabus nemoralis* in New Brunswick, 1870; *Bembidion stephensi* at

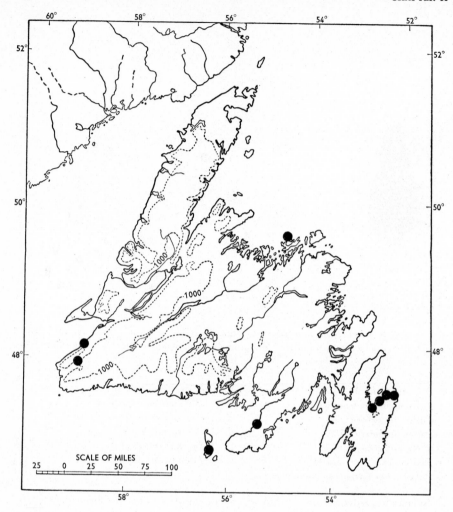

FIG. 13. *Clivina fossor* L. in Newfoundland. An introduced Carabid beetle with "immature" disjunct area. Both long- and short-
winged specimens occur on this island.

(From Faune de France.)

(Photo P. ARDÖ.)

FIG. 14. Distribution of long-winged (white) and short-winged (black) specimens of the Carabid beetle *Notiophilus biguttatus* F. in Newfoundland, its single occurrence in North America. The area of the circles is in proportion to the number of individuals investigated.

Short wing is a dominant; consequently, long-winged specimens are homozygotes and a preponderance of them indicates late colonisation. This species is a European introduction, spreading from the Avalon Peninsula in the southeast towards the west and north.

Ottawa, 1891; *Clivina fossor* at Montreal, 1915. These have since been obviously enlarging their area and so, with unusual rapidity, has *Pterostichus melanarius*, first found in Nova Scotia in 1926.

2. On GEOGRAPHICAL evidence. *Nebria brevicollis*, *Bembidion lampros*, and *Pterostichus strenuus* are known in eastern North America each from one quite small area only, the *Nebria* on the French island Miquelon, the remaining two on the eastern shore of the Avalon Peninsula. A pronouncedly "unnatural", disjunct area in Newfoundland is occupied by *Agonum ruficorne*, *Bembidion tetracolum* (fig. 12), *Carabus nemoralis*, *Clivina fossor* (fig. 13), and *Trechus rubens*. A large-scale disjunction, suggesting introduction into North America on the whole, is characteristic of *Agonum mülleri*, *Amara familiaris*, *Bembidion lampros* and *tetracolum*, *Carabus nemoralis* (fig. 7), *Clivina fossor*, *Harpalus affinis*, and *Pterostichus*

melanarius, which have an isolated, late occurrence in the Pacific Northwest (Hatch, 1953).

3. On ECOLOGICAL evidence. The following European species occur in Newfoundland only on ground strongly influenced by human culture, mainly around ports and other communities: All *Amara*'s of the list above, except *fulva* (cf. p. 142), *Bembidion lampros* and *tetracolum*, *Carabus nemoralis*, *Clivina fossor*, *Harpalus rufipes*, and *Trechus rubens*. Still more pronounced is *Pristonychus terricola*, a true indoor insect.

4. BIOLOGICAL evidence of introduction does not apply to Newfoundland Carabidae but is valid for several Curculionids (Weevils), especially those confined to *Trifolium* as food-plants (*Phytonomus meles* F., *nigrirostris* F., *punctatus* F., *Sitona lepidus* Gyll., &c.), a plant genus not represented by indigenous species on the island.

5. On TAXONOMIC evidence, *Notiophilus biguttatus*, due to the geographical distribution of its macro- and brachypterous forms, must be regarded as introduced (fig. 14). *Pterostichus strenuus*, in Europe dimorphic with respect to the hind-wings, has apparently been introduced into Newfoundland in the pure (homozygotic) brachypterous form, which possibly explains its occurrence only within a restricted area on the eastcoast of Avalon.

It is also worth while to point out that the characters referred to by Lapouge (1908, p. 19) in constituting the populations of *Carabus nemoralis* from Newfoundland and New Brunswick as belonging to a distinct, indigenous North American subspecies (also referred to by Økland, 1927, p. 355), are quite imaginary and provide no facts, which contradict the opinion that this species is a European emigrant.

The Newfoundland trade

Historical review

The trade between Newfoundland and Europe is so intimately connected with and so deeply stained by the peculiar political relations to the mother country, Great Britain, during more than four centuries, that a brief summary of early Newfoundland history seems appropriate. The most important sources have been Prowse (1895), Rogers (1911), Newton (1930), Harris (1930), Cochrane (1938), and Parkinson (1948).

The discovery of Newfoundland by the Europeans took place at a very early date. It is now regarded as a historical reality that Norsemen starting from Greenland in the year 1000 A.D. reached the coast of North America and even erected a settlement in "Vinland", though this lasted some few years only. By several earlier authors Vinland was identified either with Newfoundland or, more likely, with Nova Scotia or New England (*vide* Gathorne-Hardy, 1921, p. 224 a.f.) but, though Newfoundland was no doubt visited by the Vikings, modern authors have felt inclined to place Vinland farther south—according to Naess (1954), who based his opinion on the astronomic observations from the journeys mentioned in the Icelandic "Sagas", not north of Chesapeake Bay. The method of Naess seems, in spite of its somewhat unexpected result, to be more reliable than that of Löwe (1951), who, according to the plants mentioned in the old travel account, located Vinland somewhere between Maine and Long Island.

It has been suggested by Iversen (1938) that plants such as *Sisyrinchium montanum* Greene (*angustifolium* auctt., nec Mill.) were brought back to Greenland from North America by the Norsemen and that other species may have been carried in the opposite direction. Even if this possibility is admitted[1], there seems to exist no case of animal distribution requiring a similar explanation.

The definite incorporation of Newfoundland in the European trade was started by John Cabot's rediscovery of the island in 1497, only five years after the famous first voyage of Columbus. Cabot was sent out from Bristol and for more than three centuries Newfoundland's closest naval connection was with southwestern England. Though Cabot had discovered a new *land*, it was the surrounding *sea* that was exploited, not only by English, but in the earlier part of the 16th century mainly by French and Iberian fishermen. The island itself was used as nothing but an immense fishing-depot, with ports actively frequented in the summer months but left practically uninhabited during the winter. From the very beginning the Avalon Peninsula in the southeast was the predominant centre of this trade.

No wonder that the colonization of Newfoundland went on very slowly. Only occasionally a few crews may have been left behind over winter for preparatory work in the ports. The first known serious attempt to establish a settlement was made by John Guy from Bristol, who in 1610, with his "Company", chose Cupids on the Conception Bay of Avalon as a permanent residence. This small colony lasted only a few years. A more successful settlement was established at Ferryland on the eastcoast of Avalon in 1621; this was inhabited, with interruptions, for more than 50 years.

However, any attempt to colonize the island was met with heavy opposition from the fishermen and their customers (merchants and shipowners) in the ports of southwestern England. "From the very beginning of the sixteenth century they

---

[1] This opinion has been opposed by Böcher (1948, p. 19–24). Cf. also p. 250.

had conducted a profitable business in organizing the annual fishing expeditions to Newfoundland. They were opposed to any permanent settlement with its consequent laws and regulations which would interfere with their authority. It suited them better to send their fleets westward each spring to take possession of the stages, flakes, and cook-rooms which they had left at the end of the preceding season, to catch and cure fish there during the summer, then to abandon the place in the autumn. If there were any settlers, they would occupy the harbours and coves which the merchants had been accustomed to use and so interfere with their business. Accordingly they tried hard to prevent any settlement, or at least to keep it as low as possible" (Cochrane, 1938, p. 56). In 1633, on an influential petition from the southwestern ports, the Privy Council issued an order, called the "Western Charter", on which all subsequent regulations concerning Newfoundland were based for more than a century and a half. Among the rules laid down here was one giving the jurisdiction of every port to the "Fishing Admiral", that is the captain of the ship arriving first in the spring. Another, especially directed against settlement: "All owners of ships trading to Newfoundland forbidden to carry any persons not of ships Company or such as are to plant or do intend to settle there." A complementary rule, issued in 1637, deprived settlers the right to live less than six miles from the shore (!)

These and other obstacles contributed to keep the number of resident settlers very low for a long time. The approximate figures of Prowse (1895, p. 698 a.f.) give a total permanent population of Newfoundland during the last quarter of the 17th century not exceeding 3000 men. In summer they were greatly outnumbered by the crews of fishing-vessels; already in 1644 the English alone exceeded 10,000 (Prowse, l.c., p. 190). French settlements seem not to have existed before 1662, at Placentia (westside of Avalon), and about 1670, on St. Pierre. Not until the later half of the 18th century did the total permanent population of Newfoundland exceed the seasonal fishermen in number.

The extraordinary conditions prevailing in Newfoundland during a period of almost three centuries were bound to stamp the trade with the mother country. The large fishing-fleets leaving the ports of southwestern England every spring were destined for a poor, almost uninhabited country, a bad market for goods of any kind. The crews' own supplies gave no full cargo. The ships sailed *in ballast*. At the end of the fishing season they returned fully loaded, as a rule not directly home but to the foremost consumers, the catholic countries in southern Europe, and thence back to England in the late fall, often likewise in ballast. This triangular traffic was carried on to an almost unchanged extent as long as sailing-vessels ruled the sea, that is to the middle of the 19th century. The first steam-line calling at Newfoundland, connecting it with Halifax, was opened in 1842 (Harris,

1930, p. 431). Already at that time several introduced European insects had become established on the island (below, p. 215).

The history of the French islands *St. Pierre* and *Miquelon* has much in common with that of Newfoundland proper. Though already colonized about 1670 by the French, they later stood under British supremacy during the main part of two long periods: 1713–63, 1778–1815. I was told by Mr. Mathews, of Poole, that this Dorset port upheld an intermittent direct trade with St. Pierre, probably about 1800. From the report of the astronomer Cassini, in 1768 (Prowse, 1895, p. 570), we learn that at that time the French fishing-fleets arriving at St. Pierre every spring belonged to many different ports, from Honfleur on the Seine to Bayonne on the Bay of Biscay. However, European animals hitherto observed on St. Pierre-Miquelon are not necessarily introduced from France; the Ground-beetle *Nebria brevicollis* F., the Lamellicorn beetle *Aegialia rufa* F., and the Weevil *Trachodes hispidus* L., unknown elsewhere in North America, may as well have arrived from the British Isles. Not even the period of prohibition in U.S.A., when St. Pierre served as a too well-known staple of French spirits, certainly packeted in nice straw cases, seems to have had particular importance for the introduction of European animals. This is a confirmation of the view stressed in this chapter, that transport of ballast is superior to any kind of cargo as an instrument for synanthropous dispersal.

The ballast-traffic

There are many records from Newfoundland as well as from England indicating the regular use of ballast on board the sailing-vessels of the North Atlantic trade.

When, in 1611, John Guy, the founder of Newfoundland's first permanent settlement, published "Certaine orders for the ffishermen", he gave them the form of 8 rules and the *first* of these ran (cited from Prowse, 1895, p. 99): "Ballast or anything hurtful to Harbours not to be throwne out but be carried ashore— Penalty £ 5 for every offence".

This instruction was repeated as point 2 of the "Western Charter" of 1633: "No ballast to be thrown out to prejudice of harbor", and as number 1 of the "Lawes, Rules, and Ordinances whereby the Affaires and fishery of Newfoundland are to be governed untill the Parlam^t shall take further order", of 1653: "That noe Ballast, Prest stones nor anything else hurtfull to the Harbours bee throwne out to the prejudice of said Harbours, but that it be carryed ashore and layd where it may not doe annoyance".

Even in 1712 the appointed Governor of Newfoundland, Sir Nicholas Trevanion, included, as No. 13, a point of similar content into his "Fishery Scheme".

Among records given for 1618 by Sir Richard Whitbourne, acting as Commissioner of Vice-Admiralty, in order to illustrate various disorders committed in the Newfoundland ports, was: "Harbours frequented by English near 40 in number, almost spoiled by casting out their balast and presse stones into them".

The quotations above show sufficiently *that ballast was brought to Newfoundland in great quantities*, at least in the 17th and 18th centuries, and that as a rule *it was delivered on the shore*. It is easily understood that this procedure involved the best imaginable chances for fruits and seeds of plants, as well as for all kinds of animals associated with the soil, to be carried across the Atlantic.[1] This has already been clearly realized by W. J. Brown (1940, 1950).

Those harbours of Newfoundland in the first line affected by the conditions just described were of course the oldest ones, which in a remarkable way were concentrated to the eastern coast (map, fig. 15). Apparently St. John's, the present capital of the country, predestined by its sheltered position, was the most frequented port even in the 16th century (*vide* for instance Prowse, 1895, pp. 70, 72, 113; Rogers, 1911, pp. 19, 23, 25, 26) though probably it was not the first place to be permanently settled. Fishing-trade and settlement were almost exclusively concentrated to the Avalon Peninsula, including the first French colony, Placentia, on its western shore. This lead of the Avalon has been kept ever since and at present it houses about 45 per cent of the population. In accordance herewith the fauna and flora of this part of the island contains a larger European element than any other district in North America. As already mentioned above (p. 147), this is evident in the case of Carabid beetles (map, fig. 11), of which 19 introduced species occur on the east coast of Avalon; four of them are confined to this part of the island (*Bembidion lampros* Hbst., *Pristonychus terricola* Hbst., *Pterostichus melanarius* Ill., *P. strenuus* Panz.). In the Iso-Myriapods, 20 introduced species (54 per cent of this element in Newfoundland) are restricted to the Avalon Peninsula.

Two isolated, early colonized parts of Newfoundland are the twin islands St. Pierre-Miquelon, settled by the French about 1670 and still in French possession, and the islands Twillinggate and Fogo in the northeast, colonized about 1700. Both areas show faunal vestiges of a direct connection with Europe: on Fogo-Twillinggate the isolated occurrence of the Carabid beetles *Bembidion tetracolum* Say (*ustulatum* auctt.) (fig. 12) and *Clivina fossor* L. (fig. 13), both in the short-

---

[1] It seems reasonable to assume that the isolated occurrence of certain European Molluscs on small islands off the coast of Avalon can be explained by the fact that sailing-vessels arriving from Europe, especially at low tide, used to discharge their ballast here before entering the port of destination on the mainland of the Peninsula. Brooks & Brooks (1940, p. 58 a. f.) regarded these species as old relicts on the small islands in question, a rather adventurous hypothesis, which does not explain why the species concerned occur in Europe.

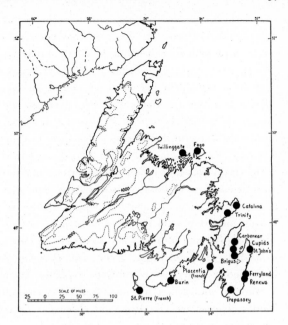

FIG. 15. The most frequented ports in the Newfoundland trade before the 19th century.

winged form, incapable of flight; on St. Pierre-Miquelon the three beetles mentioned above (p. 157).

The *western* parts of Newfoundland, the climatically most favoured, served for centuries as a base for the French fishery and had no permanent settlement at all. In the period after 1764 the French were downright forbidden to stay over winter (Prowse, 1895, p. 318; Newton, 1930, p. 144). Not until 1877 was the colonization of the west coast started by the English and shortly afterwards some French lobster factories were established, the first one at Port-au-Choix in the northwest (Harris, 1930, p. 673 a.f.). In spite of this the European faunal element is quite pronounced on the west coast and includes even species (*Amara aulica* Panz., *A. fulva* DeG., *Harpalus rufipes* DeG., among Carabid beetles) which are lacking in the east. Possibly the active trade of modern times with Nova Scotia has contributed to the Newfoundland fauna some "second-hand" European species, first arrived in the Halifax region or on Cape Breton Island (the three species mentioned all occur in Nova Scotia). A good proof of late appearance is, as mentioned above (p. 151), that *Amara aulica* and *Harpalus rufipes*, now widely distributed and abundant, were not captured by any of the entomologists who made intensive collections in western Newfoundland between 1905 and 1915. The former was first taken in Nova Scotia in 1929 (Fall, 1934), the latter on Prince Edward Island in 1937, in Nova Scotia in 1938, in New Brunswick in 1939.

At least it seems more reasonable to suppose that these species have arrived in Newfoundland from the adjacent mainland, either carried by ship, or flying (all three of them are capable of flight), than that they should have been introduced directly from Europe, for instance to Corner Brook on the west coast.

If the non-resident French fishermen of earlier centuries had been partly responsible for the introduction of European species into western Newfoundland, this would be supposed to have resulted in the appearance there of species unknown elsewhere in the Maritime Provinces of Canada, such as the beetles *Nebria brevicollis* F., *Aegialia rufa* F., and *Trachodes hispidus* L., on St. Pierre-Miquelon.

In 1951 I was told by an old fisherman of St. Pierre that even in later years sailing-vessels sometimes went in ballast from the west coast of Newfoundland, at least from the Port-au-Port region off St. George's Bay, to St. Pierre. The isolated occurrence on the French islands (in part also on the Burin Peninsula situated just opposite) of such westcoast species as the Carabid beetles *Amara avida* Say, *Harpalus rufipes* DeG., and *Patrobus longicornis* Say, all favoured on cultivated ground, may possibly be explained thereby.

Some of the earliest introductions in Newfoundland, for instance the ground-beetles *Agonum mülleri* Hbst. and *Bembidion bruxellense* Wesm. (*rupestre* auctt.), which are more abundant and widespread there than anywhere else in North America, may very well have used this island as an accumulator from which waves of air-borne emigration started and reached the mainland.

*

In order to understand the effect of the animal transport with man here suggested, it is also necessary to get a clear idea of where and how the ballast was taken on the European coast. Both the composition of the introduced faunal element in Newfoundland and the history of the North Atlantic trade have shown that English ships and English ports have played the foremost role. Unfortunately, published English records on the ballast-traffic seem to be very scarce. The brief description given here has therefore been compiled mainly from information generously supplied by persons living in or closely connected with the southwestern ports: in Poole by Mr. Edwin F. J. Mathews and the late Mr. Horace P. Smith, respectively present and former borough historian; in the Bideford district by the late Mr. Vernon C. Boyle of Westward Ho!, who was deeply interested in the matter; in Barnstaple by Mr. Alfred E. Blackwell, Head Librarian; in Bristol by Miss Elizabeth Ralph, City Archivist. Especially profitable was the study of Poole harbour journals, from 1813 and some years thereafter, liberally put at my disposal by the present owner, Mr. E. E. Kendall, aged 84, former Harbour Comissioner.

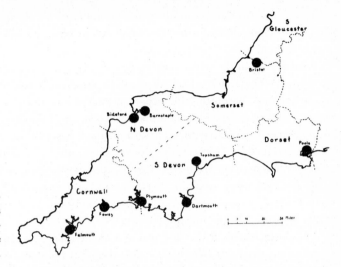

FIG. 16. The foremost British ports of the Newfoundland trade before the 19th century.

The British ports regularly mentioned in every treatise on the history of Newfoundland (e.g. by Prowse, 1895), all situated in southwestern England (in Devon and Cornwall, in addition Poole in Dorset, and Bristol), are marked on the map, fig. 16. Their trade with Newfoundland goes back to the early 16th century, as described above, and did not lose its outstanding importance until steamers outranged sailing-vessels towards the end of the last century.

Sometimes the ships went to Portugal or Spain on their way out to load salt for the fishery but as a rule they sailed directly to Newfoundland. Published records give very little information concerning to what extent they then used to go in ballast but Braddick (1953, p. 30) mentions an example from Topsham showing that in the winter season (Sept.–March) 1763–64 every second ship passing through from Exeter, with unknown destination, was in ballast. Miss Ralph informs me that as early as the 17th century a "ballast master" was appointed in Bristol, for whom special rules, orders, and instructions were established.

Far more detailed records were obtained from the unpublished "Lists of Arrivals and Sailings for the Port of Poole", placed at my disposal by Mr. Kendall and covering a short period from and including the year 1813 (fig. 17).

Diagram 1 summarizes the Newfoundland trade from Poole during two years. In the first of these, counted from September 1st 1813 to August 31st 1814 (records for the remaining four months of 1814 being lost), 38 sailing-vessels left Poole for Newfoundland, 21 of them partly or fully loaded with ballast amounting to more than 1,100 tons altogether. In 1815 (January 1st to December 31st) the figures were: 57 ships, 17 of them partly or fully loaded with ballast to a total amount of 1,180 tons. An estimation of the tonnage of British soil exported to Newfoundland from Poole alone during the course of four centuries would give an imposing figure indeed!

Poole seems on the whole to have played a very important role, underestimated by Prowse (1895) and others, in the Newfoundland trade. According to an act passed in 1778, permitting the export of limited quantities of cereals "for the use of the fisheries at Newfoundland, Nova Scotia, and Labrador" (Gribble, 1830, p. 607), Poole was allowed to send greater quantities than any other British port. The maximum intensity of the Poole trade with Newfoundland (according to Mr. Mathews) lasted from the later decades of the 18th century to about 1815 (*vide* also Parkinson, 1948, p. 244). Not until about 1800, did Liverpool catch up with Poole in importance to the Newfoundland trade (Parkinson, 1948, pp. 243, 248). The direct traffic finished in the 1880's.

The ports visited in the first place by Poole sailors of this time, according to information from Mr. Mathews, were Brigus, Carbonear and Placentia on the Avalon Peninsula, Burin in the south, Trinity and Catalina on the Bonavista Peninsula, and Fogo and Twillinggate in the northeast (fig. 15).

There is no reason to believe that the Newfoundland sailing trade of other southwestern ports differed essentially from that of Poole, but details such as the ballast procedure have been lost, due to lack of published records. For the concrete picture gathered from the old harbour papers of Poole, we are entirely obliged to the piety and foresight of a man, Mr. Kendall, who saved them from the fate of similar documents of other ports.

From a biological point of view it is also worth observing that, according to the diagrams 1 and 2, the export of ballast reached its maximum in March and April, with a second, less pronounced, in the fall. The spring maximum was no doubt still more evident before the permanent settlement of Newfoundland was started. This may have contributed to the selection of the animal and plant species which managed to cross the Atlantic as stowaways (cf. below, p. 210).

As to the kind of vessels taking part in this kind of transatlantic traffic, Mr. Boyle informed me that they were usually schooners of about 80 to 120 tons (figs. 18–19) and that 24 days would be a good passage for a ship of this kind from the North Devon coast to Newfoundland.

FIG. 17. A page from "Lists of Arrivals and Sailings for the Port of Poole", April 1814. Of the 9 ships mentioned, all but one are destined to Newfoundland and 7 of these carried ballast besides the cargo.

The bottom item runs: — "In the John & Mary, [Captain] Collins, for Newfoundland. [Cargo] 60 tons. Ballast 10 [tons]."

Published by kind permission of the owner, Mr. E. E. Kendall, Poole.

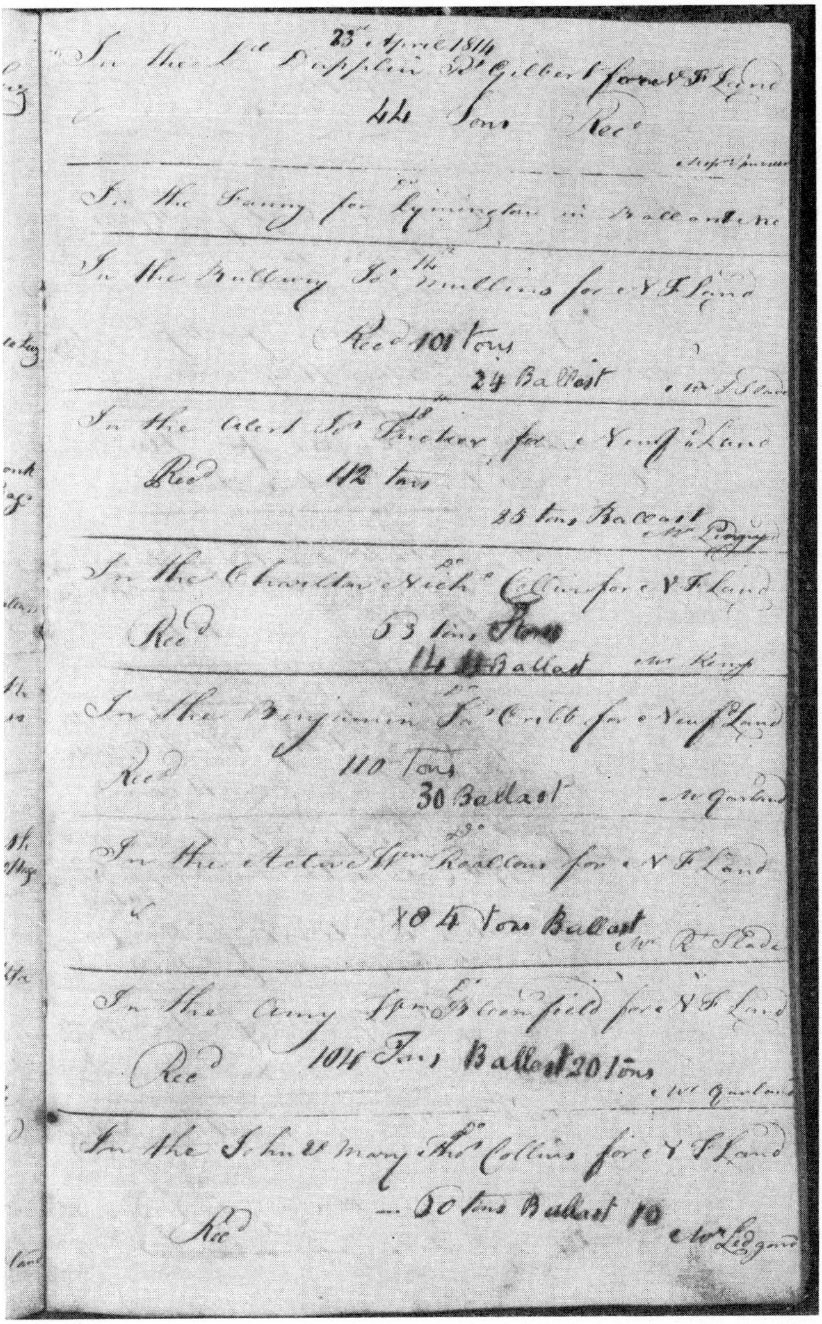
23d April 1814
In the Ld Dupplin Jno Gilbert for N F Land
44 Tons Recd
In the Fanny for Lymington in Ballantine
In the Bulkeley Jno Mullins for N F Land
Recd 101 Tons
24 Ballast
Mr J Slade
In the Alert Jno Tucker for Newfoundland
Recd 112 tons
25 tons Ballast
In the Charlotte Richd Collins for N F Land
Recd 53 tons Stores
14 Ballast Mr Kemp
In the Benjamin Jno Cribb for Newfoundland
Recd 110 Tons
30 Ballast Mr Garland
In the Active Wm [illegible] for N F Land
& 84 tons Ballast
Mr Rd Slade
In the Amy Wm Bloomfield for N F Land
Recd 104 Tons Ballast 20 tons
Mr Garland
In the John & Mary Thos Collins for N F Land
— 60 tons Ballast 10
Recd Mr Lidgard

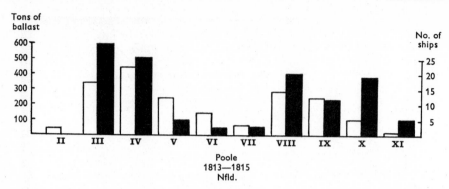

DIAGR. I. Ships (white) and ballast (black) from Poole, Dorset, destined to Newfoundland during two years, I.IX. 1813–31.VIII. 1814, and 1815. (The records of September–December 1814 are missing.)

The next important task is to find out from where the ballast was taken in the English ports. The kind of soil or other materials used of course determined the kind of living organisms which may be supposed to have found their way on board.

As far as Poole is concerned, I was told by Mr. Kendall that the ballast heaps on the quay, visible in fig. 21, consisted partly of material brought in by ships arriving in ballast from other ports, for instance from the Iberian Peninsula, and partly of stones, bricks, mortar, &c., from the town (for instance remnants from demolished houses). A similar case was related from Bideford through Mr. Boyle: The schooner "Katie", in 1905, took in 20 tons of builders' rubbish (broken bricks, mortar and stone) in Exeter on her way home to Appledore. It seems justifiable to regard this as the normal kind of ballast. The simplest way for a vessel to get ballast before sailing was to have it taken on board from the same wharf where she had discharged her load and the stuff most usually available there was no doubt builders' rubbish. For Bristol Miss Ralph speaks of stones and rubble obtained from the banks of River Avon. Later, after 1880, coastal vessels, at least, were using limestone as ballast, an economical method of carrying lime to the farmers (according to information from Mr. John Keast, Streatham, London).

A different kind of ballast was regularly used by vessels from Bideford, including Appledore, and Barnstaple, as described by Mr. Boyle: —"The ballast was always from the beaches, and sand was liked best. The vessels would be laid on Sandridge at Appledore and given a list, so that when the tide was out the crew could jump out and heave the sand up over the side with shovels. About 40 tons would be enough."—This locality, "The Crow" (figs. 23, 25) north of Appledore, was investigated in 1954 (below, p. 178).

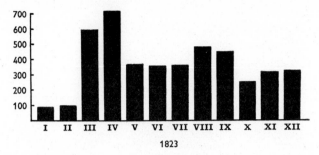

1823

DIAGR. 2. Outward ballast from Poole in 1823, regardless of destination. Total 4,298 tons.

Both diagrams (1–2) based on unpublished records from "Lists of Arrivals and Sailings for the Port of Poole", generously made available by Mr. E. E. Kendall, former Harbour Comissioner, Poole.

However, the kind of ballast used in the Bideford-Barnstaple district seems to have been an exception. Above all the ships would not as a rule take it from the tidal zone because the soil there is almost constantly mixed in with mud, which is difficult to clean away from the hold afterwards, and also because it is moist, requiring too much work in proportion to its weight after it has dried out.

A vivid picture of how the ballast was obtained in past days comes out from interviews made by Mr. Boyle in 1952 with a number of old sea captains from North Devon, of which the following are cited: —

Mr. Samuel Daniel, sailor, aged 85, says: "In about 1892 I sailed in a new schooner, the Snowflake, 120 tons, to Newfoundland. We were in ballast. In Runcorn and Liverpool you cannot get gravel from beaches, so we had stone and earth and rubble brought in carts from builders' demolitions, or deads from excavations. Another cargo from Runcorn she took out was coal for Harbour Grace [Avalon Peninsula]. I am not sure but I believe that river mud was never used as ballast in our vessels."

Captain W. J. Slade, Master of wooden schooners and ketches, Bideford: "Some vessels would sail without ballast, some with little. I once took a cargo of coal to Court Macsherry in Ireland for a farmer. The onus of getting ballast for me to come away was on him. He got me some tons from the site of a tumble-down shed[1], stones, broken slates, mortar and rubbish. Then he went off up the lanes and got a few cartloads from a hedge. It was earth and grass. When I got back here I tipped it overside in this river."

Captain William Quance, aged 83: "In October 1888 I sailed in the wooden barquentine Fanny from Appledore to St. John's, Newfoundland, in ballast. The ship had been built in Barnstaple in 1878. We were loaded with gravel ballast got

---

[1] An excellent opportunity for the indoor Carabid *Pristonychus terricola* Hbst. to get on board!

FIG. 18. "Little Minnie", two-masted topsail schooner, built 1866 at Padstow on the north coast of Cornwall. Finally belonging to J. Stephens of Fowey.

Dimensions: 82.0 ft × 21.2 ft × 10.2 ft. Tonnage: 98 net register.

She was in the Newfoundland trade and was lost in the ice off the island and the captain was killed, prior to 1899.

Published by due permission of Mr. H. Oliver Hill, through Mr. David R. Mac-Gregor, London.

from those banks of gravel close inside the Taw-Torridge Bar [i.e. 'The Crow'; *vide* below, p. 178]. Barges came alongside (30 tons each) [*vide* fig. 25] to give it to us. This gravel is in great demand by builders to make mortar, so when we got to St. John's 23 days later, the gravel was all taken away at the quay in carts."

Captain J. R. Pile, aged 65, coasting trade (not Newfoundland): "When I was a boy in a ketch we were over at Clonakilty [south of Cork, Ireland] and to get ballast we had to row about the harbour in the ship's boat and pick up stones on the beaches."

Mr. Mathews informs me that Irish ports, such as Waterford, Limerick, and Youghal in Cork, were sometimes called at by Poole vessels on their way to New-

Henley Island. Labrador.

FIG. 19. A Poole brig, possibly the "Carbonear" (belonging to Harrison, Slade & Co.), off Henley Island, Chateau Bay, Strait of Belle Isle, southern Labrador. Ships of this type, about 100 tons, were commonly used in the Newfoundland fishing trade.
   Drawn in 1857 by William Gosse of Poole (a brother of Philip Henry Gosse) and published in his "Sketches of Newfoundland & Labrador" (Ipswich, about 1858). — Made available by Mr. E. F. J. Mathews, Poole.

foundland. In the 18th century there was also periodically a very important direct trade between Ireland and Newfoundland (Prowse, 1895, pp. 283, 345) and ballast-transport westward from Ireland occurred frequently (Parkinson, 1948, p. 211). Ballast of the varied content described by Captain Slade from Court Macsherry may therefore very well occasionally have been carried to Newfoundland.

The triangle traffic, England–Newfoundland–Iberian Peninsula–England, described above (p. 156) may also have resulted in the introduction of plants and animals with ships from southern Europe returning to England in ballast. Mr. G. H. Ashe, Colyton, Devon, told me that he suggested the Weevil *Sitona gemellatus* Gyll., restricted on the British Isles to southern Devon where it feeds on *Ononis arvensis*, to have been introduced in that way. Can this possibly be applied to the occurrence of another southern Weevil, *Otiorrhynchus auropunctatus* Gyll., in Ireland?[1] It would be wise not to neglect this point of view altogether, when defining the so-called "Lusitanian element" of the British fauna and flora.

Application to other parts of North America

The conditions of trade and the use of ballast may have developed in a similar way in other parts of the Maritime Provinces of Canada and especially in *Nova Scotia*, the history of which in many points is similar to that of Newfoundland. The permanent colonization of Nova Scotia was started in the 1630's, in the beginning mainly by the French. The English did not become predominant until more than a century later and the last French colony, Louisburg on Cape Breton Island, was surrendered in 1758. The first settlement at Halifax (British) took place in 1749.

Nova Scotia was frequented by British vessels of very much the same provenience as Newfoundland, originating from the southwest of England. For instance, as Mr. Mathews informed me, there was periodically an intense but publicly underestimated traffic between Poole and Nova Scotia.

In connection with the discovery of the European weevil *Barynotus squamosus* Germ. (*schönherri* Zett.), Harrington (1891, p. 22) mentions the ballast heaps at Sidney, Cape Breton Island, "formed by vessels discharging their ballast of stone, earth, etc., before loading coal, and many species of introduced plants are found on, or about them." The ground-beetle *Carabus granulatus hibernicus* Lth., restricted in North America to Nova Scotia and New Brunswick, has no doubt arrived with ballast taken in Ireland. This and *Bembidion properans* Steph. are the only European introductions among Carabid beetles in Nova Scotia, unknown in Newfoundland (table 2). Among Weevils (Curculionids) the same applies to *Barynotus moerens* F., *Otiorrhynchus scaber* L., *Tropiphorus obtusus* Bonsd. and *tomentosus* Mrsh., and *Tychius picirostris* F.

---

[1] Carpenter (1895, p. 215) writes about *Otiorrhynchus auropunctatus:* "It is certainly remarkable that so comparatively large an insect should have been overlooked by the older naturalists; not a specimen is to be found in the collection of that prince of Irish entomologists, the late A. H. Haliday." The species is not parthenogenetic; the late Mr. E. O'Mahony informed me that he had seen mating couples several times.

Bideford (incl. Appledore) and Barnstaple were connected by direct trade also with *Prince Edward Island*, especially in the period from 1840 to 1890, according to Mr. Boyle. It is worth mentioning, then, that the introduced Carabid beetle *Harpalus rufipes* DeG. was first found on Prince Edward Island in 1937, and is now rapidly spreading.

Brown (1950, p. 197) has drawn attention to the fact that during the Napoleonic Wars British ships were seeking timber at ports in the Maritime Provinces of Canada and that "large quantities of ballast" were landed when they arrived there. As reported by Fowler (1901) St. Andrew's in *New Brunswick* seems to have been an important centre for this export of lumber and, consequently, "probably no locality of equal area in Canada can boast of a larger percentage of foreign plants in its Flora than that which flourishes on the streets and in the neighborhood of St. Andrew's".

The ground-beetles *Carabus granulatus* L. and *nemoralis* Müll., and the click-beetle *Agriotes sputator* L. were first observed in North America in New Brunswick (Brown, 1940).

New England served as a gateway for European introductions in a more restricted way (*vide* map, fig. 10). The first colonization and early history of this region were largely different. As early as the beginning of the 17th century it had the character of a permanent settlement and, though England tried to monopolize the trade, this was always more diversified than in the Canadian East and gained full independence in 1776. It is therefore easily understood that in part other animals and plants were introduced into northeastern U.S.A. For instance, the ground-beetles *Carabus auratus* L. and *cancellatus* Ill., of which at least the first mentioned has become established in New England, are not permanent inhabitants of the British Isles and must have arrived from the European mainland; likewise the Centiped *Pachymerium ferrugineum* C. L. Koch, widely distributed in Europe but not recorded from the British Isles.

Similar, more numerous instances are to be found among plant-feeding insects, apparently introduced with their hosts, such as the following Weevils (Curculionidae), introduced into the northeastern United States but unknown in Canada: *Elleschus scanicus* Payk., *Gymnetron netum* Germ., *Polydrosus impressifrons* Gyll., *Stomodes gyrosicollis* Boh., all lacking in the British Isles. One species at least, the Alfalfa Weevil (*Phytonomus posticus* Gyll.), has been imported directly to the Middle West, to Utah, possibly "in the straw packing about fragile imported packages" (Howard, 1930, p. 115), from where it is spreading rapidly in all directions (fig. 6).

Apparently, due to the early permanent colonization, there was little need for ballast in ships destined to New England, which in itself was a good market for all kinds of European products. However, the Lamellicorn beetle *Aegialia arenaria*

F., inhabiting the sand-dunes of the coast and known in North America only from Massachusetts (Darlington, 1927), was no doubt a ballast passenger. It was found on "The Crow", one of the investigated ballast-places of North Devon (below, p. 178).

All kinds of cattle had to be imported from Europe. It requires only moderate imagination to guess how slow was the procedure of loading these animals on board the old sailing-vessels. Meanwhile, of course, various dung-feeding insects were flying on board and as the rich supply of suitable food was perpetually renewed, they had no reason to leave the ship during the voyage. It is anyhow almost surprising what a rich assortment of for instance European dung-beetles, genus *Aphodius*, was carried across: 14 of the 41 species occurring in the British Isles are now well established in the United States, 10 of them also in Canada. All 3 British species of the likewise dung-feeding Hydrophilid genus *Sphaeridium* were also introduced into North America, both on the Atlantic and the Pacific coast (Brown, 1940, p. 70–71; Hatch, 1946, p. 78).

A third important reception area for European introductions was the *Pacific Northwest*. It seems that many of the introduced species of that region arrived comparatively late (*vide* list of beetles, Hatch, 1953, p. 25–29) and probably in part as secondary adventives from original centres of introduction in eastern North America. This may also be true in cases where, to our present knowledge, the Middle West constitutes an interruption of the area of a species. Even if it is actually lacking there, the climatic conditions alone may be responsible.

There is, however, quite a series of European species, notably among insects, occurring in North America exclusively on the Pacific side of the continent, for instance the following Coleoptera:

Carabidae:

Acupalpus meridianus L.
* Amara anthobia Villa
* Anisodactylus binotatus F.
Bradycellus harpalinus Serv.

* Calathus fuscipes Gze.
* Pristonychus complanatus Dej.
Tachys parvulus Dej.
* Trechus obtusus Er.

Curculionidae:

Ceuthorrhynchus assimilis Payk.
Otiorrhynchus cribricollis Gyll.

Otiorrhynchus meridionalis Gyll.
Sitona lineatus L.

* = taken in greenhouses (partly or exclusively).

For these a direct importation from Europe must be assumed (except for *Otiorrhynchus cribricollis* which may have arrived from its secondary centre in Australia, and perhaps the almost cosmopolitan *Pristonychus*). The late arrival of most European species into the Pacific Northwest, compared with eastern U.S.A., is at least partly due to the fact that the Panama Canal was not opened until 1914.

Hatch (1949) has made intense investigations of the greenhouse fauna in Washington, Oregon, and British Columbia, and found it surprisingly rich. Not only the obligatory terrestial Isopods (Wood-lice) but also insects, especially Coleoptera, were strongly represented, in part by species not regularly confined to this kind of habitat, among these several Europeans, as marked in the list above. Hatch (l.c., p. 162) is certainly right in his conclusion: "To the extent to which greenhouse species are introduced, it is probable that the shipment of nursery stock and other plant materials have played an important if not exclusive role in their dispersal. And some of these species may first have found their way into this country through the medium of greenhouse shipments" (cf. also below, p. 216). This applies also to a surprisingly large number of European indoor Spiders (genus *Theridium* and others) found exclusively in the Pacific Northwest (*vide* list, p. 94 a.f.).

However, there are also other European introductions in the Northwest, seemingly without any connection with greenhouses. Most of them occur also in northeastern North America (for examples, *vide* p. 138) and are there regarded as having arrived with ballast. Some of them may have reached the Pacific coast by subsequent transcontinental dispersal, either actively or with man, but others apparently are completely isolated in the Northwest. It seems reasonable to suppose that at least the majority of them has reached also this region by ballast transport and probably, in spite of the distance, directly from Europe.

In order to get an idea of to what extent ballast was used in this trade, I contacted the officials of the foremost ports of the Pacific Northwest and recieved two answers of considerable interest.

The first was from Tacoma, Wash., forwarded by Miss Elfriede Gudelius of the Public Library, indicating that in sailing ship days, when big square-riggers arrived on Puget Sound from foreign ports to load wheat and lumber, they were often in ballast.

The second reply was from Portland, Oreg., and sent by the General Manager of the port, Mr. J. J. Winn, Jr., who, referring to a letter from his predecessor in office, quotes as follows:

"In the old days, ending with World War I, sail vessels came in ballast to load wheat (mostly) for Europe. They all discharged earthen ballast—usually rocky stuff or sand which the stevedore companies removed and dumped into low lands abutting on the river. For many years the 'ballast' dock was in the vicinity of the present Terminal I; later it was in the Linton area in the vicinity of the present Gasco plant, as I recall."

It thus seems clear that an introduction of foreign plants and lower animals in ballast may have played a considerable role also on the Pacific coast of North America. Apparently in the same way, the Carabid beetle *Colpodes buchanani* Hope was introduced into Oregon from SE Asia (Malkin & Hatch, 1953) and it is perhaps only surprising that countries facing the Pacific, especially on corresponding latitudes of E Asia, have contributed so little to this immigration. Probably ships arriving from there used to carry full load.

Animals of a pronounced synanthropic type may of course have been carried to the Pacific coast already with the earlier settlers, as exemplified by Essig (1934).

Investigations on ballast-places in Southwestern England

Several facts mentioned in the foregoing part of this chapter, in animal distribution as well as in the history of the Atlantic trade, suggest the British Isles and above all the Southwest of England as the main region of departure for animals which have been unintentionally introduced from Europe into North America. It was therefore quite natural that I should wish to make a direct field study of the insect fauna around the old ports of this region, especially on the ballast-places, if these could still be located. These investigations were carried out in 1954, between May 21st and June 1st. On April 7th the same year I had already had the opportunity of a few hours collecting on the Avon banks in Bristol.

Most of the English ports mentioned in the old records of the Newfoundland trade (*vide* Prowse, 1895, pp. 37, 40, 56, 81–82, &c.) are situated from Poole, Dorset, in the south, along the southwestern peninsula to Bristol on the west coast, the majority in Devon (map, fig. 16). I visited the following: Poole, Topsham, Dartmouth, Plymouth, Bideford (Appledore), Barnstaple (incl. Fremington), and Bristol.

By means of preceding correspondence with initiate persons in every port and inquiries on the spot after my arrival, I tried to find out the exact position of the place where in old days sailing-vessels used to take on ballast, and in this respect, thanks to most generous information from Mr. Mathews and the late Mr. Boyle, both mentioned above, was especially successful at Poole and Bideford. In case no exact information was available, the collecting was made as close to the *oldest* parts of the port as possible, or on spots which for other reasons seemed most likely to have been used as ballast-places.

The terricolous fauna was the main object of collecting and I tried to obtain complete lists of the following groups of animals: *Coleoptera, Hemiptera Heteroptera;*

Araneae; Chilopoda, Diplopoda, Oniscoidea (Isopoda terrestria)[1]; and shell-bearing *Mollusca*. Quantitative figures were pursued only for *Carabid* beetles; of these every observed specimen was captured. The predominating or otherwise charac-teristic *plants* were noted in order to describe the nature of the locality in a simple way.

The identification of animal and plant species was carried out by myself, with the exceptions accounted for below.

Account of collecting

I. **Poole** (Dorset), 21–23.V. 54.—The actual site of the old ballast-place is still known and, according to the late Borough Historian, Mr. H. P. Smith, was marked on older maps as "Ballast Quay". It was situated on the eastern tip of the Hamworthy Peninsula (map, fig. 20) and the ballast-heaps were reproduced on an engraving from the year 1833 (fig. 21), generously put at my disposal by Mr. Edwin F. J. Mathews, the present Borough Historian. The intensity of ballast transport from Poole to Newfoundland has already been described (p. 162 a.f.).

The actual spot has now become industrialized and built over with wharfs and stores but there is a small open patch of grassland left, less than 100 metres south of the previous ballast-heaps, and here, as well as on similar ground inside the new power station, collecting was carried out.

a—Tip of Hamworthy Peninsula, immediately inside the concrete quay. Hard, dry, open soil (artificial filling of gravel and clay, with pebbles and pieces of brick). Vegetation (according to Mr. Mathews similar to that of the true Ballast Quay during the first decade of this century):

Bellis perennis	*Sarothamnus (Cytisus) scoparius*
Cirsium arvense	*Trifolium campestre (procumbens)*
Dactylis glomerata	*T. pratense*
Lotus corniculatus	*Ulex europaeus*
Poa pratensis	*Vicia angustifolia*
Plantago coronopus	*V. cracca*
P. lanceolata	*Vulpia bromoides*
P. media	

The collected animal species (*vide* list, p. 186 a.f.), very few in number due to the extreme dryness of soil, were distributed among the following groups (num-ber of "emigrant" species[2] in brackets):

---

[1] For *Chilopoda, Diplopoda*, and *Oniscoidea*, the collective name *"Iso-Myriapoda"* has been used.

[2] "Emigrants" are here understood to mean only those species which are regarded as European introductions in North America.

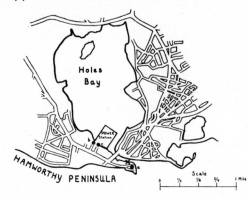

FIG. 20. The old central part of Poole. Cross = old ballast place. a–c = author's collecting places.

Coleoptera	17	(6)	species	Chilopoda	2	(2)	species
Carabidae	8	(3)	»	Diplopoda	0		»
Curculionidae	0		»	Oniscoidea	2	(2)	»
Araneae	3	(0)	»	Mollusca	2	(1)	»

Specially considered groups [1]: 14 species, 8 "emigrants" [2] = 57 per cent.

b—Inside the power plant on the northern side of the Hamworthy Peninsula, about 800 metres from the ballast-place (map, fig. 20). Artificial, open soil, of the same kind as in the preceding locality but partly not so dry, in spots bare. Vegetation:

Achillea millefolium
Anisantha (Bromus) sterilis
Artemisia vulgaris
Ballota nigra
Calystegia (Convolvulus) sepium
Capsella bursa-pastoris (coll.)
Cerastium vulgatum
Cirsium arvense
C. vulgare (lanceolatum)
Coronopus didymus
Epilobium hirsutum

Equisetum arvense
Geranium dissectum
Holcus lanatus
Hordeum murinum
Hypochaeris radicata
Poa annua
P. trivialis
Plantago lanceolata
P. major
Ranunculus repens
Rumex crispus

[1] "Specially considered groups" here and in the following include: *Carabidae, Curculionidae, Dermaptera, Opilionida, "Iso-Myriapoda"* and *Mollusca*.

FIG. 21. The Port of Poole in the year of 1833, seaside view.

Artist J. M. Gilbert. On stone by L. Haghe, Day & Haghe Lithographers. Published by R. A. Grove, Lymington, Hants. — Inscription: "To the Merchants, Shipowners & Inhabitants of Poole, This View of the Harbour, is most Respectfully inscribed, by their obedient servant, Rich[d]. And[w]. Grove." (Copy received by the courtesy of Mr. E. F. J. Mathews, Poole.)

The arrows indicate two ballast heaps.

Senecio jacobaea	*T. pratense*
S. vulgaris	*T. repens*
Sisymbrium officinale	*Tussilago farfara*
Trifolium hybridum	*Vicia angustifolia*

In addition *Alopecurus sp.*, *Crepis sp.* (possibly *capillaris*), and *Taraxacum sp.* In spots the cosmopolitan moss *Funaria hygrometrica* (det. Dr. R. Tuomikoski). In a moist ditch *Juncus effusus*.

Collected animal species ("emigrants" in brackets):

Coleoptera	79	(27) species	*Araneae*	14	(3) species	
Carabidae	29	(13) »	*Opilionida*	2	(1) »	
Curculionidae	10	(3) »	*Iso-Myriapoda*	8	(8) »	
Hem. Heteroptera	7	(0) »	*Mollusca*	4	(2) »	
Dermaptera	1	(1) »				

Specially considered groups: 54 species, 28 "emigrants" = 52 per cent.

c—Along a small salt-water pond connected with the sea by a ditch, situated inside the power plant (map, fig. 20). Clayish soil, bare and covered by a carpet of green algae close to the water, higher up with:

Artemisia vulgaris	*Matricaria maritima maritima*
Hordeum murinum	*Spergularia salina*

and *Atriplex sp.* (sterile).

Animals collected in the litoral zone (obvious salinity):

Coleoptera	8 species	*Hem. Heteroptera*	2 species
Carabidae	5 »	*Isopoda*	1

None of these occur in North America.

II. **Topsham** (S. Devon), 25.V. 54.—This small town was formerly an important harbour for the transatlantic trade. Even ships sailing from Exeter, through the canal, were supplied with ballast at Topsham (Braddick, 1953, p. 30), especially in the period 1760–1870 (according to Major A.B. Gay, of the R. Albert Mem. Museum, Exeter). The actual site of the place where ballast was taken seems no longer to be remembered. I collected on the inside of the quays and banks on the eastern side of the mouth of the canalized River Exe, within the limits as well as immediately north of the town. Hard, dry, open soil (mainly artificial: coke, bricks, gravel, &c.). Vegetation, depressed and mostly thin:

Capsella bursa-pastoris	*Senecio vulgaris*	
Matricaria matricarioides	*Sisymbrium officinale*	
Plantago major	*Stellaria media*	
Poa annua	*Trifolium repens*	
Ranunculus repens	*&c.*	

Collected animal species:

Coleoptera	34 (16) species	*Dermaptera*	1 (1) species
Carabidae[1]	22 (10) »	*Araneae*	4 (o) »
Curculionidae	1 (1) »	*Iso-Myriapoda*	5 (5)
Hem. Heteroptera	2 (o) »	*Mollusca*	2 (1) »

Specially considered groups: 31 species, 18 "emigrants" = 58 per cent.

III. **Dartmouth** (S. Devon), 27.V. 54.—Mr. Percy Russel, Hon. Curator of the Dartmouth Borough Museum, called my attention to the place still marked "Ballast Cove" on the new Ordnance Survey map (sheet 20/85). It is situated on the eastern (Kingswear) side of the harbour, opposite the Royal Naval College, and consists of a small, shallow salt-water bay, now separated from the shore by the railway. By this means the shape of the cove has certainly been changed considerably and so have the original flora and fauna of its shore, now stony and barren. The latter consisted only of the Ground-beetle *Agonum ruficorne* Gze. and a Bristle-tail, *Petrobius sp.* (immature). The railway embankment, with accompanying quays, has a synanthropous vegetation of the usual weed-type, and an utterly scarce fauna:

Coleoptera	13 (6) species	*Dermaptera*	1 (1) species
Carabidae	4 (2) »	*Araneae*	3 (o) »
Curculionidae	o »	*Iso-Myriapoda*	4 (4) »
Hem. Heteroptera	5 (o) »	*Mollusca*	3 (2) »

Specially considered groups: 12 species, 9 "emigrants" = 75 per cent. The figure is unreliable because of the poor material.

IV. **Plymouth** (S. Devon), 26.V. 54.—No records could be obtained of the places where ballast was taken. On the advice of Mr. A. A. Cumming, Curator of the City Museum & Art Gallery, I investigated the eastern side of the older (eastern) of the two harbour basins, especially along the quays at its entrance, which has not yet become fully industrialized but is largely covered with grass and weeds. The soil is hard, dry and stony, mixed in with coke, &c.

Vegetation (mostly depressed, but more or less continuous):

---

[1] In addition, *Bembidion concinnum* Steph., abundant in the tidal zone.

Brassica nigra
Dactylis glomerata (dom.)
Daucus carota
Festuca ovina
Kentranthus ruber
Lotus corniculatus
Plantago lanceolata

Potentilla reptans
Reseda luteola
Senecio vulgaris
Trifolium campestre
T. repens
Urtica dioica

In addition *Crepis sp.* (possibly *capillaris*) and *Taraxacum sp.*

Collected animals:

Coleoptera	17	(6) species	*Araneae*	6	(2) species
Carabidae	10	(4) »	*Opilionida*	1	(1) »
Curculionidae	1	(1) »	*Iso-Myriapoda*	6	(6) »
Hem. Heteroptera	3	(0) »	*Mollusca*	5	(2) »
Dermaptera	1	(1) »			

Specially considered groups: 24 species, 15 "emigrants" = 63 per cent.

V. Appledore, pr. Bideford (N. Devon), 29–30.V. 54.—Concerning this place, I obtained extremely valuable information from the late Mr. Vernon C. Boyle, of Westward Ho!, a well-known expert of the old North Devon trade (*vide* above, p. 160 a.f.). He told me that on leaving the estuaries of the rivers Torridge (Bideford area) and Taw (Barnstaple area), sailing-vessels took on board ballast mainly from the sandridge situated on the confluence of the two rivers' mouth, straight N. of Appledore, and generally known as "The Crow". The ballast thus consisted of sand, which was either directly heaved up with shovels at low tide or brought alongside in small barges. The normal rise and fall of tide here is 20 feet.

a—"The Crow" (map, fig. 22; figs. 23, 25). The collecting was carried out on the very tip of the peninsula, the only part accessible at any tide. The soil is pure sand, in the upper tidal zone partly mixed with gravel. Higher up a pronounced chain of low sand-dunes bound by *Ammophila* and, on their inside, a depressed vegetation, continuous only in spots:

Ammophila arenaria
Anagallis arvensis
Cirsium arvense
Cynoglossum officinale
Erodium cicutarium

Euphorbia paralias
E. portlandica
Ononis repens repens
Senecio jacobaea

Collected animals:

Coleoptera	34	(12) species	*Araneae*	12	(2) species
Carabidae	12	(4) »	*Opilionida*	1	(1) »
Curculionidae	6	(1) »	*Mollusca*	1	(0) »
Hem. Heteroptera	5	(0) »			

Specially considered groups: 20 species, 6 "emigrants" = 30 per cent.

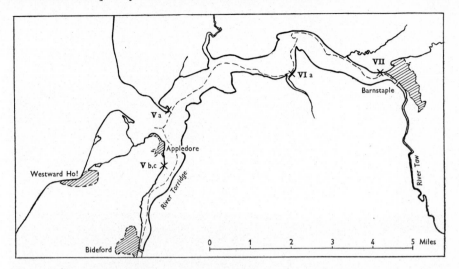

F I G. 22. The Bideford–Barnstaple district of North Devon.
Crosses indicate the author's collecting places; "V a" is "The Crow".
The broken line is the deepest channel of the rivers Taw and Torridge used by
ships.

Of particular interest are the Lamellicorn beetle *Aegialia arenaria* F. and the
weevil *Philopedon plagiatus* Schall. (fig. 26). The former has been introduced into
Massachusetts (Darlington, 1927), the latter on several localities in the Maritime
Provinces of Canada (Brown, 1940, p. 76; 1950, p. 202).

In the tidal zone north of the tip, on the east side of the peninsula, the soil was
heavily mixed with mud. The vegetation consisted of scattered *Salicornia sp.* and
thin crusts of green algae.

Recorded *Coleoptera*, all extremely abundant:

Bembidion (Cillenus) laterale Sam. *Bledius spectabilis* Kr.
Dichirotrichus pubescens Payk.

None of these occurs in North America.

b—The quarry immediately south of Appledore close to the western bank
of River Torridge (fig. 24). Captain Schiller of Appledore, aged 75, told me that
sailing-vessels took gravel and stones as ballast from this place. The bottom of the
quarry, where the collecting was carried out, is a dry, hard, stony plane, with
scattered loose heaps of stones and gravels. The vegetation was discontinuous,
rich in species, and had a pronouncedly synanthropous character:

(Photo the author 30.V. 1954.)

FIG. 23. The Taw-Torridge Bar, called "The Crow", viewed from the south (Appledore side) at low tide.

On the sand-flat (the same as in fig. 25) ballast was commonly taken by sailing vessels in olden days.

Achillea millefolium
Alliaria petiolata
Bellis perennis
Carduus crispus
Cerastium vulgatum
Chaerophyllum temulum
Chrysanthemum leucanthemum
Cirsium arvense
C. vulgare (lanceolatum)
Dactylis glomerata
Galium aparine
Geranium dissectum
G. robertianum
Holcus lanatus
Hypochaeris radicata
Lolium perenne
Lotus corniculatus
Matricaria maritima inodora

Melilotus altissima
Myosotis arvensis
Plantago media
P. major
Poa annua
P. trivialis
Ranunculus repens
Rumex crispus
Senecio jacobaea
Silene cucubalus (vulgaris)
Solanum dulcamara
Sonchus oleraceus
Trifolium campestre (procumbens)
T. pratense
T. repens
Ulex europaeus
Urtica dioica
Vicia angustifolia

(Photo the author 30.V. 1954.)

FIG. 24. The quarry south of Appledore (locality V b) seen from the river-side (River Torridge).
Stones and earth from the quarry were said to have been used as ship's ballast.

In addition *Agrostis ? stolonifera* (sterile), *Crepis sp.*, *Rubus "plicatus"*, and *Scrophularia sp.*

Collected animals:

Coleoptera	95 (29) species		*Araneae*	25 (2) species	
Carabidae	32 (11) »		*Opilionida*	1 (1) »	
Curculionidae	15 (4) »		*Iso-Myriapoda*	16 (13) »	
Hem. Heteroptera	11 (0) »		*Mollusca*	10 (2) »	
Dermaptera	1 (1) »				

Specially considered groups: 75 species, 32 "emigrants" = 43 per cent.

Some of the species recorded above (including *Stomis*, *Simplocaria semistriata*, *Sitona lepidus*, and those living on Ulex) were collected on a slightly moister pasture between the quarry and the river bank, with *Trifolium repens* as dominating plant.

c—Along a salt-water ditch inside the stone wall which follows the river bank immediately below the quarry (loc. b). Muddy, soft marsh-soil, with *Beta*

vulgaris maritima, Glaux maritima, Puccinellia maritima (dom.), *Triglochin maritimum,* &c.

Collected animals:

Coleoptera	9 species	
Carabidae	4 »	No "emigrants".

VI a. Fremington, pr. Barnstaple (N. Devon), 1.VI. 54 (map, fig. 22).—This little port, situated about 2 miles west of Barnstaple, was selected on the advice of Mr. Alfred E. Blackwell, Curator of the North Devon Athenaeum, his reason being that this is the only place along the Taw estuary where in- and outgoing ships to and from Barnstaple come close to land (cf. fig. 22) and thus would be easily accessible to vessels requiring ballast. The collecting was carried out along the quay, on dry and hard, artificially filled-out soil (mainly coke). Dominating plants were the three *Trifolium* species, *campestre* (*procumbens*), *pratense,* and *repens.*

Collected animals:

Coleoptera	49 (18) species	*Araneae*	8	(1) species	
Carabidae	15 (7) »	*Opilionida*	1	(1) »	
Curculionidae	13 (6) »	*Iso-Myriapoda*	8	(8) »	
Hem. Heteroptera	6 (0) »	*Mollusca*	8	(3) »	
Dermaptera	1 (1) »				

Specially considered groups: 46 species, 26 "emigrants" = 57 per cent.

b—Muddlebridge, east of Fremington. On saline clayish soil around upper tidal limit, at the bottom of a small estuary. Among bunches of straw and leaf in dense vegetation of *Phragmites communis.* The Carabid beetle *Pogonus chalceus* Mrsh. under *Halimione* (*Obione*) *pedunculata.*

Collected animals:

Coleoptera	16 (2) species	
Carabidae	11 (2) »	

FIG. 25. Barges taking sand and gravel at low tide on "The Crow", north of Appledore (visible in the background to the left), N. Devon.

In old days the stuff was then shovelled on board the larger vessels used in the transatlantic fishing trade. At the time of the photo (about 1900), the gravel was principally used for concrete work.

Photo taken by a Mr. Fox and published by permission of the National Maritime Museum, London, through Mr. David R. MacGregor.

VII. **Barnstaple** (N. Devon), 31.V. 54.—According to Gribble (1830, p. 547), "the exports [from Barnstaple], the earliest statement of which refers to 1742, were principally to Newfoundland". Actually, Barnstaple ships started the Newfoundland fishing trade much earlier; there is a record from 1593 (l.c., p. 622). It is possible that ballast, when used by vessels leaving this port, was taken on "The Crow" off Appledore (*vide* pp. 164, 178) and no records of a certain ballast-place within the limits of the town are available. On the other hand, the woollen goods &c. which seem to have constituted the main cargo for Newfoundland may occasionally have contained seeds, living insects &c. and there is reason to believe that ballast was sometimes taken on board even in Barnstaple proper.

On the advice of Mr. Blackwell, I chose as collecting-place the northern bank of River Taw, immediately west of the mouth of the small River Ye, thus in the westernmost part of the town. This is the part of the harbour where land is most easily accessible to larger vessels, even at low tide. The selected place is situated inside the quay and the railway embankment and is partly cultivated (allotment-gardens). The vegetation otherwise consists of weeds, with *Poa annua* as completely dominating plant.

Collected animals:

Coleoptera	56 (29) species	*Araneae*	5	(0) species
Carabidae	25 (13) »	*Opilionida*	1	(1) »
Curculionidae	3 (3) »	*Iso-Myriapoda*	8	(6) »
Hem. Heteroptera	3 (0) »	*Mollusca*	7	(3) »
Dermaptera	1 (1) »			

Specially considered groups: 45 species, 27 "emigrants" = 60 per cent.

VIII. **Bristol** (Somerset), 6.IV. 54.—According to information kindly given by Miss Elizabeth Ralph, City Archivist of the Council House, a "ballast master" was appointed in Bristol from about the 17th century and the orders to be observed by him included the establishment of a "ballast wharf" where ships might collect and deposit ballast. The exact site of this wharf is not known but Mr. Walter Minchinton suggests, in a letter to Miss Ralph, that the ballast came "from the neighbourhood of the Avon Gorge and the Downs", that is from the banks of River Avon in the northwestern part of the town, possibly from the quarries dug in the steep rock.

A short collecting trip, in company with Mr. P. Ardö, was made on the left (Somerset) side of the Avon Gorge on both sides of the Clifton Suspension Bridge, around upper tidal limit, thus in more or less saline localities.[1] The vegetation

---

[1] Several species collected at Bristol are no true inhabitants of saline localities (for instance *Amara aenea* DeG. and *Agonum dorsale* Pont. among Carabid beetles, many of the Staphy-

(Photo P. ARDÖ.)

FIG. 26. The Dung beetle *Aegialia arenaria* F. and the Weevil *Philopedon (Cneor-rhinus) plagiatus* Schall., both occurring on "The Crow" (fig. 23) and introduced into North America. These sluggish, flightless insects may easily be swept down by heavy wind on to the tidal flat where ballast was taken (fig. 25). Swedish specimens.

was not noted. Due to the early season the results were poor, for instance no spiders were found.

Collected animals:

Coleoptera	27	(7) species	Dermaptera	1	(1) species
Carabidae	12	(3) »	Iso-Myriapoda	7	(5) »
Curculionidae	1	(1) »	Mollusca	6	(4) »
Hem. Heteroptera	2	(0) »			

Specially considered groups: 27 species, 14 "emigrants" = 52 per cent.

linids, &c.). Apparently due to the early time of year, they had not managed to make their definite selection of habitat after hibernation.

It should also be mentioned that, according to specimens preserved at the Bristol Museum, the ground-beetles *Clivina collaris* Hbst. and *fossor* L. have been taken on the Avon banks. Both of them are European introductions into North America but they were not found by me on the investigated ballast-places.

*

In the fauna of the investigated, stated or supposed, ballast-places, the importance of species which have been carried over to North America, is quite obvious. Within the specially considered groups (*Carabid* and *Curculionid* beetles, *Dermaptera, Opilionida*, "*Iso-Myriapoda*", and *Mollusca*), the said element amounts to between 43 and 75 per cent of the species on *waste ground*. On pure sand and on saline localities it is less pronounced or even absent.

Lists of animals collected on the ballast-places in SW England

Genera and species in alphabetical order. — Locality numbers as given above (p. 173 a.f.). — Abundance recorded for common species, (c), only.

† = occurring in North America, †† = in Newfoundland, and regarded as introduced.
* =   ,,   ,,   ,,   ,,   ** = ,,   ,,   , and regarded as indigenous.

These symbols are placed in brackets in case only old records from North America (not later than Leng, 1920) are available.

Coleoptera

Carabidae
83 species vide table 5 (p. 193).

Hydrophilidae
Helophorus brevipalpis Bed. V c.
† *Megasternum boletophagum* Mrsh. V b.
Ochthebius impressicollis Cast. (det. V. Hansen) V c.
O. marinus Payk. (det. V. Hansen) V c
†† *Sphaeridium scarabaeoides* L. V a.

Silphidae
Ablattaria laevigata F. VI a, VII.
Silpha tristis Ill. V a, b, VI a.

Staphylinidae
† *Aleochara bipustulata* L. I a.

†† *Amischa analis* Gr. V b, VI a.
A. decipiens Sharp I b, V b, VII.
Astenus longelytratus Palm (*angustatus* auctt., nec Payk.) I b.
Astilbus canaliculatus F. V c, VI a, VII, VIII.
Atheta (Dinaraea) angustula Gyll. (contr. L. Brundin) V b.
A. (Dimetrota) atramentaria Gyll. I a.
A. (Acrotona, "Oxypoda") exigua Er. I a.
(*) *A. (Acrotona) fungi* Gr. I a, V b, VII.
A. (s. str.) oblita Er. (det. L. Brundin) I b.
(†) *A. (Acrotona) orbata* Er. (contr. L. Brundin) V a.
A. (s. str.) triangulum Kr. (contr. L. Brundin) V a.
A. (Thinobaena) vestita Gr. I c (c), VIII (c).

Bledius spectabilis Kr. V a (c).
Conosoma lividum Er. I b.
C. testaceum F. (*pubescens* Gr.) I b, c.
Falagria obscura Gr. I c, VI b.
Halobrecta flavipes Th. VIII.
(✠) *Hypocyptus longicornis* Payk. V b.
Lathrobium geminum Kr. I b.
Lesteva heeri Fauv. VI b.
(†) *Mycetoporus splendidus* Gr. I b.
Myrmecopora uvida Er. I c (c).
† *Oxytelus tetracarinatus* Block V a.
Paederus fuscipes Curt. V c (c).
P. litoralis Gr. I b, II, III, V b, VI a,
VII, VIII.
Philonthus (*Gabrius*) *astutus* Er.
(det. V. Hansen) V a.
† *Ph. concinnus* Gr. VII.
† *Ph. cruentatus* Gmel. I b.
Ph. fimetarius Gr. V b, VIII.
† *Ph. fuscipennis* Mnh. I b, II, III,
IV (c), V a (c), VII.
Ph. laminatus Crtz. V b.
Ph. marginatus Stroem VIII.
(†) *Ph.* (*Gabrius*) *nigritulus* Gr. VI a,
VII.
† *Ph. varians* Payk. (genital slide) II,
VII.
† *Ph. varius* Gyll. I b, V a, c, VII,
VIII.
Philorinum sordidum Steph. V b.
Quedius curtipennis Bernh. (*fuligi-
nosus* Britten; genital slide) VII.
† *Q. fuliginosus* Gr. (*subfuliginosus*
Britten; genital slide) V b.[1]
Q. maritimus J. Sahlb. (*umbrinus*
Er., p.p.; genital slide) III.
(††) *Q. picipennis* Payk. (*molochinus* Gr.)
V b.
Q. picipes Mnh. V b.
Q. rufipes Gr. I a, b, III, IV, V b.
Q. schatzmayri Grid. (contr. E.
Gridelli) I b, IV, V b, VII.
Q. tristis Gr. I a, b, II, IV, V a, b,
VI a, VII.

Sipalia circellaris Gr. I b, V b.
† *Staphylinus ater* Gr. VI a.
(†) *S. caesareus* Ced. II.
† *S. olens* Müll. I a, III.
Stenus brunnipes Steph. I b, V b,
VI a.
** *S. canaliculatus* Gyll. VI b.
S. clavicornis Scop. V b, VI b, VII,
VIII.
S. flavipes Steph. VIII.
S. formicetorum Mnh. (genital slide)
V c.
S. fulvicornis Steph. I b, VII.
S. impressus Germ. VII.
** *S. juno* F. VI b.
S. nanus Steph., coll. V b (2 ♀).
S. picipes Steph. V b.
S. similis Hbst. V b.
S. subaeneus Er. (det. O. Renkonen)
V b.
Stilicus orbiculatus Payk. VII.
(†) *Tachinus rufipes* DeG. I b, VI a, VII.
T. subterraneus L. VIII.
†† *Tachyporus chrysomelinus* L. I b (c),
II, III, V b, VI a, VII, VIII.
T. hypnorum F. II, III, IV, V a, b,
VI a, VII.
† *T. nitidulus* F. I b.
T. obtusus L. V b, VI a.
T. pusillus Gr. I b.
T. solutus Er. I b (c), VII.
Xantholinus angustatus Steph. I b,
II, III, IV, V b, VI a, VII, VIII.
Zyras (*Myrmedonia*) *limbatus* Payk.
I a.

Histeridae

† *Hister purpurascens* Hbst. I b, II,
VII.

Lampyridae

Lampyris noctiluca L. VIII (larva).

---

[1] Hatch (1949), who reported *Quedius fuliginosus* Gr., new to North America, did not consider *curtipennis* Bernh. The identification is therefore somewhat uncertain.

Cantharidae

†† *Cantharis rufa* L. III, Vb.
C. rustica Fall. Vb, VIa.
Malachius viridis F. VIa.
Rhagonycha limbata Th. VII.

Elateridae

†† *Agriotes lineatus* L. VII.

Byrrhidae

** *Cytilus sericeus* Forst. Ib, Vb.
†† *Simplocaria semistriata* F. Ib, Vb, VIa.

Nitidulidae

(†) *Meligethes aeneus* F. Ib, VII.
M. flavipes Sturm (det. O. Sjöberg) Ib.
M. picipes Sturm (det. O. Sjöberg) Ib.

Cryptophagidae

Atomaria fuscata Schnh. (det. O. Sjöberg) Va.
Cryptophagus (*Micrambe*) *vini* Panz., Bruce Vb (c).

Phalacridae

Olibrus aeneus F. II.
O. liquidus Er. Ib.
Stilbus testaceus Panz. Ib.

Lathridiidae

Corticarina (*Melanophthalma*) *fuscula* Gyll. Vb.
(†) *C.* (*M.*) *gibbosa* Hbst. Vb (c)
Enicmus transversus Ol. VIa.

Coccinellidae

Coccidula rufa Hbst. Ib,Vb.
†† *Coccinella* (*Adalia*) *bipunctata* L. Ib.
C. (*Thea*) *22-punctata* L. Ib.
C. (*Propylaea*) *14-punctata* L. Ib.
C. (*s. str.*) *7-punctata* L. Ia, b, Va,b.
Micraspis (*Tytthaspis*) *16-punctata* L. Vb (c).

Rhizobius litura F. Ib (c), Vb, VII.
Subcoccinella 24-punctata L. VIa.

Oedemeridae

Oedemera lurida Mrsh. Ib, Vb, VIa.
Oe. nobilis Scop. Va, b.   •

Anthicidae

Anthicus humilis Germ. Ic.

Tenebrionidae

Melanimon tibiale F. Va.
Phylan gibbus F. Va (c).

Scarabaeidae

† *Aegialia arenaria* F. Va.
†† *Aphodius fimetarius* L. Vb.
† *A. granarius* L. (det. B.-O. Landin) Vb, VII.
(†) *A. rufipes* L. Vb.

Cerambycidae

Clytus arietis L. Vb.

Chrysomelidae

Chalcoides fulvicornis F. Ib.
Chrysomela banksi F. Vb.
† *Phaedon cochleariae* F. VIII (c).
Ph. tumidulus Germ. VIa.
† *Phyllotreta undulata* Ktsch. Va.

Curculionidae

Apion aestivum Germ. VIa.
A. apricans Hbst. VIa
A. assimile Kby. VIa.
A. flavipes Payk. Ib, Vb.
A. hookeri Kby. Vb.
A. nigritarse Kby. Vb, VIa.
A. ononicola Bach Va.
A. ononis Kby. Va (c).
A. sanguineum DeG. (*miniatum* Germ.) Ib, Vb, VIa.
A. ulicis Forst. Vb (c).
A. violaceum Kby. Ib.
A. virens Hbst. Vb.
† *Ceuthorrhynchus assimilis* Payk. VII.
C. hirtulus Germ. Va.

C. troglodytes F. I a, b.
Cionus alauda Hbst. V b.
C. scrophulariae L. V b (c).
Cneorrhinus (Atactogenus) exaratus Mrsh. I b.
Liosoma deflexum Panz. I b.
†† Otiorrhynchus ligneus Ol. VI a.
†† O. ovatus L. VI a.
† O. rugosostriatus Gze. I b.
†† O. sulcatus F. I b, II, IV, V b, VIII.
†† Philopedon plagiatus Schall. V a (c).
Phytonomus ononidis Chvr. V a.
† Ph. posticus Gyll. (variabilis Hbst.) VI a.

Polydrosus confluens Steph. V b.
Sibinia potentillae Germ. I b.
Sitona griseus F. V a.
†† S. hispidulus F. V b, VI a.
† S. humeralis Steph. VI a.
†† S. lepidus Gyll. (flavescens Mrsh.) V b.
† S. lineatus L. V b (c), VII.
S. puncticollis Steph. VI a.
S. regensteinensis Hbst. V b.
S. sulcifrons Thunb. I b, V b, VI a.
† Tychius (Miccotrogus) picirostris F. I b, VI a, VII.

Hemiptera Heteroptera
(det. F. Ossiannilsson)

Arenocoris falleni Schill. V a, b.
Beosus maritimus Scop. III.
Chartoscirta cocksi Curt. V b.
Coreus marginatus L. VI a.
Dicranomerus agilis Scop. V a.
Dolycoris baccarum L. V b.
Drymus sylvaticus F. I b, II, IV, V b, VI a.
Eurygaster testudinaria Geoffr. VI a.
Harpocera thoracica Fall. III.
Lygus rugulipennis Popp. II.
Megalonotus chiragra F. I b, IV, V b, VI a, VII.
M. praetextatus H.-S. V a.
Nabis myrmecoides Costa I b, V b, VI a.

N. rugosus L. II, V b, VIII.
Palomena prasina L. V b.
Peritrechus nubilus Fall. I c.
Piesma quadrata Fieb. I c.
Podops inuncta F. VII.
* Salda littoralis L. V b.
Scolopostethus affinis Schill. I b, IV, VI a, VII.
S. decoratus Hahn V a.
S. puberulus Horv. III.
Stenodema calcaratum Fall. I b.
S. laevigatum L. I b, V b.
Stygnocorus fuligineus Geoffr. I b, III, V b.
Syromastus rhombeus L. f. quadrata F. V a.

Dermaptera
†† Forficula auricularia L. I b, II, III, IV, V b, VI a, VII, VIII.

Araneae
(det. W. Hackman)

Dysderidae
† Dysdera crocata C. L. Koch IV, V b.

Theridiidae
* Ctenium (Robertus) lividum Bl. I b.

† *Theridium bimaculatum* L. I b, V a.
† *Th. ovatum* Cl. I b (c).

Linyphiidae
Dicymbium nigrum Bl. I b.
Lepthyphantes tenuis Bl. V b, VI a.
Linyphia clathrata Sund. I b, V a,
VI a.
L. pusilla Sund. V b.
Stenomyphantes bucculentus Cl. (*lineatus* L.) I a, V a, b, VII.

Erigonidae (*Micryphantidae*)
Oedothorax fuscus Bl. V b.
Oe. retusus Westr. V b.
Silometopus interjectus Cambr. I b.
Styloctetor romanus Cambr. V a.

Araneidae
Araneus redii Scop. V b.
Meta merianae Scop. V b.

Tetragnathidae
Pachygnatha degeeri Sund. I b, V b,
VI a, VII.
P. listeri Sund. I b.
** *Tetragnatha extensa* L. V b.

Agelenidae
Agelena labyrinthica Cl. II, V b.

Pisauridae
Pisaura mirabilis Cl. I b, V b.

Lycosidae
Alopecosa pulverulenta Cl. I b, V b,
VI a, VII.
Arctosa leopardus Sund. V b (c).

A. perita Latr. V a.
Pardosa nigriceps Thor. V a.
* *P. palustris* L. I a.
P. proxima C. L. Koch IV, V b.
P. pullata Cl. I a, III, V a.
Trochosa ruricola DeG. II.
T. terricola Thor. VI a.
Xerolycosa miniata C. L. Koch V a.

Gnaphosidae
Drassodes lapidosus macer Thor. II,
IV, V b.
Zelotes pedestris C. L. Koch V b.

Clubionidae
Cheiracanthium erraticum Walck.
V a.
Clubiona compta C. L. Koch V b.
C. neglecta Cambr. I b, IV, V a, VI a.
C. reclusa Cambr. I b, II, V a, VII.
C. terrestris Westr. III.
†† *Micaria pulicaria* Sund. I b, IV, V b,
VI a.
Phrurolithus festivus C. L. Koch V b.

Xysticidae
Xysticus cristatus Cl. I b, II, IV,
V b, VI a, VII.
X. kochi Thor. V b.

Philodromidae
** *Tibellus maritimus* Menge V a.

Salticidae
Euophrys frontalis Walck. V b.
Eu. molesta Cambr. V b.
Heliophanes flavipes C. L. Koch V b.

Opilionida

(det. W. Hackman)

Lacinius ephippiatus C. L. Koch I b.

†† *Phalangium opilio* L. I b, IV, V a, b,
VI, VII.

Chilopoda
(det. E. Palmén)

†† *Cryptops hortensis* Leach Vb, VIa, VII.

†† *C. parisi* Brol. III, IV.

†† *Haplophilus subterraneus* Leach Ia, IV, VIa, VII, VIII.

†† *Lithobius forficatus* L. Ia, b, II, III, Vb, VIa, VII.

Diplopoda
(det. E. Palmén)

†† *Brachyiulus littoralis* Verh. Vb.

†† *Cylindroiulus britannicus* Verh. Vb.

†† *C. frisius* Verh. Vb.

†† *C. silvarum* Mein. Vb.

†† *C. teutonicus* Pocock Ib.

Glomeris marginata Vill. VIII.

†† *Ophyiulus fallax* Mein. Vb, VIII.

† *Polydesmus angustus* Latz. Ib.

†† *P. inconstans* Latz. (*coriaceus* Por.) Vb, VIa.

Schizophyllum sabulosum L. Vb, VII.

Tachypodoiulus albipes C. L. Koch Vb, VII, VIII.

Oniscoidea (Isopoda Terrestria)
(det. E. Palmén)

†† *Androniscus dentiger* Verh. Vb.

Armadillidium depressum Brdt. Vb.

† *A. vulgare* Latr. Ia, b, IV, Vb, VIa, VII.

Ligia oceanica L. Ic.

†† *Oniscus asellus* L. Ib, II, III, IV, Vb, VIa, VII, VIII.

† *Philoscia muscorum* Scop. Ib, II, IV, Vb, VIII.

†† *Porcellio scaber* Latr. Ia, b, II, III, IV, Vb, VIa, VII, VIII.

†† *Trichoniscus provisorius* Racov. II.

Mollusca (shell-bearing)
(det. H. W. Waldén)

Ashfordia granulata Alder IV, Vb.

** *Cionella* (*Cochlicopa*) *lubrica* Müll. Ib, Vb, VIa, VII, VIII.

C. (*C*). *minima* Siem. VII.

Clausilia bidentata Stroem II, Vb, VIa, VIII.

†† *Discus rotundatus* Müll. III.

Helicella (*Candidula*) *caperata* Mont. Ia, b, Va, b, VIa, VII.

H. (*Cernuella*) *virgata* Da Costa II, IV, Vb, VIa, VII.

† *Helix aspersa* Müll. Ib, IV, VIII.

† *Hygromia* (*Trichia*) *hispida* L. Ib, III, VIa, VII, VIII.

†† *H.* (*T*.) *striolata* Pfeiff. VIa, VII.

Lauria cylindracea Da Costa IV, Vb.

† *Monacha* (*Theba*) *cantiana* Mont. VIII.

† *Oxychilus alliarius* Müll. Vb.

† *O. cellarius* Müll. Ia.

†† *O. draparnaldi* Beck II, IV, Vb, VIa, VII.

† *O. helveticus* Blum VIII.

Retinella nitidula Drap. Vb.

Vitrina pellucida Müll. Vb, VIa.

TABLE 4. Animals found on ballast-places in S. W. England.

	Number of species		
	Total	Eur.-American	Introduced into N. Amer.
Coleoptera	242	72	68 = 28 %
Carabidae	83	22	21 = 25 %
Curculionidae	37	12	12 = 32 %
Others	122	38	35 = 29 %
Hem. Heteroptera	26	1	0
Dermaptera	1	1	1 = 100 %
Araneae	45	8	4 = 9 %
Opilionida	2	1	1 = 50 %
Chilopoda	4	4	4 = 100 %
Diplopoda	11	8	8 = 73 %
Isopoda Terr.	8	6	6 = 75 %
Mollusca	18	10	9 = 50 %
All animals	357	111	101 = 28 %

The Carabid beetles

Special attention was paid to Carabid beetles, every specimen of this group being collected in order to get an idea of the relative abundance of the different species. The results are given in table 5.

From the survey given there, it seems appropriate to draw attention to the following points:

1. Of 83 Carabid species collected on the ballast places, 21 are here regarded as introduced into North America, that is 25 per cent.

2. Of 40 Carabid species regarded as introduced into North America from Europe (table 2, p. 144), these 21 species make no less than 53 per cent. If 3 species are removed from the list, because they are not permanent inhabitants of the British Isles (*Amara anthobia, Carabus auratus* and *cancellatus*) and 2 species (*Clivina collaris* and *fossor*), found by other collectors on the Avon banks at Bristol (p. 186), are added to the "ballast species", it appears that out of 37 North American species of Carabidae which may have been introduced from the British Isles, no less than 23, that is 62 per cent, have been observed on the stated or supposed ballast-places of southwestern England.

3. Another point of importance is the *frequency* and *abundance* of the "emigrants" among Carabids collected on the ballast-places (Diagr. 3 and 4); only the occurrence on "waste places" is here considerd. If frequency is determined by the num-

TABLE 5. Carabid beetles collected on the ballast-places. Symbols as in the list of species, p. 186 a.f.

	A. Waste places									B. Saline places				C. Sand
	I a, b	II	III	IV	Vb	VIa	VII	Total: Number of		I c	Vc	VIb	VIII	Va
	Poole	Topsham	Dartmouth	Plymouth	Appledore	Fremington	Barnstaple	localities	specimens	Poole	Appledore	Fremington	Bristol	Appledore
Abax ater Vill.	—	—	—	—	6	—	—	1	6	—	—	—	—	—
Acupalpus dubius Schky. .	o + 7	—	—	—	11	—	—	2	18	—	—	—	—	—
A. meridianus L.	o + 1	—	—	—	2	—	42	3	45	—	—	—	—	—
Agonum atratum Dft. . .	—	—	—	—	—	—	—	—	—	—	1	24	6	—
A. dorsale Pont.	o + 7	—	—	—	—	—	2	2	9	—	—	—	1	—
A. micans Nic.	—	—	—	—	—	—	—	—	—	—	—	3	—	—
A. mülleri Hbst.	—	—	—	—	4	—	1	2	5	—	—	—	—	1
A. obscurum Hbst.	—	—	—	—	3	—	—	1	3	—	—	—	—	—
A. ruficorne Gze.	—	1	—	—	—	—	—	1	1	—	—	7	—	—
Amara aenea DeG. . . .	o + 14	18	—	3	2	7	32	6	76	—	—	—	2	2
A. aulica Panz.	o + 1	—	—	—	—	—	—	1	1	—	—	—	—	—
A. communis Panz. . . .	—	—	—	—	2	—	—	1	2	—	—	—	—	—
A. convexior Steph. . . .	o + 2	—	—	—	—	—	—	1	2	—	—	—	—	—
A. convexiuscula Mrsh. . .	—	4	—	—	—	—	—	1	4	2	—	—	—	—
A. equestris Dft..	o + 1	—	—	—	—	—	—	1	1	—	—	—	—	—
A. familiaris Dft.	—	14	—	—	—	1	4	3	19	—	—	—	—	—
· *A. lunicollis* Schiø. . . .	—	—	—	—	3	—	—	1	3	—	—	—	—	—
A. montivaga Sturm . . .	—	—	—	—	—	1	—	1	1	—	—	—	—	—
A. ovata F.	—	1	—	12	—	—	3	3	16	—	—	—	1	—
A. plebeja Gyll.	o + 2	2	—	—	6	—	30	4	40	—	—	—	—	—
A. similata Gyll.	o + 10	2	—	—	—	—	—	2	12	—	—	—	—	—
A. tibialis Payk.	o + 2	—	—	—	1	—	—	2	3	—	—	—	—	—
† *Anisodactylus binotatus* F. .	o + 13	1	—	—	—	—	1	3	15	—	—	—	—	—
† *Asaphidion flavipes* L. . .	o + 6	—	—	—	—	—	1	2	7	—	—	—	—	—
Badister bipustulatus F. . .	—	—	—	—	2	—	1	2	3	—	—	—	—	—
Bembidion assimile Gyll. .	—	—	—	—	—	—	—	—	—	—	—	3	—	—
B. concinnum Steph. . . .	—	—	—	—	—	—	—	—	—	—	—	1	17	—
B. guttula F.	—	—	—	—	—	—	—	—	—	—	—	—	1	—
B. iricolor Bed.	—	—	—	—	—	—	—	—	—	—	—	6	26	—
† *B. lampros* Hbst.	o + 12	2	—	—	17	1	6	5	38	—	—	—	—	—
B. laterale Sam.	—	—	—	—	—	—	—	—	—	—	15	—	—	—
B. lunulatum G.-F. . . .	—	—	—	—	—	—	—	—	—	—	1	—	—	—
B. minimum F.	—	—	—	—	—	—	—	—	—	—	3	—	—	—
B. normannum Dej. . . .	—	—	—	—	—	—	—	—	—	1	—	—	—	—
† *B. properans* Steph. . . .	—	1	—	—	11	—	1	3	13	—	—	—	6	—

13 – 565597 *Lindroth*

	I a, b	II	III	IV	Vb	VIa	VII	Total: loc.	Total: spec.	I c	V c	VI b	VIII	V
B. quadrimaculatum L. . . .	—	—	—	—	1	—	—	1	1	—	—	—	—	—
†† B. tetracolum Say (ustulatum auctt.)	0 + 2	—	—	—	—	—	—	1	2	—	—	—	—	—
B. varium Ol.	—	—	—	—	—	—	—	—	—	1	17	—	—	—
† Bradycellus harpalinus Serv.	0 + 3	—	—	—	—	—	1	2	4					
B. verbasci Dft.	0 + 3	5	1	1	1	4	13	7	28	—	—	—	—	—
Broscus cephalotes L. . . .	—	—	—	—	—	—	—	—	—	—	—	—	—	—
Calathus erratus Sahlb. . . .	—	—	—	—	—	—	—	—	—	—	—	—	—	—
† C. fuscipes Gze.	5 + 0	—	—	2	—	1	—	3	8	—	—	—	—	1
C. melanocephalus L. . . .	1 + 0	1	—	—	—	1	—	3	8	—	—	—	—	
C. mollis Mrsh.	—	1	—	—	—	1	—	3	3	—	—	—	—	—
Carabus violaceus L. . . .	—	—	—	—	1	—	—	1	1	—	—	—	—	5
Demetrias atricapillus L. .	0 + 7	—	1	—	2	7	3	5	20	—	—	1	—	
Dichirotrichus pubescens Payk.	—	—	—	—	—	—	—	—	—	3	15	—	—	—
Dromius linearis Ol. . . .	0 + 4	—	—	1	2	3	1	5	11	—	—	—	1	
D. melanocephalus Dej. . .	—	—	—	—	—	—	1	1	1	—	—	—	—	
Dyschirius globosus Hbst. .	—	—	—	—	—	—	—	—	—	—	—	3	—	8
Eurynebria complanata L. .	—	—	—	—	—	—	—	—	—	—	7	—	—	—
†† Harpalus affinis Schrk. (aeneus F.)	13 + 17	28	—	28	—	7	4	5	97	—	—	—	—	
H. anxius Dft.	—	—	—	—	—	—	—	—	—	—	—	—	—	
H. attenuatus Steph. . . .	1 + 0	—	—	—	—	—	—	1	1	—	—	—	—	—
H. latus L.	0 + 1	—	—	—	—	—	—	1	1	—	—	—	—	—
H. puncticeps Steph. (angusticollis J. Müll.) . . .	—	—	—	3	1	2	—	3	6	—	—	—	—	
H. rubripes Dft.	8 + 0	1	—	—	3	—	1	4	13	—	—	—	—	
†† H. rufipes DeG. (pubescens Müll.)	0 + 11	3	—	—	27	—	5	4	46	—	—	—	—	—
H. seladon Schaub.	—	3	—	—	—	—	11	2	14	—	—	—	—	—
H. tardus Panz.	0 + 1	—	—	—	—	—	—	1	1	—	—	—	—	—
H. tenebrosus Dej.	—	—	—	9	—	—	—	1	9	—	—	—	—	—
** Loricera pilicornis F. . . .	—	1	—	—	—	—	—	1	1	—	—	2	—	—
Metabletus foveatus G.-F. .	1 + 3	1	—	—	—	—	—	2	5	—	—	—	—	
Microlestes maurus Sturm .	—	—	—	—	1	—	—	1	1	—	—	—	—	
†† Nebria brevicollis F. . . .	26 + 3	13	—	3	7	1	1	6	54	—	—	—	—	
N. salina Frm. (degenerata Schauf.)	9 + 0	—	—	—	—	—	—	1	9	—	—	—	—	
†† Notiophilus biguttatus F. .	—	—	1	—	5	4	2	4	12	—	—	—	—	—
N. palustris Dft.	—	—	—	—	—	—	2	1	2	—	—	—	—	—
N. substriatus Steph. . . .	0 + 1	—	—	—	—	2	—	2	3	—	—	—	—	—
Olisthopus rotundatus Payk.	—	—	—	19	—	—	—	1	19	—	—	—	—	—
Pogonus chalceus Mrsh. . .	—	—	—	—	—	—	—	—	—	4	—	1	3	

	I a, b	II	III	IV	V b	VI a	VII	Total loc.	Total spec.	I a	V c	VI b	VIII	V a
Pterostichus cupreus L. . .	—	—	—	—	4	—	—	1	4	—	—	—	—	—
P. madidus F.	o + 4	—	—	1	1	—	—	3	6	—	—	—	3	—
P. niger Schall.	—	—	—	—	—	1	—	1	1	—	—	—	—	—
P. nigita F.	—	—	—	—	1	—	—	1	1	—	—	—	—	—
† *P. strenuus* Panz.	o + 1	1	—	—	—	—	—	2	2	—	—	2	1	—
P. vernalis Panz.	—	1	—	—	7	—	—	2	8	—	—	—	—	—
P. versicolor Sturm (*coerulescens* auctt.)	—	—	—	—	—	—	1	1	1	—	—	—	—	—
Stenolophus teutonus Schrk.	o + 2	—	—	—	—	—	—	1	2	—	—	—	—	—
† *Stomis pumicatus* Panz. . .	—	—	—	1	—	—	—	1	1	—	—	—	—	—
† *Trechus obtusus* Er. . . .	o + 2	—	—	—	2	—	—	2	4	—	—	—	—	—
T. quadristriatus Schrk. .	—	3	—	—	7	—	—	2	10	—	—	—	—	—
Number of species	34	22	3	10	32	15	25	—	64	5	7	11	12	11
Number of specimens	207	107	3	63	163	43	170	—	756	11	59	53	68	96

ber of investigated localities (out of 7) inhabited by a species (Diagr. 3), it appears that the "emigrants" show a higher frequency (average: about 3 localities per species) than the rest (average: about 2 localities per species). — Still more striking is their higher abundance (Diagr. 4).

The 7 most abundant species in order of precedence, the seven "waste ground" localities (table 5) taken together, are:

Harpalus affinis   *Acupalpus meridianus*
Amara aenea   *Amara plebeja*
Nebria brevicollis   *Bembidion lampros*
Harpalus rufipes

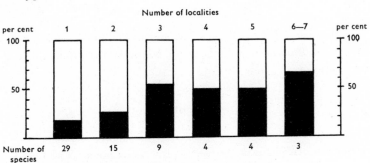

DIAGR. 3. Frequency groups of the 64 species of Carabid beetles found on waste ground (A, table 5) on 7 ballast places in SW England.
Black = "emigrants". White = non-emigrants.

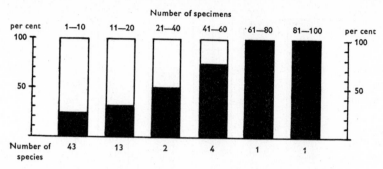

DIAGR. 4. Abundance groups of the 64 species of Carabid beetles found on waste ground (A, table 5) on 7 ballast places in SW England.
Black = "emigrants". White = non-emigrants.

Of these all but one (*Amara plebeja*) occur in North America as "emigrants".

If both frequency and abundance are considered, both on a 6 degree scale (as in diagr. 3 and 4), it appears that of 16 species topping the list 11 are "emigrants".

It certainly cannot be regarded as presumptuous to declare that the composition of the Carabid fauna, especially of its "emigrant" element, on the ballast-places investigated strongly supports the idea of a ship transport of the said element across the Atlantic.

*

Still more pronounced is the geographical composition of some other of the collected groups of animals:

Of 37 species of *Curculionids*   12 are "emigrants" = 32 per cent
,, 18   ,,   ,, *Molluscs*   9 ,,   ,,   = 50 ,, ,,
,, 23   ,,   ,, "*Iso-Myriapods*" 19 ,,   ,,   = 83 ,, ,,

On the other hand, the ballast material contains only few species of *Hemiptera Heteroptera* and *Araneae* in common with North America (for explanation, *vide* below, p. 199).

The plants

Without any pretensions to completeness, the more abundant or otherwise conspicuous vascular plants of the ballast-places were noted. The identification of some critical species was made or controlled by Mr. K. A. Mattisson, Botanical Institute, University of Lund. The complete list of observed species, divided into the three types of investigated localities, follows here:

List of vascular plants observed on the ballast-places[1]

† = occurring in North America, regarded as introduced.[2]
†† = ,, ,, Newfoundland, ,, ,, ,,
* = ,, ,, North America, ,, ,, indigenous.

A. On waste ground (loc. I a, b, II, III, IV, V b, VI a, VII).

†† *Achillea millefolium* L.
† *Alliaria petiolata* Bieb.
 (*officinalis* Andrz.)
† *Anisantha* (*Bromus*) *sterilis* L.
†† *Artemisia vulgaris* L.
† *Ballota nigra* L.
†† *Bellis perennis* L.
†† *Brassica nigra* L.
†† *Calystegia* (*Convolvulus*) *sepium* L.
†† *Capsella bursa-pastoris* L. (coll.)
† *Carduus crispus* L.
†† *Cerastium vulgatum* L.
† *Chaerophyllum temulum* L.
†† *Chrysanthemum leucanthemum* L.
†† *Cirsium arvense* L.
†† *C. vulgare* Savi (*lanceolatum* L.)
†† *Coronopus didymus* L.
†† *Dactylis glomerata* L.
† *Daucus carota carota* L.
† *Epilobium hirsutum* L.
†† *Equisetum arvense* L.
†† *Festuca ovina* L.
†† *Galium aparine* L.
† *Geranium dissectum* L.
* *G. robertianum* L.
†† *Holcus lanatus* L.
† *Hordeum murinum* L.
†† *Hypochaeris radicata* L.
 Kentranthus ruber L.
†† *Lolium perenne* L.
†† *Lotus corniculatus* L.
†† *Matricaria maritima inodora* L.
* *M. matricarioides* Less. (*discoidea* D. C.)

† *Melilotus altissima* Thuill.
†† *Myosotis arvensis* L.
† *Plantago coronopus* L.
†† *P. lanceolata* L.
†† *P. major* L.
† *P. media* L.
†† *Poa annua* L.
†† *P. pratensis* L.
†† *P. trivialis* L.
† *Potentilla reptans* L.
†† *Ranunculus repens* L.
† *Reseda luteola* L.
†† *Rumex crispus* L.
† *Sarothamnus* (*Cytisus*) *scoparius* L.
†† *Senecio jacobaea* L.
†† *S. vulgaris* L.
†† *Silene cucubalus* Wibel (*vulgaris* Moench)
†† *Sisymbrium officinale* L.
†† *Solanum dulcamara* L.
†† *Sonchus oleraceus* L.
†† *Stellaria media* L.
† *Trifolium campestre* Schreb. (*procumbens* auctt.)
†† *T. hybridum* L.
†† *T. pratense* L.
†† *T. repens* L.
†† *Tussilago farfara* L.
† *Ulex europaeus* L.
†† *Urtica dioica* L.
†† *Vicia angustifolia* L.
†† *V. cracca* L.
† *Vulpia bromoides* L.

[1] The nomenclature of species follows Clapham, Tutin, & Warburg, "Flora of the British Isles" (1952). If different from Fernald, in "Gray's Manual" (1950), or other current literature, the latter name is noted as a synonym in brackets.
[2] According to Fernald (1950); *Chaerophyllum*, *Hordeum*, and *Vulpia* according to Clapham, Tutin, & Warburg (1952).

B. On saline places (loc. I c, V c, VI b).

†† *Artemisia vulgaris* L.
  Beta vulgaris maritima L.
 * *Glaux maritima* L.
  Halimione (Obione) pedunculata L.
† *Hordeum murinum* L.
†† *Matricaria maritima maritima* L.

  Phragmites communis Trin.
 * *Puccinellia maritima* Huds.
 * *Spergularia (Spergula) salina* Presl.
  (*marina* auctt., p. p.)
†† *Triglochin maritimum* L.

C. On sand (loc. V a).

† *Ammophila (Psamma) arenaria* L.
†† *Anagallis arvensis* L.
†† *Cirsium arvense* L.
† *Cynoglossum officinale* L.
† *Erodium cicutarium* L.

  Euphorbia paralias L.
  E. portlandica L.
  Ononis repens repens L.
†† *Senecio jacobaea* L.

The plant list gives very clear evidence. Of the total number of 77 species, 72 (94 per cent) are known to occur in North America and no less than 65 (84 per cent) are there regarded as European introductions, 44 species (57 per cent) also in Newfoundland.

If only the flora of waste ground (63 species) is considered, all plants except *Kentranthus ruber* (wich is originally introduced in the British Isles) are recorded from North America and all the rest, except *Geranium robertianum* and *Matricaria matricarioides*, are regarded as adventives from Europe, that is 95 per cent! 42 of these (67 per cent) occur in Newfoundland.

It may be concluded that ballast transport has been still more efficient in carrying plants across the Atlantic than in carrying the lower terrestrial fauna. This is not surprising, considering the generally higher resistance and longer diapause (period of rest) in plant diaspores by which they no doubt as a rule are more suited to endure the voyage.

The reduced number of species common to Europe and North America among the plants of saline localities and of pure sand is in conformity with the results obtained from the fauna (below, p. 199).

The selection of animal species which managed to cross the Atlantic

The successful transport of an animal species with ballast from one continent to another involves a long series of lucky chances. One would be inclined, perhaps, to regard the selection of species which survived the adventure as a matter of pure chance too, provided that the species in question regularly occurs on places where ships took ballast. This is not so. From the account above it is evident that certain groups of animals, for instance Carabid beetles and "Iso-Myriapods", have crossed the Atlantic, or at least made successful settlements on the other side, more often than plant bugs (*Hemiptera Heteroptera*), Spiders (*Araneae*) and others. This, of course, is not due to their taxonomic position but to one or more characteristic features of their natural history.

By grouping the animals found on the English ballast-places according to *such* principles, instead of taxonomically, it would be possible to fix the foremost qualifications favouring transport with ballast. The necessary analysis of the ecological requirements and of certain other biological properties of the species was carried out for all *Coleopterous* insects observed on the ballast-places (table 6).

The biological and ecological properties recorded in the 7 columns of table 6 are valid for the fullgrown insect (imago), the larva in several species having a different biology. The method used is defensible from the point of view that the imago (especially a fertilized female) is far more important for a successful colonization of an oversea area than is the larva.

Let us first consider the columns of table 6 separatedly.

1st column. The planticolous species (p) constitute 28 per cent (48 species) of the 174 Coleoptera from the ballast-places *not* introduced into North America, but only 19 per cent (13 of 68 species) of the "emigrants". *Terricolous species are favoured*, as has already been pointed out by Brown (1940, 1950). Similarly, Molluscs and Iso-Myriapods are strongly represented among the introduced forms, whereas very few of the many planticolous Hemiptera and Araneae (true spiders) were carried over. Planticolous forms were less likely to be taken on board with the material generally used as ballast (above, p. 164) and, if this happened, they ran the risk of being blown overboard due to their habit of climbing.

2nd column. The hygrophilous species (h) constitute 25 per cent (44 species) of the "non-emigrants", but only 6 per cent (4 species) of the "emigrants". *Xero- and mesophilous species are favoured*, partly because *dry* ballast was more usual, partly because there was considerable risk of desiccation during the long voyage or, if the ballast became wet, the cause was usually salt water, which is injurious to normal hygrophilous insects.

3rd column. The "emigrants" and the remaining species were distributed on the three investigated kinds of soil as follows:

	waste ground	pure sand	saline localities
"Emigrants"	61 species = 90 %	6 = 9 %	1 = 1 %
Others	130 ,, = 75 %	14 = 8 %	30 = 17 %

The essential difference depends on the fact that *almost no species from saline localities* (in the collected material only the Chrysomelid beetle *Phaedon cochleariae* F.), and no halobiontic (salt-demanding) species, *were introduced into North America*. This may sound absurd but must be explained by the fact that the ballast, at least as a rule, was not taken from the tidal zone (cf. above, p. 165). The soil there was wet, heavy to handle, and eventually lost part of its valuable weight; it was often muddy and difficult to clean out of the ship afterwards.

4th column. There is no difference between phytophagous beetles (p) and species requiring other kinds of food, the former group constituting 25 per cent (17 species) of the "emigrants" and likewise 25 per cent (44 species) of the remainder.

5th column. A slight difference is found between polyphagous and oligo- or monophagous species, that is those specializing on restricted kinds of food. The former group makes 85 per cent (58 species) of the "emigrants", 79 per cent (137 species) of the remainder. One would have expected a clearer demonstration of the fact that a more or less pronounced monophagy disfavours introduction over long distances. Apparently the figures are not quite representative, as is clear from a somewhat different calculation on Curculionids (below, p. 210).

6th column. The constantly short-winged (brachypterous) species and those occurring in both macro- and brachypterous individuals (dimorphic species) (b and d of column 6) are better represented among the "emigrants", 32 per cent (22 species), than in the rest, 25 per cent (44 species). *Flightless insects no doubt had more chance to stay onboard* during the voyage, escaping the risk of being blown into the sea. The *Hemiptera*, as a rule capable of flight in the adult stage, and the true spiders (*Araneae*), most of which are able to ascend by "ballooning", at least as young, are also very poorly represented among the introduced species. It is characteristic that the only true spider both occurring in the English ballast-material and regarded as a European introduction in the fauna of Newfoundland (Hackman, 1954, p. 40), is *Micaria pulicaria* Sund., a pronounced ground-species without the habit of ballooning, found on four of the eight investigated ballast-places.

7th column. Five of the species observed on the ballast-places are constantly *parthenogenetic* (*Amischa analis*, and four species of *Otiorrhynchus*), only females being known, and all of them have been carried over to North America. *This is another proof of the extraordinary advantage of this form of reproduction* for the dispersal of a species: for a single specimen, in any stage of development, to be deposited in a suitable spot, is sufficient to colonize a new area! The parthenogenesis in Coleoptera, with very few exceptions (Suomalainen, 1953), is combined with polyploidy (increase of chromosome number) and possibly this in itself effects a higher viability in comparison with related bisexual forms and species (Lindroth, 1954 e). The aspect of parthenogenesis in the first place applies to Curculionids (Weevils; below, p. 210). Concerning the Staphylinid *Amischa analis* Gr., *vide* Strand (1951). In some *Iso-Myriapods*, too, a more or less constantly partheno-genetic reproduction has largely contributed towards the wide passive dispersal (mainly with man) of these species. In the Newfoundland fauna this applies to the Chilopod *Lamyctes fulvicornis* Mein. (Palmén, 1954, p. 144), the Diplopod *Proteroiulus fuscus* a. St. (Palmén, 1952, p. 17), and the Oniscoid *Trichoniscus pusillus pusillus* Brandt (Palmén, 1951, p. 2).

Another animal, the extremely rapid dispersal of which may be attributed at least in part to parthenogenesis, is the euryhaline Mollusc *Hydrobia* (*Potamopyrgus*) *jenkinsi* Smith (*vide* Bondesen & Kaiser, 1950). Its original home is unknown but it may have been carried to NW. Europe by human transport from America. The Lumbricid worms *Allolobophora caliginosa* Sav., *Bimastus tenuis* Eis., *Dendrobaena subrubicunda* Eis., *Eisenia rosea* Sav., and *Eiseniella tetraedra* Sav., almost cosmopolitan in distribution and evidently introduced into North America from Europe, are likewise parthenogenetic, at least in part (Gavrilov, 1935, 1940; Muldal, 1952; Omodeo, 1952, p. 246), and this may also apply to the rest of peregrine Oligochaeta.

Functionally similar are hermaphroditic species capable of self-fertilization. Possible examples among terrestrial (and, in part, limnic) animals are to be found among *Mollusca* and *Oligochaeta*. Of the species dealt with in this book, *Arion ater* L. (Künkel, 1916, p. 409 a.f.; Perrot, 1939) and several species of *Lymnaea* (Hubendick, 1951, p. 32) are considered capable of self-fertilization[1] and the same has been supposed with respect to the form of *Deroceras laeve* Müll. with reduced penis (Boettger, 1932, p. 402; Meeuse & Hubert, 1949, p. 25), as well as for members of the following families (in part even the same species), which have crossed the North Atlantic by human agencies: *Arionidae, Helicidae, Limacidae, Physidae, Planorbidae*, and *Zonitidae* (*vide* bibliography in Larambergue, 1939, p. 41–43). The occurrence of self-fertilization in Oligochaeta has been suggested in those cases, in which reproduction was observed in isolated individuals, as in *Dendrobaena octaedra* Sav. and *Eisenia foetida* Sav., both of world-wide distribution, but parthenogenesis, as in the species mentioned above, seems equally probable.

*

---

[1] It must be regarded as very difficult to separate, conclusively, selffertilization from parthenogenesis in hermaphroditic animals without cytological investigation.

TABLE 6. Coleoptera from the ballast places of southwestern England divided into certain biological and ecological groups.

1st column. Selection of stratum.[1]

t   = terricolous (ground-living); (t) = regularly climbing the vegetation
p   = planticolous (plant-living).

True subterraneous species were not considered.

2nd column. Selection of moisture.[1]

x   = xerophilous (preferring dry places); (x) = less pronounced
m   = mesophilous (intermediate)
h   = hygrophilous (preferring wet places); (h) = less pronounced.

3rd column. Selection of soil.[2]

c   = on waste ground; (c) = also on sand or (and) saline soil
s   = on pure sand (loc. V a)
t   = on saline soil (tidal zone, ± clayish).

4th column. Selection of food.[1]

p   = phytophagous (feeding on living plants, incl. mosses and fungi)
z   = zoophagous (feeding on other animals)
s   = schizophagous (feeding on decomposing organic matters)
o   = zoo- or schizophagous; m = mixed diet.

5th column. Specialisation on food.[1]

m   = monophagous (restricted to plants or animals belonging to one single genus)
o   = oligophagous (restricted to plants or animals belonging to one single family or corresponding group)
p   = polyphagous (taking more diversified food).

6th column. Means of dispersal.[1] [2]

m   = macropterous (stated or supposed to fly); (m) = brachypterous in other areas
b   = brachypterous (fligthless)[3]; (b) = macropterous in other areas
d   = dimorphic (occurring on the ballast places in both forms).

7th column. Means of reproduction.[1]

s   = bisexual; p = parthenogenetic.

---

[1] According to general knowledge of the species.
[2] According to observations on the ballast places.
[3] The following species seem to be flightless in spite of comparatively well developed hind-wings: the species of *Quedius* and *Staphylinus, Chrysomela banksi.*

	1	2	3	4	5	6	7
Species regarded as European introductions into North America in bold face types	stratum	moisture	soil	food selection	food specialisation	dispersal	reproduction
Fam. Carabidae							
Abax ater	t	m	c	z	p	b	s
Acupalpus dubius	t	h	c	m	p	m	s
A. meridianus	**t**	**m**	**c**	**m**	**p**	**m**	**s**
Agonum atratum	t	h	t	m	p	m	s
A. dorsale	t	(x)	c	m	p	m	s
A. micans	t	h	t	m	p	m	s
A. Mülleri	**t**	**m**	**(c)**	**m**	**p**	**m**	**s**
A. obscurum	t	(h)	c	m	p	(b)	s
A. ruficorne	**t**	**h**	**(c)**	**m**	**p**	**b?**	**s**
Amara aenea	**t**	**x**	**(c)**	**m**	**p**	**m**	**s**
A. aulica	**(t)**	**m**	**c**	**m**	**p**	**m**	**s**
A. communis	t	m	c	m	p	m	s
A. convexior	t	m	c	m	p	m	s
A. convexiuscula	t	m	(c)	m	p	m	s
A. equestris	t	m	c	m	p	m	s
A. familiaris	**t**	**m**	**c**	**m**	**p**	**m**	**s**
A. lunicollis	**t**	**m**	**c**	**m**	**p**	**m**	**s**
A. montivaga	t	(x)	c	m	p	m	s
A. ovata	t	(x)	c	m	p	m	s
A. plebeja	t	m	c	m	p	m	s
A. similata	t	m	c	m	p	m	s
A. tibialis	t	x	c	m	p	m	s
Anisodactylus binotatus	**t**	**m**	**c**	**m**	**p**	**m**	**s**
Asaphidion flavipes	**t**	**(h)**	**c**	**z**	**p**	**m**	**s**
Badister bipustulatus	t	m	c	m	p	m	s
Bembidion assimile	t	h	t	z	p	d	s
B. concinnum	t	h	t	z	p	m	s
B. guttula	t	h	t	z	p	(m)	s
B. iricolor	t	h	t	z	p	m	s
B. lampros	**t**	**m**	**c**	**z**	**p**	**(b)**	**s**
B. laterale	t	h	t	z	p	(b)	s
B. lunulatum	t	h	t	z	p	m	s
B. minimum	t	h	t	z	p	m	s
B. normannum	t	h	t	z	p	m	s
B. properans	**t**	**m**	**(c)**	**z**	**p**	**d**	**s**
B. quadrimaculatum	t	m	c	z	p	m	s
B. tetracolum (*ustulatum*)	**t**	**m**	**c**	**z**	**p**	**(b)**	**s**
B. varium	t	h	t	z	p	m	s

	1	2	3	4	5	6	7
Bradycellus harpalinus	(t)	m	c	m	p	(m)	s
B. verbasci	(t)	m	c	m	p	m	s
Broscus cephalotes	t	x	s	z	p	m	s
Calathus erratus	t	x	s	m	p	(b)	s
C. fuscipes	**t**	**m**	**c**	**m**	**p**	**b**	**s**
C. melanocephalus	t	m	c	m	p	(b)	s
C. mollis	t	x	s	m	p	(m)	s
Carabus violaceus	t	m	c	z	p	b	s
Demetrias atricapillus	p	x	(c)	m	p	m	s
Dichirotrichus pubescens	t	h	t	m	p	m	s
Dromius linearis	p	x	(c)	m	p	(b)	s
D. melanocephalus	p	x	(c)	m	p	m	s
Dyschirius globosus	t	m	t	z	p	b	s
Eurynebria complanata	t	(h)	s	z	p	m	s
Harpalus affinis (*aeneus*)	**t**	**x**	**(c)**	**m**	**p**	**m**	**s**
H. anxius	t	x	s	m	p	m	s
H. attenuatus	t	x	c	m	p	m	s
H. latus	t	m	c	m	p	m	s
H. puncticeps (*angusticollis*)	t	(x)	c	m	p	m	s
H. rubripes	t	x	c	m	p	m	s
H. rufipes (*pubescens*)	**t**	**m**	**c**	**m**	**p**	**m**	**s**
H. seladon	t	m	c	m	p	m	s
H. tardus	t	x	c	m	p	m	s
H. tenebrosus	t	x	c	m	p	m	s
Loricera pilicornis	t	h	(c)	z	p	m	s
Metabletus foveatus	t	x	c	z	p	b	s
Microlestes maurus	t	x	c	z	p	(b)	s
Nebria brevicollis	**t**	**m**	**(c)**	**z**	**p**	**m**	**s**
N. salina (*degenerata*)	t	m	c	z	p	m	s
Notiophilus biguttatus	**t**	**m**	**c**	**z**	**p**	**d**	**s**
N. palustris	t	m	c	z	p	(b)	s
N. substriatus	t	m	c	z	p	m	s
Olisthopus rotundatus	t	x	c	m	p	d	s
Pogonus chalceus	t	h	t	z	p	(b)	s
Pterostichus cupreus	t	m	c	z	p	m	s
P. madidus	t	m	(c)	z	p	b	s
P. niger	t	m	c	z	p	m?	s
P. nigrita	t	h	c	z	p	m	s
P. strenuus	**t**	**(h)**	**(c)**	**z**	**p**	**(b)**	**s**
P. vernalis	t	h	c	z	p	d	s
P. versicolor (*coerulescens*)	t	m	c	z	p	m	s
Stenolophus teutonus	t	(h)	c	m	p	m	s
Stomis pumicatus	**t**	**m**	**c**	**m**	**p**	**b**	**s**
Trechus obtusus	**t**	**m**	**c**	**m**	**p**	**(b)**	**s**

	1	2	3	4	5	6	7
T. quadristriatus	t	x	c	m	p	m	s
Fam. Hydrophilidae							
Helophorus brevipalpis	t	h	t	z	p	m	s
Megasternum boletophagum	**t**	**m**	**c**	**s**	**p**	**m**	**s**
Ochthebius impressicollis	t	h	t	z	p	m	s
O. marinus	t	h	t	z	p	m	s
Sphaeridium scarabaeoides	**t**	**m**	**s**	**s**	**p**	**m**	**s**
Fam. Silphidae							
Ablattaria laevigata	t	m	c	m	p	b	s
Silpha tristis	t	m	(c)	m	p	b	s
Fam. Staphylinidae							
Aleochara bipustulata	**t**	**m**	**c**	**o**	**p**	**m**	**s**
Amischa analis	**t**	**m**	**c**	**o**	**p**	**m**	**p**
A. decipiens	t	m	c	o	p	m	s
Astenus longelytratus	t	m	c	z	p	m	s
Astilbus canaliculatus	t	m	c	o	p	b	s
Atheta angustula	t	(h)	c	o	p	m	s
A. atramentaria	t	m	c	s	p	m	s
A. exigua	t	(h)	c	o	p	m	s
A. fungi	t	m	c	o	p	m	s
A. oblita	t	m	c	o	p	m	s
A. orbata	**t**	**(x)**	**s**	**o**	**p**	**m**	**s**
A. triangulum	t	m	c	o	p	m	s
A. vestita	t	h	t	o	p	m	s
Bledius spectabilis	t	h	t	p	o	m	s
Conosoma lividum	t	m	c	o	p	b	s
C. testaceum (*pubescens*)	t	m	c	o	p	m	s
Falagria obscura	t	m	c	o	p	m	s
Halobrecta flavipes	t	h	t	o	p	m	s
Hypocyptus longicornis	**t**	**m**	**c**	**s**	**p**	**m**	**s**
Lathrobium geminum	t	(h)	c	z	p	(b)	s
Lesteva heeri	t	h	t	o	p	b	s
Mycetoporus splendidus	**t**	**m**	**c**	**z**	**p**	**m**	**s**
Myrmecopora uvida	t	h	t	o	p	m	s
Oxytelus tetracarinatus	**t**	**m**	**s**	**s**	**p**	**m**	**s**
Paederus fuscipes	t	h	t	z	p	m	s
P. litoralis	t	m	c	z	p	b	s
Philonthus astutus	t	m	s	o	p	m	s
Ph. concinnus	**t**	**m**	**c**	**s**	**p**	**m**	**s**
Ph. cruentatus	**t**	**m**	**c**	**s**	**p**	**m**	**s**
Ph. fimetarius	t	m	c	s	p	m	s
Ph. fuscipennis	**t**	**m**	**(c)**	**s**	**p**	**m**	**s**
Ph. laminatus	t	m	c	o	p	m	s
Ph. marginatus	t	m	t	s	p	m	s

	I	2	3	4	5	6	7
Ph. nigritulus	t	m	c	o	p	m	s
Ph. varians	t	m	c	s	p	m	s
Ph. varius	t	m	(c)	s	p	m	s
Philorinum sordidum	p	m	c	p	p	m	s
Quedius curtipennis	t	m	c	z	p	b¹	s
Q. fuliginosus (*subfuliginosus*)	t	m	c	z	p	b¹	s
Q. maritimus	t	m	c	z	p	b	s
Q. picipennis (*molochinus*)	t	m	c	z	p	b¹	s
Q. picipes	t	m	c	z	p	b¹	s
Q. rufipes	t	(x)	c	z	p	b¹	s
Q. schatzmayri	t	(x)	c	z	p	b¹	s
Q. tristis	t	m	c	z	p	b¹	s
Sipalia circellaris	t	m	c	o	p	b	s
Staphylinus ater	t	(x)	c	z	p	b¹	s
S. caesareus	t	m	c	z	p	b¹	s
S. olens	t	(x)	c	z	p	b¹	s
Stenus brunnipes.	t	(h)	c	z	p	b	s
S. canaliculatus	t	h	t	z	p	m	s
S. clavicornis	t	m	(c)	z	p	m	s
S. flavipes.	t	(h)	t	z	p	b	s
S. formicetorum	t	h	t	z	p	m	s
S. fulvicornis	t	h	c	z	p	m	s
S. impressus	t	m	c	z	p	m	s
S. juno	t	h	t	z	p	m	s
S. "nanus"	t	(h)	c	z	p	m	s
S. picipes	t	(h)	c	z	p	m	s
S. similis	t	h	c	z	p	m	s
S. subaeneus	t	(h)	c	z	p	m	s
Stilicus orbiculatus	t	m	c	o	p	m	s
Tachinus rufipes	t	m	c	s	p	m	s
T. subterraneus	t	m	t	s	p	m	s
Tachyporus chrysomelinus	t	m	c	o	p	m	s
T. hypnorum	t	m	(c)	o	p	m	s
T. nitidulus	t	m	c	o	p	m	s
T. obtusus	t	m	c	o	p	m	s
T. pusillus	t	m	c	o	p	m	s
T. solutus.	t	m	c	o	p	m	s
Xantholinus angustatus	t	m	c	z	p	m	s
Zyras limbatus.	t	m	c	o	o	m	s
Fam. Histeridae							
Hister purpurascens	t	m	c	o	p	m	s

¹ *Vide* footnote 3, p. 202.

	1	2	3	4	5	6	7
Fam. Lampyridae							
Lampyris noctiluca	t	m	c	z	o	b	s
Fam. Cantharidae							
Cantharis rufa	**p**	**m**	**c**	**m**	**p**	**m**	**s**
C. rustica	p	m	c	m	p	m	s
Malachius viridis	p	m	c	m	p	m	s
Rhagonycha limbata	p	m	c	m	p	m	s
Fam. Elateridae							
Agriotes lineatus	**t**	**m**	**c**	**m**	**p**	**m**	**s**
Fam. Byrrhidae							
Cytilus sericeus	t	m	c	p	o	m	s
Simplocaria semistriata	**t**	**m**	**c**	**p**	**o**	**m**	**s**
Fam. Nitidulidae							
Meligethes aeneus	**p**	**m**	**c**	**p**	**o**	**m**	**s**
M. flavipes	p	m	c	p	p	m	s
M. picipes	p	m	c	p	p	m	s
Fam. Cryptophagidae							
Atomaria fuscata	t	m	s	p	p	m	s
Cryptophagus vini	p	m	c	p	o	m	s
Fam. Phalacridae							
Olibrus aeneus	p	m	c	p	o	m	s
O. liquidus	p	m	c	p	o	m	s
Stilbus testaceus	p	m	c	p	p	m	s
Fam. Lathridiidae							
Corticarina fuscula	t	m	c	p	p	m	s
C. gibbosa	**p**	**m**	**c**	**p**	**p**	**m**	**s**
Enicmus transversus	t	m	c	p	p	m	s
Fam. Coccinellidae							
Coccidula rufa	p	(h)	c	z	p	m	s
Coccinella bipunctata	**p**	**m**	**c**	**z**	**p**	**m**	**s**
C. 22-punctata	p	m	c	z	p	m	s
C. 14-punctata	p	m	c	z	p	m	s
C. 7-punctata	p	m	c	z	p	m	s
Micraspis 16-punctata	p	m	c	z	p	m	s
Rhizobius litura	t	x	c	z	p	b	s
Subcoccinella 24-punctata	p	m	c	p	p	b	s
Fam. Oedemeridae							
Oedemera lurida	p	m	c	p	p	m	s
Oe. nobilis	p	m	(c)	p	p	m	s
Fam. Anthicidae							
Anthicus humilis	t	m	t	o	p	m	s
Fam. Tenebrionidae							
Melanimon tibiale	t	x	s	s	p	m	s
Phylan gibbus	t	x	s	s	p	b	s

	1	2	3	4	5	6	7
Fam. Scarabaeidae							
Aegialia arenaria	t	**x**	**s**	**s**	**p**	**b**	**s**
Aphodius fimetarius	t	**m**	**c**	**s**	**p**	**m**	**s**
A. granarius	t	**m**	**c**	**s**	**p**	**m**	**s**
A. rufipes	t	**m**	**c**	**s**	p.	**m**	**s**
Fam. Cerambycidae							
Clytus arietis	p	m	c	p	o	m	s
Fam. Chrysomelidae							
Chalcoides fulvicornis	p	m	c	p	m	m	s
Chrysomela Banksi	t	m	c	p	m	b[1]	s
Phaedon cochleariae	**p**	**h**	**t**	**p**	**o**	**m**	**s**
Ph. tumidulus	p	h	c	p	o	m	s
Phyllotreta undulata	**p**	**m**	**s**	**p**	**o**	**m**	**s**
Fam. Curculionidae							
Apion aestivum	p	m	c	p	m	m	s
A. apricans	p	m	c	p	m	m	s
A. assimile	p	m	c	p	m	m	s
A. flavipes	p	m	c	p	m	m	s
A. hookeri	p	m	c	p	m	m	s
A. nigritarse	p	m	c	p	m	m	s
A. ononicola	p	x	s	p	m	m	s
A. ononis	p	x	s	p	m	m	s
A. sanguineum (*miniatum*)	p	m	c	p	m	m	s ·
A. ulicis	p ·	(x)	c	p	m	m	s
A. violaceum	p	m	c	p	m	m	s
A. virens	p	m	c	p	m	b	s
Ceuthorrhynchus assimilis	**p**	**m**	**c**	**p**	**o**	**m**	**s**
C. hirtulus	p	m	s	p	o	m	s
C. troglodytes	(p)	(x)	c	p	o	m	s
Cionus alauda	p	m	c	p	m	m	s
C. scrophulariae	p	m	c	p	o	m	s
Cneorrhinus exaratus	t	(x)	c	p	o	b	s
Lisoma deflexum	(p)	m	c	p	o	b	s
Otiorrhynchus ligneus	**t**	**(x)**	**c**	**p**	**p**	**b**	**p**
O. ovatus	**t**	**m**	**c**	**p**	**p**	**b**	**p**
O. rugosostriatus	**t**	**(x)**	**c**	**p**	**p**	**b**	**p**
O. sulcatus	**t**	**m**	**c**	**p**	**p**	**b**	**p**
Philopedon plagiatus	**t**	**x**	**s**	**p**	**p**	**b**	**s**
Phytonomus ononidis	p	x	s	p	m	b	s
Ph. posticus (*variabilis*)	**p**	**m**	**c**	**p**	**o**	**(b)**	**s**
Polydrosus confluens	p	(x)	c	p	o	b	s

---

[1] *Vide* footnote 3, p. 202.

	1	2	3	4	5	6	7
Sibinia potentillae	p	(x)	c	p	o	m	s
Sitona griseus	p	x	s	p	o	m	s
S. hispidulus	(p)	(x)	c	p	o	d	s
S. humeralis	p	m	c	p	o	(m)	s
S. lepidus (*flavescens*)	p	m	c	p	o	m	s
S. lineatus	p	m	c	p	o	(m)	s
S. puncticollis	p	m	c	p	o	(m)	s
S. regensteinensis	p	(x)	c	p	o	(b)	s
S. sulcifrons	p	m	c	p	m	(b)	s
Tychius picirostris	p	m	c	p	o	m	s

Summarizing, then: to be judged especially fit to survive transport in ballast across the Atlantic and to becoming settled in North America, a terrestrial animal, e.g. an insect, should combine the following six properties: it lives on the ground (terricolous), has no pronounced moisture requirements (non-hygrophilous), prefers open ground of a waste-place character (at least it is not halobiontic, salt-demanding), is not dependant on special kind of food (polyphagous), is flightless, and has a parthenogenetic reproduction. The only species of Coleoptera from the English ballast-places filling all these requirements are the four *Otiorrhynchus* weevils and, sure enough, they all crossed the Atlantic.

It is of considerable interest to illustrate, in form of a diagram (diagram 5), *to what extent the beetles of the ballast places combine the six "favourable qualities"* just mentioned, keeping "emigrants" and the remaining species apart. The difference is striking: 73 per cent of the "emigrants", but only 46 per cent of the rest, combine more than 3 of the 6 "favourable qualities".

A similar calculation has been made for *Carabid* beetles alone (diagram 6), omitting the mode of reproduction (last column of table 6), because all species are bisexual, but adding the stage of hibernation (according to Lindroth, 1945, 1949). This may be regarded as having some influence because the transport of a fullgrown beetle (above all of a fertilized female) gives the maximum chance for a successful colonization. Most ships in the Newfoundland trade left England in the spring (above p. 162) and constant imaginal hibernators were therefore favoured. These make 71 per cent (15 species) of the 21 "emigrants" but 66 per cent (41 species) of the remaining species; only among the latter there are some species (6 in number: *Amara convexiuscula, A. equestris, Calathus mollis, Dichirotrichus pubescens, Eurynebria complanata,* and *Trechus quadristriatus*), in which the larval hibernation is practically without individual exceptions. — Of the Carabidae of

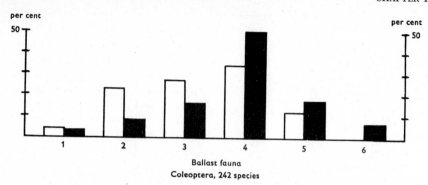

DIAGR. 5. Combination of one to six ecological and biological characters (table 6, columns 1–3, 5–7; and p. 209) favouring ballast transport, among 242 species of Coleoptera observed on ballast places in SW England.
Black = "emigrants" (67 species).   White = non-emigrants.

the ballast-places, all of the 21 "emigrants" but only 81 per cent (51) of the remaining 62 species combine more than 3 "favourable characters", as shown in diagram 6.

*

The estimation of characters favouring ballast-transport was also carried out by comparing the species introduced into Newfoundland with the "non-emigrants" of the English ballast-places. The Carabid and Curculionid families were selected for this purpose.

Carabidae	planti-colous	hygro-philous	saline localities	macro-pterous
Introduced Newfoundland species (23)	0	5 = 22 %	0	14 = 61 %
"Non-emigrants" of ballast-places (63)	3 = 5 %	20 = 32 %	14 = 23 %	46 = 74 %

The difference in the other factors of table 6, as well as in the stage of hibernation, was insignificant in this case.

Curculionidae	planti colous	oligo- or monophagous	macro-pterous	bisexual
Introduced Newfoundland species (29)	15 = 52 %	15 = 52 %	13 = 45 %	16 = 55 %
"Non-emigrants" of ballast-places (25)	24 = 96 %	25 = 100 %	18 = 72 %	25 = 100 %

The advantage of a polyphagous choice of food is very striking in this case, and also the predominance of flightless forms among introduced species.

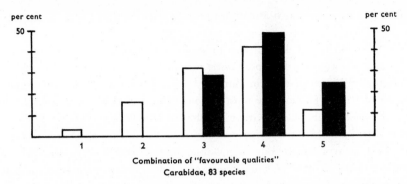

DIAGR. 6. Combination of one to five "favourable qualities" (table 6, columns 1–3, 5–6; and p. 209), among 83 species of Carabid beetles observed on ballast places in SW England.
Black = "emigrants" (21 species). White = non-emigrants.

From the above it can be concluded that the selection of animal species which managed to cross the Atlantic by ship, first and foremost in ballast, has not been a random one. Forms associated with cultivated soil, possessing low moisture requirements, little specialization of food and little power of active dispersal were always favoured, especially if these properties were combined with parthenogenetic reproduction.

Eastward transport

The entire preceding part of this chapter has been devoted to the European introductions into North America. Turning to the reverse phenomenon, the American element in the fauna of Europe, we find quite a different picture: this element plays an inferior role in the European fauna.

On page 125 a summary is given (table 1) of the animal species common to Europe and North America, belonging to certain selected taxonomic groups and listed on page 17–124. The total number of species is 908. Of these no less than 309–344 species (33–38 per cent) are considered (at least in part) to be introduced with man from Europe to North America. In comparison herewith, the American introductions in Europe are quite unimportant, amounting to 27–34 species (3–4 per cent).

The difference is especially striking in some groups of lower terrestrial animals. In the case of *Carabid* beetles, 37–38 species were introduced from Europe to North America, none in the opposite direction; in *Chilopods* (Centipedes) 12–13 (0) species, in *Diplopods* (Millipedes) 15 (0) species, in *Terrestrial Isopods* (Woodlice) 21–22 (0) species, in *Lumbricids* (Earthworms) 15 (2) species. Schubart (1929,

p. 316) has already drawn attention to this remarkable fact, as far as Diplopods are concerned.

The situation is well-known also to applied entomologists. They noticed that the number of originally European *insect pests* in North America is higher than that of originally American ones in Europe. A few instances of the latter type are mentioned below (p. 222), the most famous being the Colorado Beetle (*Leptinotarsa decemlineata* Say), the Grape Phylloxera (*Phylloxera vitifoliae* Fitch), and the Woolly Aphis (*Eriosoma lanigerum* Hausm.). "The Fall Webworm" (*Hyphantria cunea* Drury) has become a potential pest in southeastern Europe. "The Northern Army Worm" (*Leucania unipuncta* Haw.), with an almost cosmopolitan distribution, is also said to be of North American origin.

Still more insignificant is the group of American animals not associated with agricultural plants which have been unintentionally introduced into Europe and become naturalized outdoors. For instance, only two cases of this kind have been observed among the Coleoptera: the Longicorn beetle *Neoclytus acuminatus* F. and the small Weevil *Stenopelmus rufinasus* Gyll. Both are now widely distributed, the former in the regions surrounding the northern part of the Adriatic Sea, the latter in western Europe. Both have been imported with their foodplants, the *Neoclytus* (arrived before 1850; Müller, 1949–53, p. 148–149) with American timber, the *Stenopelmus* (since 1898) with the water-fern *Azolla caroliniana* Willd. which is of North American origin but generally cultivated in Europe as an ornament in ponds and pools.

This is fully in accordance with the geographical character of the *European flora*. It has sent hundreds of emigrants west across the Atlantic, which is illustrated above on the Newfoundland flora (p. 146) and the vegetation of the English ballastplaces (p. 196; *vide* also Gilmore, 1932), but weeds and other recent introductions originating in North America, completely naturalized and widely distributed in Europe, are surprisingly scarce. Well-known instances are[1]: —

Elodea canadensis Michx.[2] — Transamerican, N to N. Labr. — Europe (widely, since 1836), N to N Sweden.
Epilobium glandulosum Lehm. (incl. *adenocaulon* Haussk.)[2] — Transamerican. — Europe (widely, since later part of 19th century), N to C Finland.
Erigeron canadense L. — Transamerican. — Europe (generally), N to N Sweden. Almost cosmopolitan.
Juncus tenuis Will. (*macer* Gray).[3] — N. America (generally), also C. & S. America. — Europe (widely, since before 1850), N to C Sweden. N. Africa. Australia.

---

[1] For further information, *vide* Jessen & Lind, 1922–23, Hultén, 1950, Fernald, 1950, and Clapham, Warburg, & Tutin, 1952.
[2] Probably originally cultivated in Europe and escaped.
[3] By some students, e.g. Heslop Harrison (1953), regarded as native in Ireland.

Lepidium densiflorum Schrad. — Transamerican (but probably introduced in the east). — Europe (generally but often casual), N to N Norway. Also in other continents.

Matricaria matricarioides Less. (*discoidea* D.C., *suaveolens* Pursh., nec L.). — Transamerican, native of NW America & NE Asia. — Europe (generally, since about 1850), N to northernmost Scand. S. America, New Zealand.

Oenothera biennis L.[1] — N. America E of Rocky Mts. — Europe (generally, since 18th century), N to C Finland.

Oxalis stricta L. —Transamerican, S to Mexico. — Europe (widely, since before 1700), N to C Finland. Also in other continents.

Veronica peregrina L.[1] — Transamerican, also C & S America. — W & C Europe (since 18th century), N to Denmark.

To these should be added some 15–20 species of North American origin, locally and mostly only temporarily established, especially on the British Islands. —On *Ranunculus cymbalaria* Pursh., vide below (p. 244).

This is a poor representation, indeed! It should also be observed that several of the above plants are late arrivals, apparently introduced after modern steam trade had commenced.

Turning back to *animals*, there is only one ecological group in which North American species unintentionally introduced into Europe are far more numerous than those transported in the opposite direction: the *hothouse animals*, more or less unable to establish themselves out of doors.

European hothouse species of North[2] American origin.

A. *Terrestrial animals.*

Formicidae
Crematogaster lineolata Say
Ponera opaciceps Nyl.

Araneae
Eperigone maculata Banks

Mollusca
Hawaiia minuscula Binn.

Helicodiscus parallelus Say
Opeas pumilum Pfeiff.
Subulina octona Brug.
Zonitoides arboreus Say[3]

Lumbricidae
Bimastus beddardi Mich.
Eisenia carolinensis Mich.

---

[1] Probably originally cultivated in Europe and escaped.
[2] Some of these may possibly come from parts of America south of the U.S.A.-Mexican boundary.
[3] In part established in outdoor conditions.

B. *Freshwater animals.*

Mollusca

Gyraulus parvus Say	*Lymnaea columella* Say
Helisoma duryi Weth.	*L. cubensis* Pfeiff.
H. tenuis Phil.	*Physa ancillaria* Say
H. trivolve Say	*Ph. gyrina* Say
Lymnaea catascopium Say	*Ph. heterostropha* Say[1]

The corresponding European element in North America is almost non-existent.

The reasons for its poor effect

Judging from the present character of trade and exchange of goods between Europe and North America, one would perhaps feel inclined to expect that an unintentional transport of animals and plants across the Atlantic would have been more easily realized in an eastward direction. There is more material suitable for the purpose, such as vegetable food, wool, timber, &c., shipped from North America to Europe than in the opposite direction.

The present conditions, however, are but little pertinent to the matter. It seems that the main bulk of introduced species, especially of the Europeans naturalized in North America, arrived prior to modern steam and motor traffic, the first transatlantic line of this kind being opened in 1840 (Cunard Line: Liverpool–New York). Earlier records from North America are available for at least the following European species: —

Sitotroga cerealella Ol., the Angoumois Grain Moth, is reported to have been observed in North America as early as 1743 (Essig, 1931, p. 824).

The Hessian Fly, *Mayetiola* (*Phytophaga*) *destructor*, was first described by Say in 1816 and observed on Long Island, N.Y., as early as 1779, but is usually regarded as a European introduction.

Argyroploce pomonella L., the Codling Moth, was also introduced in the 18th century.

The Carabid Beetle *Harpalus affinis* Schrk. (*aeneus* F.) was described from North America in 1805 by Beauvois under the name of *viridiaeneus*, a clear synonym.

Similarly, the father of North American entomology, Thomas Say (1787–1834), described some insects and other arthropods now regarded as of Old World origin, for instance the Carabid beetle *Bembidion tetracolum* Say (*ustulatum* auctt., nec L.), the Dung-beetle *Aphodius fasciatus* Ol. (*putridus* Hbst.; as *tenellus* Say), the Milliped *Nopoiulus venustus* Mein. (as *pusillus* Say; *vide* Palmén, 1952, p. 26),

---

[1] In part established in outdoor conditions.

the Wood-lice *Porcellio spinicornis* Say (*pictus* Brandt) and *P. scaber* Latr. (the latter as *niger* Say; *vide* Palmén, 1951, p. 15). Say also mentioned the occurrence in North America of *Armadillidium vulgare* Latr. and *Oniscus asellus* L.

Dejean (1828, p. 466) reports the Carabid beetle *Amara aenea* DeG. from North America and this is confirmed by a specimen in his collection (Lindroth, 1955 b, p. 111).

Randall, in 1838, described the Carabid *Clivina collaris* Hbst. (as *elongata*; *vide* Lindroth, 1954 a, p. 122) and the dung-beetle *Aphodius fimetarius* L. (as *nodifrons*).

One of the *Otiorrhynchus* (*Brachyrhinus*) Weevils, the genus as a whole being introduced into North America (Brown, 1940, p. 67), was early recognized: *sulcatus* F., about 1830 (Schwarz, 1890, p. 38; Essig, 1931, p. 189).

The Pear Psylla, *Psylla pyricola* Foerst., and the Elm Leaf Beetle, *Galerucella luteola* Müll., were noticed in the U.S.A. in the 1830's (Essig, 1931, p. 848–850).

In Newfoundland, between 1827 and 1835, Philip Henry Gosse (*vide* Bruton, 1930) collected, among other insects, "*Forficula* sp." (no doubt *auricularia* L.)[1] and the beetles *Coccinella bipunctata* L., *Aphodius fimetarius* L., and two species of *Sitona*, all introduced.

Finally, according to a collection of insects made by the Norwegian naturalist Peter Stuwitz in Newfoundland in the period 1839–1842 and preserved at the Zoological Museum, Oslo, at least the following European species reached the island prior to the opening of steamer connections (with Halifax, in 1842):

Carabidae
Agonum mülleri Hbst.
A. ruficorne Gze.
Bembidion tetracolum Say
Harpalus affinis Schrk.

Elateridae
Agriotes lineatus L.

Scarabaeidae
Aphodius fimetarius L.

Curculionidae
Barynotus obscurus F.
Otiorrhynchus ovatus L.
O. sulcatus F.
Sitona lepidus Gyll. (*flavescens* Mrsh.)

It is thus evident that the old trade conditions of sailing vessels days are largely responsible for the fact that transatlantic introduction of foreign animals and plants took place almost exclusively in a westward direction. In addition, as fully discussed earlier in this chapter, the one-sided carrying of ballast westward only, seems to strengthen the case in a sufficient way.

A slightly different picture is provided by animals imported with their host plants.

---

[1] Generally, *Forficula auricularia* L. is regarded as an introduction of the 20th century (Essig, 1931, p. 923).

This traffic is still going on on a large scale and the gradually more rigorous quarantine will never be able to eliminate completely the undesirable landing of unexpected and unwelcome passengers.

As far as animals feeding upon the common agri- and horticultural plants of the temperate zone are concerned, there is a marked preponderance of species carried west across the North Atlantic (cf. p. 212) which is easily explained by the greater number of cultivated plants transferred from the Old to the New World.

In importations connected with *hothouse* gardening we meet with the reverse situation: the *eastward* transport has been strongly dominating. Above all, the botanical gardens and aquariums of Europe, erected for scientific purposes, have no doubt been more inclined to enlarge their collections with specimens of the rich flora of North America than similar institutions of the latter region to obtain European plants. It should also be observed that European animals, first arrived as hothouse inquilines into North America, very often were able to spread and become settled under outdoor conditions, whereas the corresponding element of European hothouses often arrived from subtropical, or even tropical, parts of North America and thus as a rule was prevented from leaving its artificial surroundings. Only species which happened to be introduced from Europe into cold regions, such as Newfoundland (certain Myriapods and Terrestrial Isopods; p. 108 a.f.) or the Pacific Northwest (also some species of Carabid beetles; p. 170), have also remained indoors in North America.

Another explanation

The main bulk of European species, animals as well as plants, which managed to cross the Atlantic with man and become settled in North America, even on their native continent demonstrate a high degree of dependence upon human culture. Most of the plants in question are pronounced weeds and the animals, almost all members of the lower soil fauna, belong to a corresponding synanthropic element. Many of the insect species, for instance several Weevils (*Curculionidae*), are directly bound to Crucifers, Leguminosists, and other weeds.

These plants constitute an old element in Europe, as do the corresponding animals. The first civilizations of the Occident founded upon agriculture, especially those of Hither Asia (Assyrians, Babylonians, &c.), were pronounced river cultures, immediately bordering upon deserts and steppes. Hence man got his most important culture-plants, the cereals, from the unwooded land but at the same time many useless plants invaded the arable land from the surrounding steppe and transformed into weeds. They were of course accompanied by insects and other lower animals feeding upon or otherwise connected with them.

Eventually civilization based on agriculture moved westward, forested land around the Mediterranean was developed into culture-steppe occupied by cultivated plants but also by weeds. Locally, primary steppe of this region contributed a number of additional weeds, with adherent vermin.

During the Roman age, about the beginning of our chronology, the modern colonization of Central Europe started, then slowly spread northward. The first permanent glades were cut out of the continuous forest carpet and invaded, with the aid of man, by cultivated plants—and weeds. Thus the culture-steppe conquered Europe, "step by step", the isolated patches of arable land increased and fused together. Already at the time of Columbus the coastland of Western Europe was almost devoid of forests and transformed into an artificial steppe inhabited by man's constant followers among plants and animals, invited or selfinvited. They were all ready to embark the ships and, if the voyage was favourable, to settle wherever they landed in a suitable climate, provided man had prepared the soil. Similar views, concerning the synanthropic bird fauna, have been expressed by Lack (1954, p. 200–202).

How different were conditions on the American side when transatlantic trade was starting!—The high Indian cultures, founded upon agriculture, were restricted to Central America and parts of the Andes farther south. In northeastern North America, at least, the tribes were more or less migratory and had hardly progressed beyond the neolithic stage. A very primitive form of agriculture, with maize and beans as foremost plants, was practiced by the Iroquois in the St. Lawrence valley (Coleman, 1930, p. 11). Farther south within the limits of the present U.S.A., also along the Atlantic coast, agriculture seems to have been carried on more intensively and sweet potatoes, tobacco, cotton, sunflower, &c., were cultivated. But nowhere was the plow used. The general custom was to burn over the ground and to plant some grains of maize &c. into holes dug at short distances with the aid of primitive shovels, hoes or spades (Hodge, 1907, p. 24–27). Nothing like the arable land of the contemporaneous Eastern Hemisphere was produced in this way and though some tribes planted corn in the same spots from year to year, the cultivation of the soil seems generally to have been of a more or less casual character, except among the Pueblos of the present New Mexico and Arizona, where agriculture was the dominating trade, based on irrigation.

Therefore, in North America, the chance of native steppe plants invading permanent arable land and transforming into constant weeds was considerably less than in the Old World. This holds true especially for northern coastal districts, on the Atlantic as well as on the Pacific side, partly because the Indian agriculture was very primitive there, partly because there was no direct connection with the central prairie enabling steppe plants to invade the artificial clearings. Consequently, when the White Man first arrived and permanent settlement founded upon agriculture started, there were few indigenous plants present able to intrude as weeds. This gave free entrance to the corresponding floral element from Europe which, almost free from competition, soon became dominating on cultivated and waste ground, above all within the northern half of the Atlantic coast. Around the ports of Newfoundland and Nova Scotia it is still easy to find acres of land inhabited by a purely European flora. This region was perfectly prepared then, to receive and establish the more or less synanthropic members of the European *fauna* brought in by trade, but it was very little suited to provide ships destined east with stowaways of North American origin.

The economic importance of introduced animals

It is a fact, only too well-known, that animals and plants purposely or unintentionally introduced into a foreign country often reproduce and spread very quickly and soon reach an abundance far surpassing the normal conditions in their original patria. As far as domesticated or otherwise useful animals are concerned this of course is only to the advantage of man. More numerous, however, are the instances of weeds, phytophagous insects, plant diseases, &c., which in the new continent have developed to veritable pests, though many of them in their native country do not cause much annoyance.

Theoretically, the explanation of such super-normal abundance of introduced species, animals as well as plants, may be found among any of the following three groups of facts:—

1. The environment, that is soil, climate, supply of food, &c., may be more favourable in the new country.

2. There may be more "space" available, the introduced species being able to colonize and "ecological niche" previously not, or only thinly, inhabited by indigenous species.

3. The introduced species may have escaped from its native enemies which in the original patria control its abundance.

The *first* explanation seems to hold true at least in cases where a new and more abundant host (plant or animal) is available in the new area. Thus the main reason for the mass reproduction of the Colorado beetle (*Leptinotarsa decemlineata* Say) was that it invaded land (in eastern North America and in Europe) where a new host, *Solanum tuberosum*, was enormously more abundant than the *Solanum rostratum* of its original habitat in the Rocky Mountains.—Similarly, the European vine (*Vitis vinifera*) was a more suitable host to the *Phylloxera vitifoliae* Fitch than were the corresponding American species.—Species adapting themselves to indoor conditions, especially in greenhouses, such as many Diplopods, Terrestrial Isopods (Woodlice), &c., may gain thereby, not only an almost cosmopolitan distribution, but also, due to an equal and favourable microclimate, a local abundance widely surpassing that of their original outdoor habitat.

However, these are exceptions. It seems reasonable to assume that normally an animal or plant species is perfectly adapted to climatic and other conditions prevailing in its natural habitat, that it finds its optimum where it developed (from a phylogenetical point of view), usually in the central part of its distribution area, and that a successful introduction by the aid of man into a foreign country means that it by lucky chance entered a new area with approximately the same, and not better, environmental conditions. Then this alone cannot be responsible for subsequent super-abundance.

The *second* explanation is based on the assumption that "competition" (excluding the relations between predator or parasite and prey or host) is a major factor determining the composition of fauna and flora of a given area, especially the assortment of species within a micro-habitat. Without any doubt this is true as far as sedentary organisms are concerned. Between species and individuals of higher, autotrophic plants there is a continuous competition, not only for space, but also for light and nutriment. It seems therefore defensible to explain the colonization of waste ground in towns and ports of the Canadian East by an almost unmixed European flora (*vide* above, p. 218) as at least partly due to the fact that practically no corresponding ecological element of the indigenous flora was present when the White Man arrived.

In the second place, mammals and birds, with their higher-developed psychical functions, especially their instinct for ownership of a wide area ("territory"; Germ.: Revier) around their breeding places, certainly in their normal state live under permanent (intra- as well as inter-specific) competition which is essentially different from the blind struggle for life in most non-sedentary evertebrates. The effect is that the population of for instance a certain bird species is many times sparser than if it had been regulated by food supply alone. The rapid increase of area and abundance of the English Sparrow (*Passer domesticus* L.) and the Starling (*Sturnus vulgaris* L., fig. 4), both purposely introduced into North America, may very well have been determined by the lack of indigenous competitors among birds living in the immediate neighbourhood of man.

Turning to the lower terrestrial fauna, the literature contains a good many purely theoretical assumptions but very few direct observations of interspecific competition as a major factor governing distribution. Personally, I feel especially suspicious of the slogan: "competition between near related species", because, in this connection, the ecological and not the taxonomical relationship must be decisive.

Some of the most reliable observations on competition were made on *earthworms* (fam. *Lumbricidae*), implying that "peregrine", *i.e.* the anthropochorous, more or less cosmopolitan species, after introduction into a new country, intrude upon the endemic species of the original fauna or even completely exterminate them over large areas (Michaelsen, 1903, p. 24; Smith, 1928, p. 347 a.f.). It seems also natural that the rather permanent burrow system of an earthworm should represent a sort of individual "territory", avoided by other individuals of the same or ecologically related species and that a competition about space takes place, similar to that between sedentary organisms.

Klots (1951, p. 201), Ferguson (1955, p. 188), and others remarked that the indigenous *Pieris napi* L. (Green-veined White) of North America has noticeably decreased in places where the introduced *Pieris rapae* L. (Small or Cabbage White) had become established (since 1860). It is difficult to imagine a competition for food in this case as *napi* appears to prefer wild, thinleaved Cruciferous plants, but *rapae* the thickleaved, usually cultivated forms (*Brassica*, &c.) (Petersen, 1954a, p. 195). It seems more reasonable to suggest that the normal courtship and other sexual activity of the "weaker" species (*napi*) has been disturbed by the presence of the very similar *rapae;* the upper side of the male is almost identical. This explanation may have relevance for other diurnal insects of great vagility and guided by optical sense (the scent of the male in the two *Pieris* species seems to be quite different; Ford, 1946, p. 97). For nocturnal Lepidoptera the olfactory sense governing sexual behaviour may be similarly deceived by the intrusion of a related species with similar smell of the female. Dr. Petersen (*in lit.*) suggests that, in the case of the two *Pieris* mentioned, a higher resistance against parasites in *rapae* may be an important factor for its higher viability as compared with *napi*. It would perhaps be worth while to investigate whether the purposely introduced Braconid wasp *Apanteles glomeratus* L. (p. 222) has played a role there.

From my own experience on *Carabid beetles*, I have already (Lindroth, 1949, p. 554–560) given at some length the reasons for my deeply felt doubts as to the validity of "competition" (in the limited sense, *i.e.* exclusive of predacy and parasitism) as a major factor determining the abundance or even the existence of a species in a certain habitat. In the lawns of Halifax, Nova Scotia, the introduced *Amara aenea* DeG. was so exceedingly abundant that the population density widely surpassed that of all *Amara* species together in any similar spot studied by me in Europe, and this in spite of the fact that, in abundant species, *intra*-specific competition (between individuals of the same species) must be considered stronger than *inter*-specific competition (between the individuals of different though possibly near related species). In my opinion, terrestrial habitats very seldom and then for only short periods possess a "saturated" fauna and therefore competition, in the limited sense here used, hardly constitutes a governing factor for lower animals without instincts of "ownership", except in cases where they are highly specialized, for instance in choice of food.

The *third* explanation (above) contains the most obvious facts contradicting the opinion that as a rule reduced competition is responsible for the often extraordinarily rapid dispersal of an introduced animal species, above all embodied in the method of *"biological control"* against this special form of insect pests. This is based on the assumption that the abundance of a species in its native country is balanced by natural enemies (predators, parasites and diseases) from which it partly or entirely escapes in a new area. By careful observations in the original patria, the most important of these natural enemies may be discovered, artificially reproduced and finally released in the infested country.

The best examples of success in biological control of this kind emanate from the United States. In that country, due to the extraordinarily high number of introduced culture-plants, the demands for proceedings against imported pests have been greater than anywhere else, and likewise the economical powers to carry them out.

The following examples refer to insects unintentionally or purposely exchanged between Europe and North America and are selected from Howard (1930), Essig (1931), "Handbuch der Pflanzenkrankheiten" (1949–54), and other current economic-entomological literature.

A. Species of European origin

Galerucella luteola O. F. Müll. (*xanthomelaena* Schrk.) (Elm Leaf Beetle). Introduced as early as the 1830's, now over the main part of U.S.A. and very noxious. A species of *Tetrastichus* (fam. *Chalcididae*), parasiting the eggs in Europe, and a few Tachinid flies, have been tentatively introduced.

Phytonomus punctatus F. (Clover Leaf Weevil) and *Ph. posticus* Gyll. (*variabilis* Hbst.) (Alfalfa Weevil) (*vide* map, fig. 6).[1] The latter has been successfully con-

---

[1] Flight of *Phytonomus posticus* has been frequently observed in U.S.A. It is therefore possible that macropterous homozygotes have been introduced by which the dispersal would be considerably favoured. In Europe, the species is dimorphic with respect to the hind-wings.

trolled by the Ichneumonid wasp *Bathyplectes curculionis* Thoms., introduced from Europe, the former by the fungus *Entomophthora sphaerosperma* Fres.

Pieris rapae L. (Cabbage or Small White). First recorded in N. America about 1856 (in Quebec), now widely distributed. The Braconid wasp *Apanteles glomeratus* L., imported from Europe in 1883, is now well established and useful.

Lymantria (Ocneria, Porthetria) dispar L. (Gypsy Moth). Introduced for purposes of study and unintentionally escaped about 1869, a severe pest from 1889. A large number of different enemies were imported from Europe and Japan, among others the Carabid beetle *Calosoma sycophanta* L., which has proved useful.

Euproctis phaeorrhoea Don. (*chrysorrhoea* auctt., nec L.) (Brown-tail Moth). First recorded in the 1890's (Mass.), injurious since 1897. Controlled by means of several European parasitic wasps and flies.

Argyroploce (Carpocapsa, Cydia) pomonella L. (Codling Moth). This was introduced into N. America already in the 18th century and is now generally distributed. Attempts at biological control have met with only moderate success but recently the Ichneumonid wasp *Ephialtes caudatus* Ratz., from Europe, has become established in British Columbia.

Pyrausta nubilalis Hbn. (European Corn Borer). First recorded in 1917 (Boston), now widely distributed and very disastrous. A special organisation, "The International Corn Borer Investigation", has carried out large scale rearing and transport of parasites (Ichneumonids, Braconids) from Europe.

Mayetiola (Phytophaga) destructor Say (Hessian Fly). This Cecidiomyid fly, although first described from America and known there since the 18th century, is usually regarded as a European introduction. Attempts at control have been performed with several European parasitic wasps.

Nematus (Pristiphora) erichsoni Htg.[1] (Larch Sawfly), injurious in Canada, has been effectively controlled by the aid of the European Ichneumonid wasp *Mesoleius tenthredinidis* Marl.

B. Species of North American origin

Leptinotarsa decemlineata Say (Colorado Beetle). Native of the Rocky Mountains. First introduced specimens observed in Europe as early as 1876 but not until about 1920 did it become established, in the Bordeaux region, whence it spread with terrible rapidity (*vide* map, fig. 3, p. 136). Attempts at biological control have had little success but the Carabid beetle *Lebia grandis* Hentz and a couple

---

[1] On the possibility of *Pristiphora erichsoni* being indigenous in North America, *vide* Coppel & Leius (Can. Entomol. 87. 1955, p. 107–108).

of Tachinid flies, all of them imported from N. America, have established themselves in France.

Phthorimaea operculella Zell. (Potato Tuber Moth). Probably of American origin, now almost cosmopolitan. Control by means of several parasitic wasps was attempted, *i.a.* a *Habrobracon* imported from California to France, but without noticeable success.

Phylloxera vitifoliae Fitch (*vastatrix* Planch.) (Vine Aphis or Grape Phylloxera). Indigenous in E N. America, it was introduced into California about 1858, in Europe not earlier than 1863, but now a terrible pest. No biological control has succeeded in this case; the insect is kept down by grafting European vine upon more resistant American roots.

Eriosoma lanigerum Hausm. (Woolly Aphis). Introduced from N. America before 1800, now generally distributed in Europe (except in the north). Its severe damage in Europe is accentuated by the fact that it has cancelled the yearly migration between the fruit-trees and a second host (*Ulmus*). The Chalcid wasp *Aphelinus mali* Hald. was introduced from N. America into France in 1920, has subsequently become well established in most parts of Europe and elsewhere, and proved very useful.

*

The danger of noxious insects being introduced with the continuously increasing air traffic seems to have been exaggerated. The appearance of a European Grasshopper, *Roeseliana roeselii* Hag., near the airports of Montreal was, however, interpreted in this way (Urquhart & Beaudry, 1953).

On the minimum size of a viable population

Students of animal populations often postulate that there exists a minimum number (a minimum density) of individuals constituting the population, below which the population (if isolated), or even the entire species, is unable to recover. They apparently assume that a sufficiently low number of individuals *in itself*, regardless of other factors, may be the initial stage of complete extinction.

The picture of an *introduced animal* (or plant) species colonizing a new continent is fundamentally opposite (already pointed out by Mayr, 1954, p. 174). There is no doubt that these rapidly increasing populations in many cases are descendents of one single female, fertilized before, during or after the intercontinental transport.

We are entitled to maintain that in such cases no "minimum size" of population exists, provided that the genetic constitution of the organism is sufficiently in accordance with the new environment. Eurytopic ("plastic", non-demanding) species, like the ecological ubiquists and the geographical cosmopolitans, are in little need of genetic variability, caused either by re-combinations or by mutations of genes. As has been shown by experiments, the pronouncedly diffuse thermal preferendum of a eurytopic species (the Carabid beetle *Pterostichus nigrita* F.; Lindroth, 1949, p. 50–53) may be explained by the relative insensibility of each individual, and not by the presence of a genetically heterogenous population.

And how about the *parthenogenetic* species, such as most *Otiorrhynchus* weevils and some related genera, now making their triumphal progress throughout all temperate parts of the world? Their prevalence over bisexual forms and species among immigrants is due to the fact that the introduction of one single individual, regardless of stage, is sufficient for a permanent colonization. Their genome is rigid, shut out from new combinations, and there is nothing indicating that their mutation frequency is higher than normal. The genetic constitution of these successful parthenogenetic forms is apparently suitable and has no need of improvement.

Extinction is not first and foremost a question of population density but of genetic degeneration, accentuated by unfavourable changes of environment (*vide* Mayr, 1944, p. 224).

Bibliography of Chapter II

ALFARO, A., 1941. El escarabejo de la patata (Leptinotarsa decemlineata Say). — Bol. Patol. Veg. y Ent. Agric. 10. Madrid, p. 39–80.

—— 1943. La invasion del escarabejo de la patata al iniciarse la campaña de 1943. — Ibidem. 12. p. 1–8.

BLAIR, K. G., 1931. The beetles of the Scilly Islands. — Proc. Zool. Soc. London, p. 1211–1258.

BÖCHER, T. W., 1948. Contributions to the flora and plant geography of West Greenland. I. Selaginella rupestris and Sisyrinchium montanum. — Medd. om Grønl. 147: 3. Copenhagen, p. 1–26.

BOETTGER, C. R., 1932. Die Besiedelung neu angelegter Warmhäuser durch Tiere. — Zeitschr. Morph. Ökol. Tiere. 24. Berlin, p. 394–407.

BONDESEN, P. & KAISER, E. W., 1950. Hydrobia (Potamopyrgus) jenkinsi Smith in Denmark, ilustrated by its ecology. — Oikos. I: 2 (1949). Lund, p. 252–281.

BRADDICK, L. E., 1953. The Port of Topsham—its ships and shipbuilding. — Devonsh. Assoc. Adv. Sci., Lit. & Art. 85. Torquay, p. 18–34.

BROOKS, S. T., 1936. The land and freshwater Mollusca of Newfoundland. — Ann. Carn. Mus. 25. Pittsburgh, p. 83–108.

BROOKS, S. T. & B. W., 1940. Geographical distribution of the recent Mollusca of Newfoundland. — Ibidem. 38. p. 53–75.

BROWN, W. J., 1940. Notes on the American distribution of some species of Coleoptera common to the European and North American continents. — Can. Ent. 72. Guelph, Ont., p. 65–78.

—— 1950. The extralimital distribution of some species of coleoptera. — Ibidem. 82. p. 197–205.

BRUTON, F. A., 1930. Philip Henry Gosse's Entomology of Newfoundland. — Ent. News. 41. Philadelphia, p. 34–38.

CARPENTER, G. H., 1895. Notes on a new British beetle. Otiorrhynchus auropunctatus Gyll. — Irish Nat. 4. Dublin, p. 213.

CLAPHAM, A. R., TUTIN, T. G. & WARBURG, E. F., 1952. Flora of the British Isles. — Cambridge, pp. I–LI, 1–1591.

COCHRANE, J. A., 1938. The story of Newfoundland. — Boston, p. 1–257.

COLEMAN, A. P., 1930. The geographical and ethnical background. — Cambr. Hist. Brit. Emp. 6. Cambridge, p. 1–19.

COSENS A., 1923. Reports on insects of the year. — 53rd Ann. Rep. Ent. Soc. Ont. (Ont. Dept. Agric.). Toronto, p. 10.

DARLINGTON, P. J., Jr., 1927. Aegialia arenaria Muls. in New England, with local records for other species. — Psyche. 34. St. Albans, Vt., p. 98–99.

DEJEAN, P. F. M. A., 1828. Spécies Général des Coléoptères. III. — Paris (p. 466).

ESSIG, E. O., 1931. A history of entomology. — New York, p. 1–1029.

—— 1934. The historical background of entomology in relation to the early development of agriculture in California. — Pan-Pac. Ent. 10. San Francisco, p. 1–11.

EVANS, J. W., 1952. The injurious insects of the British Commonwealth. — London, pp. I–VII, 1–242.

FALL, H. C., 1934. A new name and other miscellaneous notes. — Pan-Pac. Ent. 10. San Francisco, p. 171–174.

FERGUSON, D. C., 1955. The Lepidoptera of Nova Scotia. — Bull. N. S. Mus. Sci. 2. Halifax, p. 161–375.

FERNALD, M. L., 1950. Gray's Manual of Botany. 8th ed. — Cambridge, Mass., pp. I–LXIV, 1–1632.

FORD, E. B., 1946. Butterflies. — The New Naturalist. London, pp. I–XIV, 1–368.

FOWLER, J. J., 1901. A visit to St. Andrews, N. B., with a catalogue of plants collected in its vicinity. — Proc. Nat. Hist. Ass. Miramichi. 2. Chatham, N. B., p.21–28.

FUENTE, J. M., de la, 1918. Catalogo sistematico-geografico de los Coleopteros en la peninsula iberica, &c. — Bol. Soc. Ent. España. 1. Zaragoza.

GATHORNE–HARDY, G. M., 1921. The Norse discoverers of America. — Oxford, p. 1–304.

GAVRILOV, K., 1935. Contributions a l'étude de l'autofecondation chez les Métazoaires hermaphrodites. — Bull. Assoc. Russ. Rech. Sci. 2. Sect. Sci. Nat. & Math. Praha, p. 163–216.

—— 1940. Sur la reproduction de Eiseniella tetraedra (Sav.) forma typica. — Acta Zool. 29 (1939). Stockholm, p. 439–464.

GILMORE, M. R., 1932. Plant vagrants in America. — Papers Mich. Ac. Sci., Arts & Lett. 15. Ann Arbor, Mich., p. 65–79.

Gray's Manual of Botany, vide Fernald, 1950.

GRIBBLE, J. B., 1830. Memorial of Barnstaple. — Barnstaple, p. 1–640.

HACKMAN, W., 1954. The spiders of Newfoundland. — Acta Zool. Fenn. 79. Helsingfors, p. 1–99.

Handbuch der Pflanzenkrankheiten (P. Sorauer), 1949–54. 5. ed. IV. V. Berlin & Hamburg.

HARRINGTON, W. H., 1891. Notes on a few Canadian Rhyncophora. — Can. Ent. 23. London, Ont., p. 21–27.

HARRIS, C. A., 1930. Newfoundland, 1783 to 1867, and 1867–1921. — The Cambr. Hist. Brit. Emp. VI. Cambridge, pp. 422–437, 673–685.

HATCH, M. H., 1946a. Notes on European Coleoptera in Washington, including a new species of Megasternum. — Pan-Pac. Ent. 22. San Francisco, p. 77–80.

—— 1946b. Note on introduced species of Carabus in North America. — Bull. Brookl. Ent. Soc. 41. Brooklyn, N. Y., p. 71.

—— 1949. Studies on the fauna of Pacific Northwest greenhouses, &c. — Journ. N. Y. Ent. Soc. 57. New York, p. 141–165.

—— 1953. The beetles of the Pacific Northwest. I. Introduction and Adephaga. — Univ. Wash., Publ. Biol. 16. Seattle, Wash., p. 1–340.

HODGE, F. W. (editor), 1907–10. Handbook of American Indians north of Mexico. 1–2. — Washington, D. C., pp. 1–972, 1–1221.

HOLDHAUS, K., 1927–28. Die geographische Verbreitung der Insekten. — Handb. der Ent. (C. Schröder). 2. Jena, p. 592–1058.

—— 1954. Die Spuren der Eiszeit in der Tierwelt Europas. — Abh. Zool. Bot. Gesellsch. 18. Wien, p. 1–493.

HOLDHAUS, K. & LINDROTH, C. H., 1939. Die europäischen Koleopteren mit boreoalpiner Verbreitung. — Ann. Nat. Mus. 50. Wien, p. 123–293.

HOWARD, L. O., 1930. A history of applied entomology. — Smiths. Misc. Coll. 84. Washington, D. C., p. 1–566.

HUBENDICK, B., 1951. Recent Lymnaeidae. Their variation, morphology, taxonomy, nomenclature, and distribution. — K. Vet. Ak. Handl. (4) 3. Stockholm, p. 1–223.

HULTÉN, E., 1950. Atlas of the distribution of vascular plants in NW. Europe. — Stockholm, pp. 1–120, 1–512.

IVERSEN, J., 1938. Et botanisk Vidne om Nordboernes Vinlandrejser. — Naturhist. Tidende. 2: 8. Copenhagen, p. 113–116.

JEANNEL, R., 1941–42. Coléoptères Carabiques. 1–2. — Faune de France. 39. 40. Paris, p. 1–1173.

JESSEN, K. & LIND, J., 1922–23. Det Danske Markukrudts Historie. — K. Dansk. Vid.Selsk. Skr., Nat. Math. Afd. (8) 8. Copenhagen, p. 1–496.

JOHNSON, W. F. & HALBERT, J. N., 1902. A list of the beetles of Ireland. — Proc. R. Irish Ac. (3) 6. Dublin, p. 535–827.

KLOTS, A. B., 1951. A field guide to the butterflies of North America, east of the Great Plains. — Cambridge, Mass., pp. I–XVI, 1–349.

KROGERUS, H., 1954. Investigations on the Lepidoptera of Newfoundland. I. Macrolepidoptera. — Acta Zool. Fenn. 82. Helsingfors, p. 1–80.

KRÜGER, L., 1899. Insektenwanderungen zwischen Deutschland und den Vereinigten Staaten von Nordamerika und ihre wirtschaftliche Bedeutung. — (Ent. Verein) Stettin, pp. I–VIII, 1–174.

KÜNKEL, K., 1916. Zur Biologie der Lungenschnecken. — Heidelberg, p. 1–440.

LACK, D., 1954. The natural regulation of animal numbers. — Oxford, p. I–VIII, 1–343.

LAPOUGE, V. de, 1908. Tableaux de détermination des formes du genre "Carabus". — L'Échange. (Revue Linnéenne.) 24. Moulins (p. 19).

LARAMBERGUE, M. de, 1939. Étude de l'autofécondation chez les Gastéropodes Pulmonés, &c. — Bull. Biol. France et Belg. 73. Paris, p. 19–231.

LENG, C. W., 1920, 1927–48. Catalogue of the Coleoptera of America, north of Mexico. With 5 suppl. — Mount Vernon, N. Y.

LINDROTH, C. H., 1945, 1949. Die fennoskandischen Carabidae. Eine tiergeographische Studie. I. III. — Gbgs Vet. Vitt. Samh. Handl. (6) B. 4. Göteborg, pp. 1–709, 1–911.

—— 1954a. Random notes on North American Carabidae. (Coleopt.). — Bull. Mus. Comp. Zool. 111. Cambridge, Mass., p. 117–161.

—— 1954b. Carabidae common to Europe and North America. — Coleopt. Bull. 8. Washington, D. C., p. 35–52.

—— 1954c. Carabid beetles from Nova Scotia. — Can. Ent. 86. Ottawa, p. 299–310.

—— 1954d. Carabid beetles from eastern and southern Labrador. — Ibidem. p. 364–370.

—— 1954e. Experimentelle Beobachtungen an parthenogenetischem und bisexuellem Otiorrhynchus dubius Stroem (Col., Curculionidae). — Ent. Tidskr. 75. Stockholm, p. 111–116.

—— 1955a. The Carabid beetles of Newfoundland. — Opusc. Ent., Suppl. XII. Lund, p. 1–168.

LINDROTH, C. H., 1955 b. Dejean's types of North American Carabidae (Col.). — Opusc. Ent. 20. Lund, p. 10–34.

—— 1956. The Irish form of Carabus granulatus L. — Ent. M. Mag. 92. London, p. 7–8.

LÖWE, Á., 1951. The plants of Vineland the Good. — The Icelandic Canadian. 10: 2. Winnipeg, p. 15–22.

MALKIN, B. & HATCH, M. H., 1953. Colpodes buchanani in Oregon. — Pan-Pac. Ent. 29. San Francisco, p. 134.

MAYR, E., 1944. Systematics and the origin of species. — (Columb. Univ. Press.). New York, pp. I–XIV, 1–334.

—— 1954. Change of genetic environment and evolution. — In Huxley, Hardy, & Ford, Evolution as a process. London, p. 157–180.

MEEUSE, A. D. J. & HUBERT, B., 1949. The Mollusc fauna of glasshouses in the Netherlands. — Basteria. 13. Liège, p. 1–30.

MICHAELSEN, W., 1903. Die geographische Verbreitung der Oligochaeten. — Berlin, pp. I–VI, 1–186.

MULDAL, S., 1952. The chromosomes of the earthworms. 1. The evolution of polyploidy. — Heredity. 6. Edinburgh, p. 55–76.

NAESS, A., 1954. Hvor lå Vinland? (The location of Vinland.) — Oslo, p. 1–246.

NEEDHAM, J. G. & WESTFALL, M. J., Jr., 1955. A manual of the Dragonflies of North America (Anisoptera). — Berkeley & Los Angeles, p. 1–615.

NEWTON, A. P., 1930. Newfoundland, to 1783. — Cambr. Hist. Brit. Emp. VI. Cambridge, p. 121–145.

OEKLAND, F., 1927. Einige Argumente aus der Verbreitung der nordeuropäischen Fauna mit Bezug auf Wegeners Verschiebungstheorie. — Nyt Mag. f. Naturv. 65. Oslo, p. 339–367.

OMODEO, P., 1952. Cariologia dei Lumbricidae. — Caryologia. 4. Pisa, p. 173–275.

PALMÉN, E., 1951. A survey of the Oniscoidea (Isopoda Terr.) of Newfoundland. — Ann. Zool. Soc. Zool. Bot. Fenn. Vanamo. 14. Helsingfors, p. 1–27.

—— 1952. Survey of the Diplopoda of Newfoundland. — Ibidem. 15. p. 1–31.

—— 1954. Survey of the Chilopoda of Newfoundland. — Arch. Soc. Zool. Bot. Fenn. Vanamo. 8. Helsingfors, p. 131–149.

PALMER, M. G., 1946. The fauna and flora of the Ilfracombe district of North Devon. — Exeter, p. 1–266.

PARKINSON, C. N. (editor), 1948. The trade winds. A study of the British overseas trade during the French Wars 1793–1815. — London, p. 1–336.

PEARCE, E. J., 1926, 1927. A list of the Coleoptera of Dorset. — Dors. Nat. Hist. & Antiq. Field Club. Dorchester, pp. 1–78, 1–7.

PERROT, J.-L., 1939. Contribution a l'étude de la fécondation chez les Pulmonés Stylommatophores. Le cas de l'Arion empiricorum Fér. — Bull. Biol. France et Belg. 73. Paris, p. 408–432.

PETERSEN, B., 1954 a. Egg-laying and habitat selection in some Pieris species. — Ent. Tidskr. 75. Stockholm, p. 194–203.

—— 1954 b. Some trends of speciation in the cold-adapted Holarctic fauna. — Zool. Bidr. 30. Uppsala, p. 233–314.

PROWSE, D. W., 1895. A history of Newfoundland. — London, p. 1–742.

REEVES, G. I., 1927. The control of the Alfalfa Weevil. — Farmers' Bull., U. S.. Dept. Agric. 1528. Washington, D. C., p. 1–22.

ROGERS, J. D., 1911. Newfoundland. In: C. P. Lucas, A historical geography of the British colonies. V: 4. — Oxford, p. 1–274.

ROULEAU, E., 1949. Enumeratio plantarum vascularum Terrae-Novae. — Contr. Inst. Bot. Univ. 64. Montreal, p. 61–83.

SCHUBART, O., 1929. Zur Diplopodenfauna einer Weltstadt (Berlin). — Zool. Anz. 85. Leipzig, p. 303–316.

SCHWARZ, E. A., 1890. On Otiorhynchidae. — Insect Life (U. S. Dept. Agric.). 3. Washington, D. C., p. 37–38.

SMITH, F. 1928. An account of changes in the earthworm fauna of Illinois and a description of one new species. — Bull. Ill. State Nat. Hist. Surv. 17. Urbana, Ill., p. 347–362.

STRAND, A., 1951. The Norwegian species of Amischa Thoms. (Col. Staph.). — Norsk Ent. Tidsskr. 8. Oslo, p. 219–224.

SUOMALAINEN, E., 1953. Die Polyploidie bei den parthenogenetischen Rüsselkäfern. — Verh. Deutsch. Zool. Gesellsch. (1952). Zool. Anz., Suppl. 17. Leipzig, p. 280–289.

ULBRICH, J., 1930. Die Bisamratte. Lebensweise, Gang ihrer Ausbreitung in Europa, wirtschaftliche Bedeutung und Bekämpfung. — Dresden, p. 1–137.

URQUHART, F. A. & BEAUDRY, J. R., 1953. A recently introduced species of European grasshopper. — Can. Ent. 85. Ottawa, p. 78–79.

VALLE, K. J., 1955. Odonata from Newfoundland. — Ann. Ent. Fenn. 21. Helsingfors, p. 57–60.

VAN DYKE, E. C., 1945. A review of the North American species of the genus Carabus Linnaeus. — Ent. Amer. 24. Brooklyn, N. Y., p. 87–137.

WALKER, E. M., 1953. The Odonata of Canada and Alaska. 1. — Toronto, p. 1–292.

WING, L., 1943. Spread of the Starling and English Sparrow. — The Auk. 60. Lancaster, Pa., p. 74–87.

ØKLAND, vide Oekland.

Chapter III

THE TRUE, PRE-HUMAN RELATIONSHIP BETWEEN THE
PALAEARCTIC AND NEARCTIC FAUNAS

The so-called Amphiatlantic species

The word "Amphiatlantic" (German: amphiatlantisch) was proposed by Økland (1927, p. 352) in order to cover animal (and of course, also plant) species common to Europe and North America but absent from Asia and thus believed to form instances of direct faunal exchange across the North Atlantic. The word would be equally suitable for species common to Africa and Central or South America (if any) but is here used in the same sense as by Økland, for the northern continents only.

A true Amphiatlantic species occurs only in Europe (possibly also in the African and Asiatic parts of the Mediterranean region) and the eastern parts of North America. If the word "Amphiatlantic" is used as a historical, not merely as a geographical concept, implying that a species so termed took part in a direct faunal exchange across the North Atlantic, then even animals and plants with a wider distribution, towards the east in the Old World, to the west in North America, may be included, provided a pronounced gap can be demonstrated somewhere in the continents surrounding the North Pacific.

However, it is safer, at least for the moment, to keep such historical aspects out of the picture. The main question would then be to judge whether a seemingly Amphiatlantic distribution, in the restricted sense of the word, is an unquestionable reality or only due to incomplete knowledge of the species' area. The latter possibility must always be earnestly considered since the fauna, not only of northern Asia but also of Western North America, is far from sufficiently investigated in many groups of animals.

This reservation cannot, however, conceal the fact that a long series of animal species, belonging to different taxonomical and biological groups, show a perfectly Amphiatlantic distribution, as is amply exemplified in the list of Eur-American species (p. 17–124). Many of these have already been treated in the preceding chapter of this book and their crossing of the Atlantic was proved (or at least considered) as a quite late event, caused by introduction with man, mainly in the direction from Europe to North America.

This is, however, only part of the explanation of the Amphiatlantic type of distribution though it apparently holds true in the majority of cases, as far as terrestrial Evertebrates are concerned. Putting these aside, there still remains to be considered a good number of animal species which are—or may be—old, prehuman inhabitants of the countries bordering the North Atlantic but are absent from northern and eastern Asia as well as the Pacific side of the American continent. Let us call them the *primary Amphiatlantic* species.

The following are good illustrations of this geographical group:—

A. *Primary Amphiatlantic species or subspecies* lacking in Asia (except possibly in Novaja Zemlja) as well as in Pacific North America.

Aves

Alca torda L.
Catharacta skua Brünn.[1]
Cepphus grylle L. (except sbsp. *mandti* Mandt)
Charadrius hiaticula L., *f. typ.* (incl. sbsp. *psammodroma* Sal.)
Fratercula arctica L.
Fulmarus glacialis L., *f. typ.* (fig. 27)
Larus marinus L.
Morus (Sula) bassanus L. (fig. 28)
Phalacrocorax carbo L., *f. typ.*
Sterna dougalli Mont., *f. typ.*
Thalasseus sandvicensis Lath.
Uria aalge Pont., *f. typ.*

Lepidoptera

Anarta lapponica Thunb. W[2] (fig. 30)
Crymodes exulis Lef. (fig. 38)
Plusia (Autographa) parilis Hbn. W (fig. 31)

Hymenoptera, Formicidae

Ponera coarctata Latr. (fig. 35).

Araneae

Agyneta cauta Cambr.
Crustulina sticta Cambr.
Leptyphantes minutus Blackw.
Monocephalus parasiticus Westr.
Rhaebothorax borealis Jacks. W
Walckenaera vigilax Blackw.

Coleoptera, Staphylinidae

Micralymma marinum Ström (fig. 32)

B. Amphiatlantic species or subspecies differing from group A only in that they *extend into Western Asia.*

Aves

Erolia maritima Brünn.
Rissa tridactyla L., *f. typ.*
Sterna hirundo L., *f. typ.*
Uria lomvia L., *f. typ.*

Araneae

Bathyphantes nigrinus Westr.
Phlegra fasciata Hahn

---

[1] Perhaps no permanent resident of North America.
[2] W = "Westarctic" species (vide p. 237).

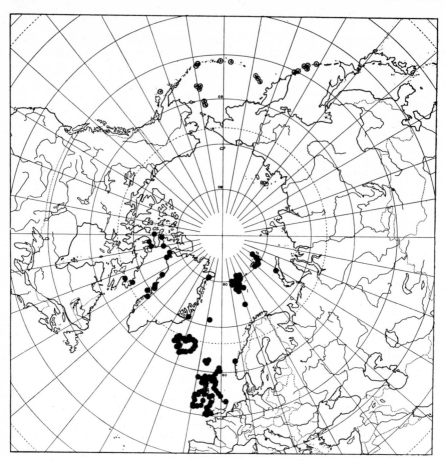

FIG. 27. Breeding area (about 1950) of the Fulmar, *Fulmarus glacialis* L. — Solid dots = *forma typica*, the Atlantic Fulmar. Pointed dots = sbsp. *rodgersii* Cass., the Pacific Fulmar. — The bird is steadily spreading in western Europe.

(After FISHER, 1952.)

(From ROSENBERG, Fåglar i Sverige.)

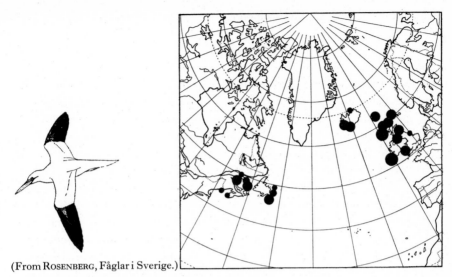

(From ROSENBERG, Fåglar i Sverige.)

FIG. 28. Breeding area of the Gannet, *Morus (Sula) bassanus* L., about 1940. Size of dots in four categories, indicating colonies of less than 100 pairs, 100–1,000 pairs, 1,000 to 10,000 pairs, and more than 10,000 pairs, respectively. (After FISHER & VEVERS, 1943.)

C. Less pronounced Amphiatlantic species, lacking in Asia (as far as known) but *Transamerican.*

Lepidoptera

Anarta leucocycla Stdgr. W
A. melanopa Thunb.

Araneae

Clubiona norvegica E. Str. W
C. trivialis C. L. Koch
Dictyna annulipes Blackw. W

Diplocentria bidentata Em.
Gnaphosa orites Chamb. W
Islandiana alata Em. W
Leptyphantes complicatus Em.
Pardosa saltuaria L. Koch
Pocadicnemis pumila Blackw.
Thanatus striatus C. L. Koch

Other Arthropods may belong here but the absence of records from Asiatic Russia is possibly due to insufficient knowledge. Instances are:—*Cidaria ruberata* Frr. and *Eupithecia gelidata* Moeschl. (Lepidoptera), *Aeschna subarctica* Walk. (Odonata).

Doubtful cases

In the above lists (A–C) of more or less pronounced Amphiatlantic animals a few species have been omitted which were regarded as primary Amphiatlantic by

several students, whereas others supposed that human transport has been responsible for their occurrence in North America.

This applies to two ants, *Tetramorium caespitum* L. and its parasite, *Anergates
atratulus* Schenck. Wheeler, and others, assumed that the *Tetramorium*, and consequently also its parasite, had been introduced from Europe with the early colonists and both species are still regarded as adventive by Smith (1951, p. 823).
This opinion was strongly opposed by Creighton (1950, p. 289): —"The discovery
of *Anergates* in America rules out the possibility that *caespitum* might have been
imported to this country"; and (l.c., p. 244):—"—I cannot agree that the first
advent of *caespitum* on this continent is a result of importation. To do so implies
that *Anergates* has also been imported. I believe that it can be demonstrated that
the probability for this having occurred is too remote to be credible."

It seems to me that Creighton has not sufficiently considered the nature of
ballast transport. If ballast was taken in great quantities from heaps of rubbish
in a port (*vide* pp. 165, 200) it is not at all unlikely that a whole *Tetramorium* nest,
with inquilines and parasites, might have been brought on board. Though scattered and disturbed during the process, it might very well have reorganized itself
during the long journey (p. 162) and become unloaded with the ballast on some
North American shore after arrival. It should also be remembered that the myrmecophilous Isopod (Woodlouse) *Platyarthrus hoffmanseggi* Brandt apparently
reached North America in the same way. Yet, *Anergates atratulus* is so rare in
Britain that it was probably carried across from the European mainland.

A much more intricate case is that of the snail *Cepaea* (*Helix*) *hortensis* O. F. Müll.
(fig. 29). This was likewise long regarded as a European introduction into North
America (*vide* Johnson, 1906, p. 79–80) though, after it had been found in "pre-
Columbian kitchen-midding deposits", Pilsbry (1894, p. 321) suggested that the
importation might have taken place with the Vikings of the eleventh century.
Later, subfossils of proposed greater age were recorded:—"in the glacial Pleistocene of Maine" (Dall, 1910, p. 20); "in a shell heap—associated with bones of the
large extinct mink—*Mustela macrodon* Prentiss.", on an island in Penobscot
Bay, Maine (Johnson, 1915, p. 131); "in a prehistoric shell-heap on Mahone Bay,
about 75 miles west of Halifax, N. S." (Wurtemberg, 1919, p. 71). Since this information was published, conchologists and zoogeographers have almost unanimously accepted *Cepaea hortensis* as indigenous in North America (Scharff, 1909,
p. 18–20; 1911, p. 39; Taylor, 1911, p. 361–362; Økland, 1927, p. 342 a.f.). Pilsbry
(1939, p. 8) also changed his view but left open the question of whether the present
separated occurrences of the species should be regarded as remnants of a wide
Holarctic area, or if they should be explained as being the result of migration
along a former transatlantic land-bridge, as advocated by Scharff. Wegener (1929,

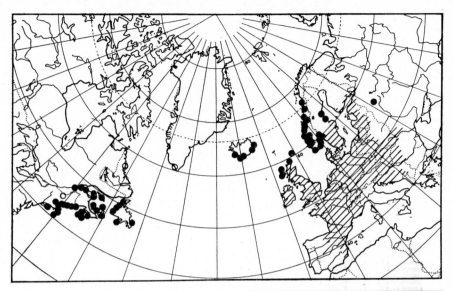

FIG. 29. Distribution of *Cepaea* (*Helix*) *hortensis* O. F. Müll. — Open circles = doubtful or accidental occurrence.

(According to JOHNSON, 1906, TAYLOR, 1911, ØKLAND, 1925, 1927, PILSBRY, 1939, &c.)

(From PILSBRY, 1939.)

p. 105) regarded the distribution of *Cepaea hortensis* as one of the strongest zoogeographical facts in favour of his theory of continental drift (*vide* below, p. 284).

It seems to me that the solution of the enigma "introduced *contra* native" in the case of *Cepaea hortensis* in North America stands and falls with the dating of the subfossil remains in Maine and Nova Scotia quoted above. The only published statement possibly allowing this, as far as I know, is the observation that in Penobscot Bay the shells were found associated with bones of an extinct species of mink. This has apparently impressed subsequent students of the question with the assumed high age of the *Cepaea*. The known history of *Mustela macrodon* Prentiss., however, is very disappointing in this respect (Anderson, 1946, p. 192–193): — "According to Hardy the animal became extinct in Maine about the year 1860. Traditionally said to have been commonly trapped along the coast of the Bay of Fundy in southern New Brunswick, —". Until further, reliably dated subfossils of *Cepaea hortensis* are discovered, nothing seems to prevent those hitherto found being of "post-Columbian" age.

The following facts may be regarded as indicators of late arrival with man of *Cepaea hortensis* into North America: —

(a) The restriction of area in North America to the sea-shore of the Northeast. There is only one old, unlocalized inland record, from northern Vermont, by A. Binney (*vide* Johnson, 1906, p. 74), which requires confirmation. In Europe (map, fig. 29), *Cepaea hortensis* is not at all restricted to coastal regions, nor to districts showing an oceanic climate. Attempts to explain its absence from inland localities as due to unsuitable edaphic and other conditions (Johnson, 1906, p. 80; Pilsbry, 1939, p. 8) are not in the least convincing since the species in Europe shows no tendency to fastidiousness in choice of soil; it cannot be termed "calciphile", more than all shell-bearing snails are, though Pilsbry (l.c.) does so. The restricted distribution in North America has no doubt *historical* reasons.

(b) The frequent occurrence of *Cepaea hortensis* in North America on small islands off the coast has been used as an argument against the theory of introduction. Actually, this argues in favour of the theory. Brooks & Brooks (1940, pp. 59, 61) found a couple of European snails (*Limax marginatus* Müll. and *Vertigo alpestris* Ald.) on small, uninhabited islands off the coast of SE Newfoundland and likewise regarded this as a sign of indigenous occurrence, but it is given a far more natural explanation by the assumption that sailing vessels discharged their ballast on these islands, especially at low tide, before entering the port of destination. As mentioned above (p. 157), tipping of ballast into the sea was prohibited in old days.

(c) The oldest record of living *Cepaea hortensis* from North America seems to be from St. Pierre-Miquelon, in 1822 (Taylor, 1911, p. 366); from Quebec in 1829, New England (Mass.) in 1837 (Johnson, 1906). Though this gives no evidence as to time and place of a possible first introduction, it suggests the Newfoundland region as the primary immigration area. The species was also unmentioned in two lists of New England shells from 1833 (according to Johnson, 1906, p. 73).

(d) A. Binney (according to Johnson, l.c., and Taylor, l.c.) observed that on the small Salt Island off Gloucester, Mass., *Cepaea hortensis* in 1837 occurred exclusively in the unbanded variety, but in 1851 he reported that the banded variety was "not uncommon" on the same island. This indicates an instability of the population contradicting the idea of old age on the spot in question. The shell character mentioned has a hereditary base and the factor "unbanded" behaves as a dominant (according to the well-known breeding experiments by A. Lang; *vide* also Boettger, 1950). Apparently Salt island was originally colonized by snails with unbanded shells, in part heterozygotes.

(e) *Cepaea hortensis*, if native in North America, would display a quite unique type of distribution. It would constitute the single Amphiatlantic animal species, the distribution of which could not be explained either by active or passive oversea dispersal or as a relict of a former circumpolar area.

Besides *Cepaea hortensis*, Økland (1927, p. 353–355) regards three species of terrestrial Arthropods as primary Amphiatlantic: the Wood-louse *Oniscus asellus* L. and two Ground-beetles of the genus *Carabus*, *nemoralis* Müll. and *problematicus* Hbst. (*catenulatus* auct.). The two first mentioned, without any doubt, are European introductions into North America; the proposed endemic North American form of *Carabus nemoralis* is a fiction (*vide* Lindroth, 1955 a, p. 27), and the records of *Carabus problematicus*, as "sbsp. *californicus* Mtsch.", from western North America are based on specimens with wrong locality labels (*vide* Lindroth, 1954a, p. 46).

There are a few more Eur-American animals, belonging to different taxonomical groups, which have a more or less pronouncedly Amphiatlantic distribution but which may be explained either by insufficient knowledge of the actual area and/or by early introduction with man into North America. Instances are the Click-beetle (*Elateridae*) *Corymbites sjaelandicus* Müll., the Moth (*Noctuidae*) *Amphipyra tragopogonis* L., the Spiders *Gonatium rubens* Blackw. and *Haplodrassus signifer* C. L. Koch, and the Snail *Vallonia excentrica* Sterki. These are to be found among species preceded by a cross in brackets (†) in the list given in Chapter I.

"Westarctic" species

The concepts "Westarctic" and "Amphiatlantic" overlap, and certain members of the first-mentioned group were enumerated above (and marked with a "W") among the Amphiatlantic species. The name "Westarctic" was, however, given from a Scandinavian point of view[1] in order to cover species of a northern or alpine character with affinities towards the west, to North America. The word was created by Th. Fries (1913) on a botanical basis and was soon applied to insects (*Lepidoptera*) by Wahlgren (1919). For more recent views on Westarctic plants, the reader is referred to Hansen (1929, p. 224 a.f.), Nordhagen (1935, p. 143 a.f.), and Nannfeldt (1940, p. 39).

The definition of a Westarctic plant or animal is that its occurrence in north-western Europe (Fennoscandia) is cut off towards the east but more or less connected with an area in North America by means of occurrences in Greenland, possibly also in Iceland and/or Spitzbergen. The concept i not merely a descriptive one, it contains implicitly the idea that these organisms have reached Fennoscandia

---

[1] In North America this group would be termed "Eastarctic"!

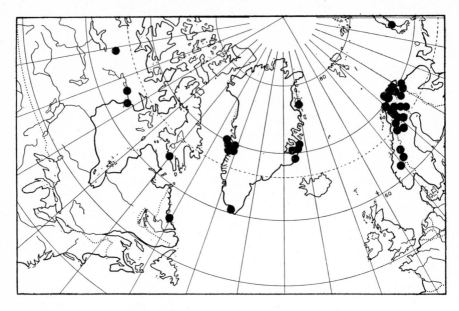

FIG. 30. Distribution of *Anarta* (*Sympistis*) *lapponica* Thunb., a "Westarctic" moth. The figured specimen is from Scandinavia.

(Photo P. ARDÖ.)

from a western direction across the North Atlantic and it is usually thought that the dispersal was facilitated by one or two now submerged land-bridges. This hypothesis was strongly opposed by Hultén (1937, e.g. pp. 126–127, 137; 1950, p. 52).

The reasons why a Westarctic species is not always an Amphiatlantic species, and *vice versa*, is that the former may occur in Pacific North America and northeastern Asia (E. of River Lena) but *not* in the mountains of Central Europe; furthermore it is supposed to show clear cold-adaption. However, the essentials of the two groups, above all the historical interpretation, are common to both. So it would seem more appropriate to deal with them in the future under one heading. If so, the term "Amphiatlantic" is much to be preferred because it is universally understood. It would be easy to make subdivisions: into *more or less pronounced* Amphi-

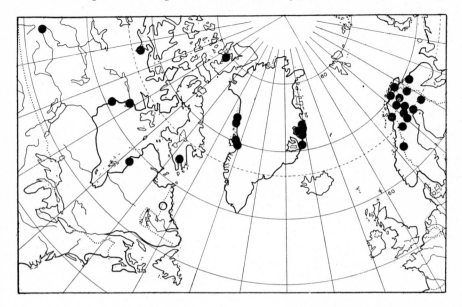

FIG. 31. Distribution of *Plusia* (*Autographa*) *parilis* Hbn., a "Westarctic" moth. The figured specimen is from Scandinavia.

(Photo P. ARDÖ.)

atlantic species (according to the size of gap on both sides of the Pacific; groups A–C above) on the one hand, into *northern, arctic, boreo-alpine,* &c., Amphiatlantic species on the other.

Westarctic animals are much fewer in number than plants are. Some of the more pronounced were enumerated above (p. 231) (and marked with a "W"). According to the definition, that is with allowance for an occurrence in *eastern* Siberia, the following are also instances of Westarctic distribution:—

Lepidoptera

Anarta funebris, Hbn.
A. melaleuca Thunb.
A. zetterstedti Stgr.

Anomogyna laetabilis Zett.
Arctia quenseli Payk.
Cidaria sabini Kby.

Colias nastes Bsd.   *Scopula frigidaria* Moeschl.
Hillia iris Zett.   *Spaelotis clandestina* Harr.
Plusia (Autographa) diasema Bsd.

Araneae

Bathyphantes pullatus Cambr.   *Hilaira frigida* Thor.
Estrandia grandaeva Keys.

Apart from the inappropriateness of using the name "Amphiatlantic" for species at the same time "Amphipacific", there are three reasons for excluding species of this type from the group.—In the *first* place, it is usually impossible to declare for certain that a considered species is actually lacking in Siberia west of the Lena River; for instance this gap exists, according to our present knowledge, in the otherwise probably circumpolar Carabid beetles *Diachila arctica* Gyll. and *Elaphrus lapponicus* Gyll.—In the *second* place, a gap of distribution (also described, for Lepidoptera, by Kusnezov, 1935) within the large West-Siberian plain, so different from the mountainous region east of Yenisei, may be due to lack of conditions of life; the limit between these regions corresponds to a rather sharp faunal limit (*vide* for instance Johansen, 1955).—In the *third* place, the western parts of Siberia during Pleistocene time, and probably more than once, have been submerged under water (Pirožnikov, 1937) and an originally equal area of distribution through northern Eurasia may have become interrupted thereby.

These objections do not prevent particularly well investigated representatives of this somewhat dubious type of Westarctic distribution being used as arguments in the discussion of transatlantic faunal connections.

The American element of the British flora

The existence of a truly American element in the flora of Ireland, to a lesser extent in western Scotland and in Wales, has long attracted the attention of botanists. Though no quite corresponding faunal element peculiar to the British Islands is known, the phenomenon has such a clear bearing upon our problem of possible transatlantic connections that it should be briefly touched upon here.

The plant species involved are:

Eriocaulon septangulare With.   W. Irel. (widely); Inner Hebrides (Skye
                                            & Coll).

Limosella subulata Ives   S. & N. Wales.
Myriophyllum alterniflorum americanum   N. E. Ireland.
   Pugsl.

Potamogeton epihydrus Raf.

Sisyrinchium angustifolium Mill.

Spiranthes romanzoffiana Cham.

Outer Hebrides (South Uist).

W. Ireland (widely).

N. E. & S. W. Irel.; Inner Hebr. (Coll & Colonsay), W. Argyllshire (Scotl.).

In North America these species have a wide distribution, all reaching New-foundland in the east, the *Spiranthes* even central Labrador; the *Sisyrinchium* goes to Anticosti Island and SE. Labrador.

The "American Group" has been carefully studied by Praeger (1932, 1934) and, most recently, by Heslop-Harrison (1953). For some unknown reason, he does not mention the *Limosella* but his list contains *Juncus tenuis* Willd. and *J. Dudleyi* Wieg., as well as *Najas flexilis* Willd. *Juncus Dudleyi* was included tenta-tively only, as probably introduced, and the same, according to other students (Clapham, Tutin & Warburg, 1952, p. 1244), applies to *J. tenuis* (cf. p. 212). Concerning *Najas flexilis*, known from several scattered stations on the European mainland and widely distributed there during inter- and early postglacial times, Heslop-Harrison himself admits that it is no more entitled to be listed in the "American" group than for instance *Lobelia dortmanna* L.

Five of the six species above (all except *Sisyrinchium*) are aquatic or grow on very wet places. Water-plants have often been brought by man, purposely (as the water-fern *Azolla caroliniana* Willd.) or unintentionally (as *Elodea canadensis* Michx.), from North America to Europe, but there seems to be no reason for a similar explanation of the six American plants in the British Isles. By means of pollen-analysis, it has even been demonstrated by Jessen (1949, p. 202) that *Eriocaulon septangulare* was growing in Irish pools already in early Atlantic time.

One animal organism, the fresh-water Sponge *Heteromeyenia ryderi* Potts, has a distribution quite similar to that of the above plants (Arndt, 1928). Its main area is in eastern North America, from Florida to Nova Scotia and Newfoundland, it is widely distributed in Ireland (Stephens, 1920) and also found on the isle of Mull in the Inner Hebrides, as well as on the Faeroes (Spärck, 1934). Any idea of human transport of *Heteromeyenia ryderi* from North America to its outposts in western Europe seems as out of touch with reality as for the corresponding plant species.

The possible explanation of the presence of an American floral (and faunal) element on the British Isles (and the Faeroes) will be discussed in the next para-graph.

The chance of spontaneous transatlantic dispersal at the present time

We have now a selection of species, mostly animals but also some plants, which more than any others are expected to show evidence of a direct exchange between Europe and North America, without the interference of man.

In order to estimate their evidence it is necessary to scrutinize the animals more concretely, so to speak more "individually", than is possible on the basis of the taxonomic and purely geographical arrangement of the preceding paragraphs. They should be grouped according to biological properties which may affect their powers of dispersal.

In this respect, the following types are represented: —

1. *Actively flying animals.* All the *birds* (16 species or subspecies) and all the *Lepidoptera* (16 species), referred to the Amphiatlantic or in widest sense "Westarctic" groups. Yet the different taxonomical and biological *groups* of birds and Lepidoptera are unequally represented.

The Amphiatlantic *birds* are all excellent flyers and closely connected with the sea, 14 are Swimmers and both of the remaining (*Charadrius hiaticula* and *Erolia maritima*) are Waders breeding on the seashore. For most of them the Atlantic breeding area is almost continuous, with stations on the Faeroes, in Iceland, Greenland, &c. (fig. 27). Exceptions are, in the first place the three species of Terns (*Sterna dougalli, S. hirundo, Thalasseus sandvicensis*) with a more southerly breeding area, but the Terns belong to the veritable gipsies of the Atlantic Ocean (*vide,* for instance, Kullenberg, 1946); in the second place *Morus bassanus* (fig. 28) which is lacking in Greenland, and *Catharacta skua,* only doubtfully recorded as breeding there.

The small breeding area of *Charadrius hiaticula* in arctic North America (incl. Greenland) is historically connected with the eastern side of the Atlantic, as demonstrated by its route of migration along the European coast. The main population of *Erolia maritima* even in Greenland stays over the winter.

It cannot be denied that all Amphiatlantic birds are easily able to cross the Atlantic or that individual birds actually do so. The Swimmers especially are able to rest and take food on the open sea. Continents more than oceans constitute obstacles to their distribution. No inland birds and no weak flyers are represented among Amphiatlantic birds. The *Passeriformes* are completely lacking.

The 16 species of *Lepidoptera* include 13 *Noctuid moths* (fam. *Noctuidae*), that is a good 80 per cent, 2 Geometers (fam. *Geometridae; Cidaria sabini* and *Scopula frigidaria*), and one Butterfly (*Colias nastes*). These figures are not at all in accordance with the proportions displayed by the faunas of countries bordering the North Atlantic:[1]

	Macrolepido-ptera, total	Butterflies (Diurna)	Noctuid moths	Geometrid moths
Newfoundland (Krogerus, 1954)	280	38 = 14 %	126 = 45 %	89 = 32 %
Greenland (Henriksen, 1939)	29	4 = 14 %	17 = 59 %	6 = 21 %
Iceland[2] (Lindroth, 1931)	28	—	14 = 50 %	12 = 43 %
Norway[1] (Haanshus, 1933)	720	96 = 13 %	257 = 36 %	237 = 33 %
British Isles[1] (Kloet & Hincks, 1945)	850	66 = 8 %	336 = 40 %	285 = 34 %
Amphiatlantic and "Westarctic" species	16	1 = 6 %	13 = 81 %	2 = 13 %

Evidently, Noctuid moths are strongly over-represented among Amphiatlantic (and geographically related) Lepidoptera. The explanation is no doubt that the members of this group are superior to other Lepidoptera in the art of flying, with the exception of the Hawk-moths (fam. *Sphingidae*) which, however, are no residents of arctic and subarctic regions. The *Anartas* numbering no less than 6 of the 13 species, are extremely rapid flyers, on the wing both night and day, though, it must be admitted, their perseverance of flight has not been investigated. Also, among the Butterflies, the genus *Colias* contains some of the most capable flyers; especially *nastes* and *hecla*, almost confined to the arctic region, are able to withstand even rather strong winds.—No records were available to me of the flight powers of the two Geometers concerned.

Crymodes exulis (fig. 38) is the member reaching farthest east of a series of three Noctuids of American origin which *via* Greenland have proceeded at least as far as Iceland on their air-borne advance (p. 254).

An instance of at least partly active dispersal across the North Atlantic is formed by the famous Monarch Butterfly (*Danaus plexippus*), a North American species regularly appearing in Britain in spite of the fact that its food plant (*Asclepias*) is not indigenous there (*vide* Ford, 1945, p. 157–159).

2. Animals especially suited for *passive aerial transport*. This applies to all of the *Araneae* listed above, 21 in number, which, at least as young, disperse themselves by "ballooning". Even if it is admitted that our present knowledge of the distribution of spiders is far from complete, implying that certain of the listed species actually belong to a more or less circumpolar type (but also that others, *not*

---

[1] Some of the figures are not quite up to date but this hardly affects the records of percentage.
[2] I have later received a revised list of Icelandic Lepidoptera by Mr. Niels L. Wolff, Hellerup (Denmark), which, however, does not essentially alter the percental figures given above.

considered, *should* belong here!), the rich representation of the *Araneae* among animals with an Amphiatlantic (or similar) distribution is quite striking. It is difficult to get away from the idea that this is a consequence of their special mode of dispersal. And it is well worth mentioning that one of the species in question, *Walckenaera vigilax*, was among the spiders included in the famous collection of "aerial plankton", made by Glick (1939) from air-planes in the U.S.A., 3 specimens captured at elevations of from 1,000 to 3,000 feet above the ground (Crosby & Bishop, 1936).

3. Flightless animals living *in close connection with seawater* and therefore liable to become dispersed by active swimming or passive transport by currents and waves. The single instance among the animals above is the Staphylinid beetle *Micralymma marinum* (fig. 32), inhabiting the tidal zone, on rocky places with a rich supply of *Fucus* and other seaweeds. Its distribution in the North Atlantic region has already been associated with the Gulfstream (Lindroth, 1931, p. 497–499) and it is difficult to understand it otherwise than as the result of direct transport.

Two other insects, confined to the seaweed drifts of the shore, the Hydrophilid beetle *Cercyon litoralis* Gyll. and the Coelopid fly *Orygma luctuosum* Meig. (Nielsen, Ringdahl & Tuxen, 1954, p. 84), have a similar Amphiatlantic distribution but probably do not endure submersion during any stage of development. The most probable explanation seems to be that they were introduced from Europe into North America.

It is a well-known fact that pieces of seaweed, seeds of terrestrial plants, &c., are regularly carried with the Gulfstream from North America to the European west-coast and the exclusive seashore plant *Mertensia maritima* L., unknown in Eurasia E. of the White Sea, is generally regarded as a Gulfstream immigrant, even by Hultén (1937, p. 64) who is otherwise extremely sceptical of all kinds of transatlantic floral exchange.

The quite isolated area of *Ranunculus cymbalaria* Pursh on the coast of SW Scandinavia, on both sides of the Swedish-Norwegian border limit, was likewise originally (Nordhagen, 1916; still by Sterner, 1945, p. 40) interpreted as the result of transport with the Gulfstream. Hultén (1937, p. 101) regarded it as an old relict-occurrence, a strained idea, but later (1950, p. 81) changed his mind, apparently in accordance with Tambs-Lyche (1937), who thought of introduction with ballast from North America. This explanation seems to be the most acceptable one.

The famous flightless *Great Auk* (*Penguinus* or *Alca impennis* L.), now extinct, once had a pronouncedly Amphiatlantic distribution (fig. 33). The limited means of dispersal of this bird refer it to the present group.

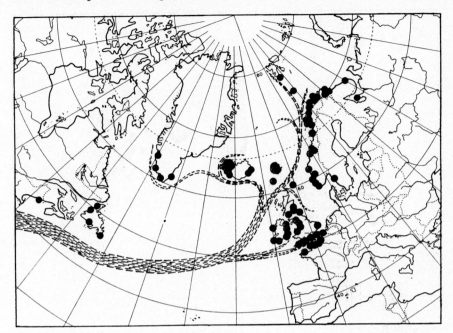

FIG. 32. Distribution of the Staphylinid beetle *Micralymma marinum* Ström (*stimpsoni* Lec.), inhabiting the tidal zone, in relation to the Gulfstream. The figured specimen is from Newfoundland.

(From LINDROTH, 1931, revised.)

(Photo P. ARDÖ.)

4. A fourth group would consist of warm-blooded animals, active in winter and therefore possibly *able to traverse the sea* between arctic islands and continents *on the ice*. This group is well represented among Circumpolar (p. 291), but not among Amphiatlantic animals, except perhaps once, temporarily, by the *Muskox* (*Ovibos moschatus* L.) (vide map by Ekman, 1922, p. 396).

5. Freshwater species with stage of development adapted to *passive transport with birds*. The Sponge *Heteromeyenia ryderi*. Like others of the fresh-water Spongillids, this species forms "gemmulae", less than 1 mm. in diameter, which

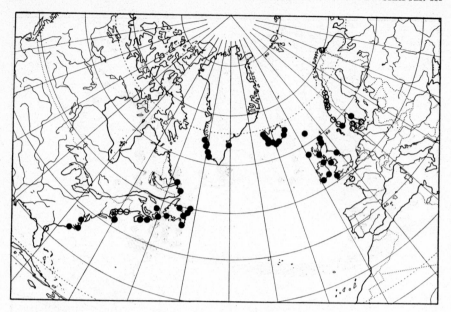

FIG. 33. The extinct Great Auk, *Penguinus* (*Alca*) *im-pennis* L. Late- and postglacial distribution. — Solid dots = on historical evidence. Open dots = subfossil remains. The figured bird belongs to the Zool. Inst., Lund.

(According to BLASIUS, 1903, EKMAN, 1922, &c.)

(Photo HANNA GRÄNS.)

are extremely resistant and constitute the normal stage of dispersal of the organism. The gemmulae may be carried by water but also, after drying up, by the wind; for greater distances, transport with birds is usually accepted as the normal means of dispersal (*vide*, for instance, Thienemann, 1950, p. 156).

It was therefore suggested by some students that bird-transport from North America might have been responsible for the European occurrence of *Heteromeyenia*

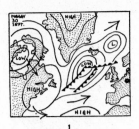 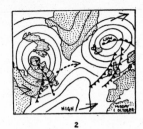 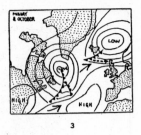

     1   2   3

FIG. 34. The situation of air pressure and winds over the North Atlantic at midday during three days, September 30th to October 2nd, 1953, with considerable influx of North American birds into the British Islands.

(From WILLIAMSON, 1954.)

ryderi. Others, for instance Scharff (1907, p. 34) and Stephens (1920, p. 247–248), regard this sponge as belonging to a very old faunal element, evidence of a former transatlantic land-connection. Arndt (1928, p. 159–163) tried to select a middle course: he stressed the probability of bird-transport from Ireland to the Faeroes but admits that the Irish population may be old. His view has been misinterpreted by Spärck (1934) who himself ascribed even to the population of the Faeroes a persistence *in situ* since the last interglacial period.

It seems advisable to consider the history of the *Heteromeyenia* in connection with the related American element of the British flora. Phytogeographers have almost unanimously accepted this as an old element too, a "relict" from a period of transatlantic land-connection. Quite recently, however, Heslop-Harrison (1953) has given voice to an opposing view: he is inclined to interpret the occurrence of these American plants in the British Isles as due to transport with migrating birds and especially draws attention to the routes of the Greenland White-fronted Goose (*Anser albifrons flavirostris* Dalg. & Sc.) which winters partly in Ireland. The weak point of Heslop-Harrison's argument is that, according to him, only one of the species in question, *Sisyrinchium angustifolium*, grows in Greenland (Böcher, 1948) an this species, it should be added, is the one least likely to be dispersed by birds.[1] He therefore feels compelled to assume that other birds have brought the plant diaspores from NE North America to Greenland, where they "changed birds", without being able, for climatic reasons, to germinate on the spot. This is a most far-fetched hypothesis.

If we are at all willing to accept bird-transport as a possible agency in the present case, it seems necessary to evaluate the chance of birds arriving in the British

---

[1] Dr. T. W. Böcher and Dr. J. Iversen have informed me, however, that the Greenlandic and the Irish *Sisyrinchium* are different. Dr. Iversen has grown both forms together. (Cf. p. 250).

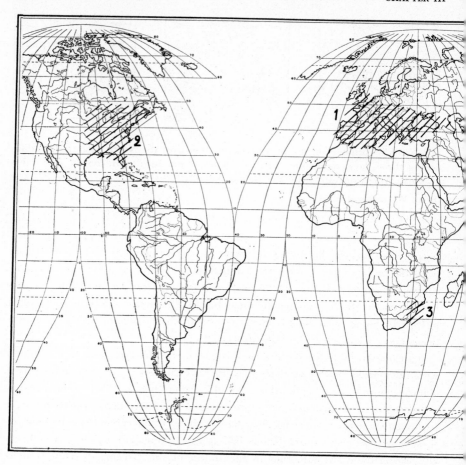

Isles *directly* from parts of North America inhabited by the plants considered, that is, not north of Newfoundland. No bird has a normal route of migration like this, it is a question of abnormal movements or pure wind-drift.

Now, Williamson (1954) has given a very interesting report of occasional appearances of American birds in the British Isles in the fall of 1953 and, what is more important, has been able to correlate the observations with the meteorological situations preceding the influx of these birds (fig. 34). Their route appeared as a clear wind-drift and the offshore drift on the American side, according to the weather, at least in one instance could have taken place as far south as Cape Hatteras. The American birds noted in Great Britain and Ireland, on this and other occasions in late years, include geese, ducks, waders, passerines, cuckoos &c. (Alexander & Fitter, 1955) and Williamson (l.c., p. 26) speaks of "the now regular

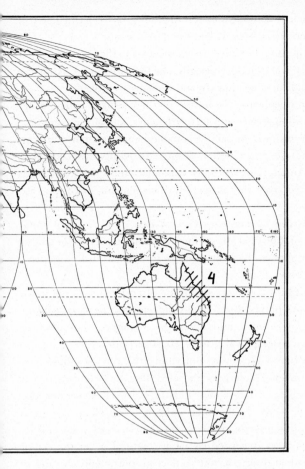

FIG. 35. World distribution of *Ponera coarctata* Latr., no doubt an old species, belonging to a very primitive group of ants.

1 = *forma typica*
2 = sbsp. *pennsylvanica* Buckl.
3 = sbsp. *boerorum* Forel
4 = sbsp. *mackayensis* Forel

The figured worker (from Smith, 1947) is of sbsp. *pennsylvanica*.

annual occurrence of nearctic waders at English reservoirs and sewage-farms". Is the sudden appearance of the American freshwater snail *Lymnaea catoscopium* Say, in "a warm engine-pond in a timber yard", in Leith, Scotland (Kevan, 1943), possibly to be explained in this way, and not through human transport?

The direct transatlantic bird-connection, direction east, is accidental but not too scarce. How great is the chance of these birds coming into contact with diaspores of the discussed plants? Heslop-Harrison (l.c., p. 114) stresses the point "that they are all aquatic, marsh or lake-margin plants". Though this statement does not apply very well to the *Sisyrinchium*, which also takes a different position in other respects, Heslop-Harrison is probably right in regarding this ecological property of the group (equally relevant for *Heteromeyen a ryderi*) as an indication in favour of bird-transport. The reasons seem to be:—

(a) Nowhere is there such a congregation of migrating birds, particularly of swimmers and waders, as on the shores of lakes and of the sea.

(b) Small objects of any kind attach themselves most easily to the feet and feather of a bird in water or on very wet places, especially together with mud. After the bird has taken wing, the mud dries up quickly and remains well fixed.

(c) Ubiquistic freshwater organisms, by means of their usually much wider geographical distribution in comparison with terrestrial ones, and at the same time their confinement to a more disjunct mosaic of suitable habitats, often of a temporary character, apparently are much better adapted to *passive* dispersal than terrestrial organisms are. Among the methods exploited, transport with birds should not be underestimated (*vide* the extract by Thienemann, 1950, p. 156–158).

(d) A special case is provided by *Potamogeton epihydrus*. The fruits of *Potamogeton* are a normal part of the food of swimming birds, especially of ducks, and Lohammar (1954) has shown that the passage through a bird's intestines highly favours the germination.

To my mind, the theory of bird-transport should be earnestly considered in the case of four of the "American" plants: *Eriocaulon septangulare, Limosella subulata, Myriophyllum alterniflorum americanum*, and *Potamogeton epihydrus;* in addition, for the single animal of this geographical group, *Heteromeyenia ryderi*.

It may sound absurd that causal appearances of wind-driven birds should have proved more efficient as an agency enlarging the area of transported organisms than birds on their normal route of migration. This is, however, a seeming discrepancy only. Dispersal of seeds, fresh-water animals, &c., along the great highways of migrating birds has gone on regularly for thousands of years and resulted in continuous species' areas, regarded by us as "natural". Yet the erratic east-west dispersal is predestined to give a better effect proportionally, because it usually means the removal into a place with a climate similar to that of the starting-point.

The two remaining plants must be treated separately. They are less hygrophilous, neither of them is a water or even a shore plant, and their diaspores are different. *Spiranthes romanzoffiana* is an Orchid with very numerous and very minute seeds which are wind-spread and must be assumed to constitute a regular component of aerial plankton. The resistance of the seeds to cold and exsiccation should be investigated experimentally. Probably the distribution of the species is more restricted by the limited possibility of the seedling finding the right fungus for mycorrhiza than by powers of dispersal.

It is difficult to understand that the globular seeds of *Sisyrinchium* could be suited for passive transport of any kind or that any vegetative part of the plant could form a substitute. A further important peculiarity of *S. angustifolium* is its occurrence on the European mainland, most often regarded as escape from cultivation, with one exception: in the Carpathians. According to repeated judgment (Lauterborn, 1927, p. 84; Böcher, 1948, p. 15) the plant here gives the impression of being indigenous. Serious consideration must therefore be given to the possibility that the small European areas of *Sisyrinchium angustifolium* are actually pre- or interglacial relicts, the remnants of a circumpolar area. At least, this hypothesis seems more plausible for the *Sisyrinchium* than for *Spiranthes romanzoffiana*, as emphasized by Hultén (1937, p. 132).

There seems to exist on the American side a small European element of boreal (non-arctic) plants corresponding to the "Americans" in Europe just treated. At least Fernald (1925, p. 272 a.f.) regards a comprehensive group of such plants, particularly in Newfoundland, as old relicts. The majority of these, however, are no doubt late introductions (*vide* above, p. 146). Heslop-Harrison (1953, p. 111) maps two species, *Carex hostiana* D.C. (*fulva* Host.) and *Potamogeton polygonifolius* Pourr. (*oblongus* Viv.), which he seems to regard as native in North America. Both are restricted to Newfoundland (incl. St. Pierre-Miquelon) and either Anticosti (*C. host.*) or Sable Island, Nova Scotia (*P. polyg.*). By Clapham, Tutin & Warburg (1952, p. 1370) *Carex hostiana* is indicated as "probably introduced" in North America. It may be appropriate to apply to the *Potamogeton* the suggestion of bird-transport put forth concerning *P. epihydrus* above. A glance through the American "Check-List" (1931) shows convincingly that stray birds on migration from Europe are not uncommon on the Atlantic coast of North America.[1]

On the American side also, like *Heteromeyenia ryderi* in Europe, there seems to exist at least one equivalent among animals, the fresh-water snail *Lymnaea* (*Radix*) *peregra* Müll., known from only two localities on the Avalon Peninsula of SE Newfoundland (Brooks & Brooks, 1940, p. 62). It is worth mentioning that the appearance of the same species ("*ovata* Drap.") on small, new-formed islands off the German Northsea coast was most likely due to bird-transport (Thienemann, 1950, p. 157). Also in other parts of Europe the distribution of this species gives evidence for an extremely high power of passive dispersal and this property of ubiquistic and more or less cosmopolitan fresh-water Molluscs is generally explained as the effect of transport with birds (Boycott, 1936, p. 123–126; Hubendick, 1947, p. 508–512, "*limosa* L.").

Whether or not the isolated occurrence of the American Amphipod *Gammarus*

---

[1] The European birds most regularly observed on the Atlantic coast of North America are: *Branta leucopsis* Bechst., *Crex crex* L., *Larus minutus* Pall., *Anas crecca* L. *f. typ.*, *Erolia alpina* L. *f. typ.*, *Philomachus pugnax* L., *Scolopax rusticola* L. *f. typ.*, *Vanellus vanellus* L. All are Swimmers or Waders.

fasciatus Say (*tigrinus* Sext.; *vide* Hynes, 1954) may be due to bird-transport, I am unable to judge. Segerstråle (1954, p. 68 a.f.) accepts this as the normal mode of dispersal for *G. lacustris* G. O. Sars.

5. Animals *without special properties* of active or passive dispersal. The ant *Ponera coarctata* Latr. (fig. 35). The sexuals, males as well as females, are winged in this species but do not make ordinary nuptial flights, the mating as a rule taking place on the ground near the nest, or even within the nest. At any rate the fertilized queens never fly (Wheeler, 1900; Michener & Michener, 1951, p. 141–142). The dispersal of this ant is therefore functionally the same as for a constantly wingless species.

Ponera coarctata inhabits a curiously broken-up area. Besides the *forma typica* of Europe and the Mediterranean region and the sbsp. *pennsylvanica* Buckl. of eastern North America, there is one subspecies endemic to South Africa (Natal) and one to Australia (Queensland) (Creighton, 1950, p. 47). The subfamily *Ponerinae* includes the most primitive of living ants (Wheeler, 1900) and must be very old, geologically speaking, not as a group alone, but also as actual species. This is confirmed by the fact that the extinct *Ponera atavia* Mayr, known by all casts from the Baltic amber (about the age of more than 40 million years), comes very close to *coarctata* (Wheeler, 1915, p. 39–40).

The present distribution of *Ponera coarctata* must be interpreted as the remnant of an almost world-wide area in Tertiary time and the occurrences on both sides of the Atlantic do not constitute evidence in favour of the theory of a direct land-connection (cf. the distribution of the beetle family *Cupedidae*, fig. 60).

The *conclusions* arising from the study of animals showing an Amphiatlantic, or similar, distribution are: —

Their present area seems understandable without accepting a late (Pleistocene) land-connection between the two continents. The existence of such (in one of the interglacial periods) would undoubtedly have resulted in a much richer faunal exchange in both directions, and a less "asymmetrical" range of distribution in the individual, actually existing cases.

On the other hand, it is not correct to regard almost all Amphiatlantic species as peripheral relics of an earlier circumpolar distribution, as do Hultén (1937) and Deevey (1949), nor to emphasize that "der Terminus 'amphiatlantische Arten' in faunagenetischer Hinsicht gegenstandslos wird" (Reinig, 1937, p. 22). Dispersal across the sea is no negligeable part of faunal and floral history.

The theories of earlier transatlantic land-connections

The Iceland—Greenland bridge

It may seem inconsistent, after the existence of a biologically efficient land-connection between Europe and North America has been denied or at least considered highly improbable, to raise again the problem of a "land-bridge" within the North Atlantic region. Land-bridges, however, are not bound to join *continents*, they may be, or have been, "blinds" connecting islands to a mainland.

Perhaps the situation is best made clear to the reader in the form of a brief account, brought up to date, of the zoogeographical conclusions to which the present writer arrived (1931) from a study of the insect fauna of Iceland, all the more as later students have agreed, at least in the essentials.

The fauna of *Iceland* is practically purely European, the American element being restricted to some few species: the Noctuid Moths *Crino sommeri* Lef., *Crymodes exulis* Lef., *Rhyacia (Caradrina) quadrangula* Zett. (figs. 36–38), and the Gnat ("Black Fly") *Simulium vittatum* Zett. (fig. 39), all of them no doubt able to arrive by air under present conditions. Possibly the Empidid Fly *Rhamphomyia hirtula* Zett. (Greenl., Icel., Scotl.) belongs to the same group. The Icelandic form of the Water-beetle *Colymbetes dolabratus* Payk., *thomsoni* Sharp, is decidedly more related to the sbsp. *groenlandicus* Aubé, of Greenland and North America (Brinck, 1940, p. 37–40) and must likewise have invaded Iceland from a western direction, by air or with drifting ice. The same is true for a genuine fresh-water animal, the small Copepod *Diaptomus minutus* Lilljeb., a Nearctic species, known also from Greenland (Poulsen, 1939, p. 29).

Even among breeding *birds*, only three Icelandic species are of clearly Nearctic origin: *Bucephala islandica* Gm., *Gavia (Colymbus) immer* Brünn., and *Histrionicus histrionicus* L. (Timmermann, 1938–49, p. 123).

As far as *vascular plants* are concerned, *Epilobium (Chamaenerium) latifolium* L. and two Orchids, *Habenaria (Leucorchis) hyperborea* L. and *H. (L.) straminea* Fern., belong to an American element (the last-named also reaching the Faeroes). All of them have seed excellently suited for wind-transport. Löwe (1950) has added some forms of doubtful taxonomic position, including polyploids, the historical interpretation of which is most delicate since a polyphyletic origin cannot be dismissed.

In all, this is a poor share of American inhabitants indeed for an island situated 900 km. or more from the British Islands and Scandinavia, but only 330 km. from Greenland which, in its turn, is separated from southern Baffin Island by the

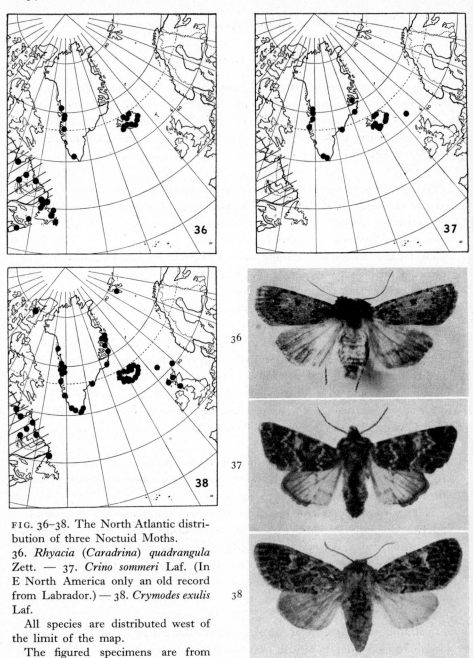

FIG. 36–38. The North Atlantic distribution of three Noctuid Moths.
36. *Rhyacia* (*Caradrina*) *quadrangula*
Zett. — 37. *Crino sommeri* Laf. (In
E North America only an old record
from Labrador.) — 38. *Crymodes exulis*
Laf.

All species are distributed west of
the limit of the map.

The figured specimens are from
Greenland.

(Photo P. ARDÖ.)

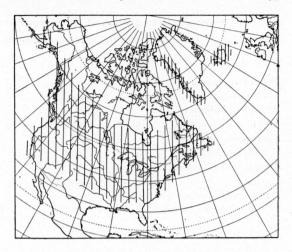

(Photo P. Ardö.)

FIG. 39. Approximate distribution of *Simulium vittatum* Zett., a species of gnat or "black fly", a regular nuisance to man and cattle.

Mainly according to A. Stone (*in litt.*) who thinks the species may be a complex one. The figured specimen is from Greenland.

only slightly wider Davis Strait (350 km.). The Nearctic element of the Icelandic insect fauna is less than one per cent!

On the *Faeroes*, as a matter of course, it is still more insignificant, consisting only of two of the Noctuid Moths just mentioned, *Crino sommeri* and *Crymodes exulis*, and, among animals other than insects, of the freshwater Sponge *Heteromeyenia ryderi* Potts, treated above (p. 245).

The fauna of *Greenland*, however, provides the great surprise within the chain of islands across the North Atlantic. This large island, almost a continent of more than 2 million square kilometers, though to more than four fifths covered with ice, traditionally belongs to America. Actually, the shortest distance to the North American mainland, in northern Labrador, is little more than half (750 km.) of the distance to the European continent, in northern Norway (1,400 km.).

The American influence on the Greenlandic fauna, as on its flora, is quite obvious but it is far from dominating. Above all it is striking how unequally large is this element among different groups of animals. In those sufficiently known and large enough to allow a comparative analysis, the share of the different geographical groups is as follows: —

256 CHAPTER III

Representative groups of the terrestrial Greenlandic fauna

(species and subspecies; obviously introduced forms omitted)

	Total	Holarctic	Palaearctic	Nearctic	Endemic
Birds (Salomonsen & Gitz, 1950)	68	30 = 44 %	9 = 13 %	18 = 27 %	11 = 16 %
Macro-Lepidoptera (Henriksen, 1939)	26	14 = 53 %	3 = 12 %	9 = 35 %[1]	—
Coleoptera (ditto; Vibe, *in litt.*)	24	7 = 29 %	11 = 46 %	6 = 25 %[2]	—
Collembola (Hammer, 1953)	46	27 = 59 %	13 = 28 %[3]	5 = 11 %	1 = 2 %
Araneae (Braendegaard, 1946, & Holm, *in litt.*)	50	21 = 42 %	11 = 22 %[3]	11 = 22 %[4]	7 = 14 %
Together	214	99 = 46 %	47 = 22 %	49 = 23 %	19 = 9 %

If the 16 endemic subspecies of *birds* are distributed among the three other geographical groups, according to their relation to other subspecies (Salomonsen & Gitz, 1950), the figures are:

37 Holarctic,   12 Palaearctic,   19 Nearctic forms

= 54 %   = 18 %   = 28 %

If, furthermore, the 7 Spiders and the single Collembol, unknown outside Greenland, are counted as Nearctic, which they probably are, the 214 species and subspecies of the list include:

106 Holarctic,   50 Palaearctic,   58 Nearctic forms

= 50 %   = 23 %   = 27 %

This means that, provided the selected groups are accepted as representative, *the terrestrial fauna of Greenland consists of one half Holarctic, and one fourth each of Nearctic and Palaearctic forms* (species and subspecies).

Before considering the fascinating question of the *reasons* for the peculiar zoogeographical character of Greenland, and the North Atlantic islands on the whole,

---

[1] Included are *Byrdia* (*Dasychira*) *groenlandica* Wocke, found in the Canadian Arctic according to Dr. Munroe (*in litt.*), and *Rhyacia* (*Euxoa*) *drewseni* Stdgr., the occurrence of which in North America proper is not quite settled (McDunnough, 1950, p. 396); furthermore, *Spaelotis* (*Amphitrota*) *clandestina* Harr. (*unicolor* Wlk.), recorded also from E Siberia but represented in N Europe by sbsp. *suecica* Aur.

[2] Including *Micralymma brevilingue* Schiø. and *Coccinella transversoguttata* Fald., occurring in Siberia but not in Europe.

[3] Including two species (*Sminthurus concolor* Mein. and *Collinsia thulensis* Jacks.) outside Greenland known from Spitzbergen only.

[4] Including *Islandiana princeps* Braend., outside Greenland known from Iceland only.

it seems appropriate to make a closer inspection of their *beetle* faunas (tab. 7, diagr. 7). We are now in a far more favourable position than in 1931, since at least a preliminary survey has been made of the Coleoptera of Baffin Island (Brown, 1937). This insect order, even from other points of view, is well suited as starting-point. It is tolerably numerous in species, even in northern regions, and, above all, it contains many flightless, not easily dispersed forms which may, in their present distribution, reflect faunal history with unusual clarity.

The detailed facts concerning the coleopterous fauna included in table 7 and diagram 7, give very clear evidence as to the zoogeographical character of Greenland. It appears that the purely *Palaearctic* element is not only quantitatively dominant (11 species), but that it furthermore contains the following *flightless* species with consequently reduced powers of dispersal:

Nebria gyllenhali f. typ.	*Otiorrhynchus arcticus* (fig. 41)
Lathrobium fulvipenne	*O. dubius*
Quedius boops	*Phytonomus elongatus.*

TABLE 7. Beetles (Coleoptera) of the Faeroes, Iceland, Greenland, and Baffin Island, regarded as indigenous, with a summing-up of their distribution in other parts of the Holarctic area.

(+) = introduced. — *a*, *b*, and *c* = different subspecies; *ab* or *bc* = both subspecies, or intermediates.

In the first column, **m** = macropterous (wings full), **b** = brachypterous (wings reduced), **(b)** = wings full, or almost so, but probably non-functionary (incl. dimorphic forms occurring in the brachypterous form only), **d** = dimorphic (both forms represented, also within the area considered).

The limit between E and W North America is supposed to run through Hudson Bay and Mississippi. Ditto between W and E Siberia is River Yenisei.

All species stated or believed to be introduced into the four island areas considered have been excluded. A division of this kind is in part a matter of personal judgment, yet the rather rigorous discharge here practised at any rate has not over-dimensioned the European element. Students interested in the species thus omitted are referred, for the Faeroes to West (1939)[1], for Iceland to Lindroth (1931)[2], for Greenland to Henriksen (1939)[3], for Baffin Island to Brown (1937).

[1] For the Faeroes, the only additional species is *Otiorrhynchus rugosostriatus* Gze. (S. G. Larsson, *in litt.*), probably introduced from the British Islands.
[2] Many imported beetles, but apparently only one native species, *Gymnusa brevicollis* Payk., have been collected since 1931 (S. G. Larsson, *in litt.*). The North American *Phymaphora pulchella* Newm. (Lindroth, 1931, p. 219) was no doubt reported by a pure mistake.
[3] For the recent discovery in Greenland of *Caenoscelis ? cryptophaga* Reitt. and *Dorytomus sp.* we are indebted to Mr. C. Vibe who kindly made the specimens available to me.

	State of wings	E. Sib.	W. Sib.	Scand.	Brit. Isl.	Faeroes	Iceland	Greenl.	Baff. & Ellesm. L.	E. N. Am. (E. of Huds. Bay)	W. N. Am. (W. of Huds. Bay)
	1	2	3	4	5	6	7	8	9	10	11
Carabidae											
Amara alpina F. (fig. 40)	(b)	ab	a	a	a	—	—	—	b	b	b
A. aulica Panz..	m	—	+	+	+	+	—	—	—	(+)	—
A. quenseli Schnh.	m	+	+	+	+	—	+	—	—	+	+
Bembidion bipunctatum L.	m	—	+	+	+	+	+	—	—	—	—
B. grapei Gyll.	d	+	+	+	—	—	+	+	—	+	+
B. redtenbacheri K. Dan.	m	—	—	—	+	+	—	—	—	—	—
Calathus fuscipes Gze.	b	—	—	+	+	+	—	—	—	—	(+)
C. melanocephalus L.	(b)	+	+	+	+	+	+	—	—	—	—
Carabus problematicus Hbst.	b	—	—	+	+	+	+	—	—	—	—
Cymindis unicolor Kby.	b	—	—	—	—	—	—	—	+	+	+
Dichirotrichus pubescens Payk..	m	—	—	+	+	+	—	—	—	—	—
Harpalus quadripunctatus Dej.	m	+	+	+	+	+	—	—	—	—	—
Loricera pilicornis F.	m	+	+	+	+	+	—	—	—	+	+
Nebria gyllenhali Schnh.	(b)	ab	a	a	a	a	a	a	—	b	b
N. nivalis Payk.	(b)	ab	a	a	a	—	—	—	b	b	b
N. salina Fairm.	(b)	—	—	+	+	+	—	—	—	—	—
Notiophilus aquaticus L.	(b)	+	+	+	+	+	+	—	—	+	+
N. biguttatus F.	d	—	—	+	+	+	+	—	—	(+)	—
Olisthopus rotundatus Payk.	d	—	—	+	+	+	—	—	—	—	—
Patrobus assimilis Chd.	b	—	—	+	+	+	—	—	—	—	—
P. atrorufus Ström	b	—	+	+	+	+	+	—	—	—	—
P. septentrionis Dej.[1]	m	+	+	+	+	+	+	+	—	+	+
Pterostichus adstrictus Eschz..	m	+	+	+	+	+	+	—	—	+	+
P. arcticola Chd.	b	—	—	—	—	—	—	—	+	+	—
P. diligens Sturm	(b)	+	+	+	+	+	+	—	—	—	—
P. haematopus Dej.	(b)	+	+	—	—	—	—	—	+	+	+
P. nigrita F.	m	+	+	+	+	+	+	—	—	—	—
Trechus fulvus Dej.	b	—	—	+	+	+	—	—	—	—	—
T. obtusus Er.	b	—	—	+	+	+	+	—	—	—	(+)
Trichocellus cognatus Gyll.	m	+	+	+	+	+	+	+	—	+	+

Taxonomical remarks, 1–8.

1. The North American *Patrobus septentrionis* Dej. is not consistently so different from the Eurasian nominal form as previously assumed (Lindroth, 1955 a, p. 84). Only the New-foundland population seems to deserve a subspecific name. Ample series from Labrador, Greenland, Iceland, and Scandinavia, have convinced me that the punctuation of head and

	1	2	3	4	5	6	7	8	9	10	11
Haliplidae											
Haliplus fulvus F. (excl. *lapponum* Thoms.)	m	—	+	+	+	+	+	—	—	—	—
Dytiscidae											
Agabus congener Payk. (coll.)	m	+	+	+	+	—	—	—	+	+	+
A. moestus Curt.	m	—	—	—	—	—	—	—	+	+	+
A. solieri Aubé	m	—	—	+	+	+	+	—	—	—	—
Colymbetes dolabratus Payk.	m	a	a	a	—	—	b	b	b	b	b
Deronectes multilineatus Falkstr.	m	+	+	+	+	+	—	—	—	+	+
Hydroporus erythrocephalus L.	m	+	+	+	+	+	—	—	—	—	—
H. lapponum Gyll.	m	+	+	+	—	—	—	—	+	+	+
H. melanocephalus Mrsh.	m	+	+	+	+	—	—	+	+	+	+
H. memnonius Nic.	m	+	+	+	+	+	—	—	—	—	—
H. nigrita F.	m	—	+	+	+	+	+	—	—	—	—
H. palustris L.	m	—	+	+	+	+	—	—	—	—	—
H. polaris Fall	m	—	—	—	—	—	—	—	+	—	+
H. pubescens Gyll.	m	—	+	+	+	+	—	—	—	—	—
Gyrinidae											
Gyrinus opacus C. R. Sahlb.	m	a	a	a	a	—	—	b	—	b	bc
Hydrophilidae											
Anacaena globulus Payk.	m	—	+	+	+	+	—	—	—	—	—
Cercyon litoralis Gyll.	m	—	—	+	+	+	+	—	—	(+)	—
Helophorus aquaticus L.	m	—	+	+	+	+	—	—	—	(+)	—
H. arcticus Brown	m	—	—	—	—	—	—	—	+	—	+
H. brevipalpis Bed.	m	—	—	+	+	+	—	—	—	—	—
H. flavipes F.	m	—	+	+	+	+	—	—	—	—	—
Megasternum boletophagum Mrsh.	m	—	—	+	+	+	—	—	—	—	(+)
Liodidae											
Hydnobius punctatus Sturm	m	+	+	+	+	+	—	—	—	—	—
Scydmaenidae											
Stenichnus collaris M. & K.	b	—	—	+	+	+	+	—	—	—	—

prothorax, more pronounced in the North American material, is a variable character even within geographically limited populations.

2. For the taxonomy of *Atheta hyperborea* Brd. and *islandica* Kr., *vide* Brundin (1943, p. 15–19).

3. *Boreaphilus nearcticus* Blair. Two ♀♀ from Baffin Island (Mus. Ottawa) were compared with the original specimens of *nordenskiöldi* Mäklin (1878, p. 25; 1881, p. 42) from Siberia,

	1	2	3	4	5	6	7	8	9	10	11
Staphylinidae											
Acidota crenata F.	m	+	+	+	+	—	+	—	—	+	+
Aleochara obscurella Gr. . . .	m	—	—	+	+	+	—	—	—	—	—
Amischa analis Gr.	m	—	+	+	+	+	+	—	—	(+)	(+)
Arpedium brachypterum Gr. .	(b)	+	+	+	+	+	—	—	—	?	—
Atheta atramentaria Gyll. . .	m	+	+	+	+	+	+	—	—	—	—
A. excellens Kr.	m	+	+	+	+	+	+	—	—	—	—
A. fungi Gr.	m	+	+	+	+	+	+	+	—	+	+
A. graminicola Gr.	m	+	+	+	+	+	+	—	—	+	+
A. hyperborea Brd.[2]	m	—	—	+	—	—	—	+	—	—	—
A. islandica Kr.[2]	m	—	?	+	?	+	+	+	—	—	—
A. melanocera Thoms. . . .	m	+	+	+	+	+	+	—	—	—	—
A. vestita Gr.	m	—	—	+	+	+	+	—	—	—	—
Autalia puncticollis Sharp . .	m	—	—	+	+	+	—	—	—	—	(+)
Boreaphilus nearcticus Blair[3] .	b	—	—	—	—	—	—	—	+	+	—
Bryoporus sp.[4]	m	—	—	—	—	—	—	—	+	+	—
Cafius xantholoma Gr.. . . .	m	—	—	+	+	—	+	—	—	—	—
Geodromicus globulicollis Zett..	m	—	—	+	+	—	+	—	—	—	—
Gnypeta cavicollis J. Sahlb. .	m	—	+	—	—	—	—	+	—	—	—
Gymnusa brevicollis Payk. . .	m	—	+	+	+	—	+	—	—	+	+
Lathrobium fulvipenne Gr. . .	b	+	+	+	+	+	+	+	—	—	—
Lesteva longelytrata Gze. . .	m	—	—	+	+	+	+	—	—	—	—
Micralymma brevilingue Schiø.[5]	b	+	+	—	—	—	—	+	+	—	+
M. marinum Ström (fiig. 32) .	b	—	—	+	+	+	+	+	—	+	—
Ocalea picata Steph.	m	—	—	+	+	+	+	—	—	—	—
Omalium laeviusculum Gyll. .	m	—	—	+	+	+	+	—	—	—	—
O. riparium Thoms.	m	—	—	+	+	+	+	—	—	—	—
Othius melanocephalus Gr. . .	b	—	—	+	+	+	+	—	—	—	—
O. myrmecophilus Kies. . . .	b	—	—	+	+	+	—	—	—	—	—
O. punctulatus Gze..	m	—	+	+	+	+	—	—	—	—	—
Oxypoda islandica Kr. . . .	m	—	+	+	+	—	+	—	—	—	—
O. soror Thoms.	b	—	—	+	+	—	+	—	—	—	—
Philonthus trossulus Nordm. .	m	—	—	+	+	—	+	—	—	—	—
Quedius boops Gr.	(b)	—	+	+	+	+	+	+	—	—	—

Mesenkin and Sopotshnoj Island, and with a series from Tolstoinos (J. Sahlberg, 1880, p. 106); all localities on the eastern side of the Yenisei estuary. Though I was unable to study the ♂ genitalia, it seems clear from external characters that the species, though closely related, as already supposed by Blair (1933, p. 95), are not identical. The vertex is excavated behind the eyes in *nearcticus* and this concavity has a strong, striated sculpture. In *nordenskiöldi*, the vertex is truncate towards the contracted neck.

4. The "*Mycetoporus sp.*" of Brown (1937, p. 110), according to the single specimen (Mus. Ottawa), is a *Bryoporus* of a species not occurring in Europe but related to *rugipennis* Pand. It is possibly *rufescens* Lec. and I have ventured to mark the distribution as "E. North America".

5. *Micralymma brevilingue* Schiø. A comparison between ample series of this species,

	1	2	3	4	5	6	7	8	9	10	11
Q. fuliginosus Gr.	(b)	—	+	+	+	+	—	—	—	—	(+)
Q. fulvicollis Steph.	(b)	—	+	+	+	+	+	—	—	+	+
Q. nitipennis Steph.	b	+	+	+	+	+	—	—	—	—	—
Q. umbrinus Er.	b	—	—	+	+	+	+	—	—	—	—
Sipalia circellaris Gr.	b	—	+	+	+	+	+	—	—	—	—
Stenus brunnipes Steph. . . .	b	—	—	+	+	+	—	—	—	—	—
S. canaliculatus Gyll.	m	—	+	+	+	—	+	—	—	+	+
S. carbonarius Gyll.	b	—	+	+	+	—	+	—	—	—	—
S. clavicornis Scop.	m	—	+	+	+	+	—	—	—	—	—
S. coarcticollis Epp.	b	—	+	+	+	—	+	—	—	—	—
S. impressus Germ.	m	—	—	+	+	+	—	—	—	—	—
S. nanus Steph. (coll.). . . .	m	—	+	+	+	—	+	—	—	?	—
S. nitidiusculus Steph.	b	—	—	+	+	+	—	—	—	—	—
Tachinus corticinus Gr. . . .	b	—	+	+	+	—	+	—	—	—	—
T. rufipes DeG.	m	+	+	+	+	+	—	—	—	(+)	(+)
Tachyporus atriceps Steph. .	m	—	+	+	+	+	—	—	—	—	—

Pselaphidae

	1	2	3	4	5	6	7	8	9	10	11
Bythinus puncticollis Denny (*validus* Aubé)	b	—	—	+	+	—	+	—	—	—	—

Cantharidae

	1	2	3	4	5	6	7	8	9	10	11
Malthodes mysticus Kies. . .	m	+	—	+	+	—	+	—	—	—	—
M. pumilus Bréb. . . . . . (*atomus* Thoms.)	m	—	—	+	+	+	+	—	—	—	—

Elateridae

	1	2	3	4	5	6	7	8	9	10	11
Hypnoidus riparius F.	m	—	+	+	+	+	+	—	—	—	—

Helodidae

	1	2	3	4	5	6	7	8	9	10	11
Helodes minuta L.	m	—	—	+	+	+	—	—	—	—	—

Byrrhidae

	1	2	3	4	5	6	7	8	9	10	11
Byrrhus fasciatus Forst. . . .	m	+	+	+	+	+	+	+	—	+	+
Cytilus sericeus Forst.	m	—	+	+	+	+	+	—	—	+	+
Simplocaria tessellata Lec.[6] . .	m	—	—	—	—	—	—	+	—	+	+
S. semistriata F.	m	—	—	+	+	+	—	—	—	(+)	—

Crytophagidae

	1	2	3	4	5	6	7	8	9	10	11
Caenoscelis? cryptophaga Reitt.[7]	m	—	—	—	—	—	—	+	—	+	—

including "types" from Greenland (Mus. Copenh.) and Brown's specimens from Baffin Island (Mus. Ottawa), and of *dicksoni* Mäkl. from arctic Siberia, 11 localities, between the mouth of River Yenisei and St. Lawrence Bay in the Bering Strait (Swed. Riksmus.), has convinced me that they all belong to one species. The differences from *brevilingue* mentioned

	1	2	3	4	5	6	7	8	9	10	11
Coccinellidae											
Coccinella transversoguttata Fald.	m	+	+	—	—	—	—	+	—	+	+
C. 11-punctata L.	m	+	+	+	+	—	+	—	—	(+)	+
Scymnus limonii Donis.	m	—	—	+	+	—	+	+	—	—	—
Scarabaeidae											
Aphodius lapponum Gyll.	m	+	+	+	+	+	+	—	—	—	—
Chrysomelidae											
Chrysomela staphylea L.	b	b	a	a	a	a	a	—	—	(a)	—
Phyllodecta polaris Sp.-Schn.	m	—	—	+	—	—	+	—	—	—	—
Curculionidae											
Apion cruentatum Walt.	b	—	—	+	+	+	+	—	—	—	—
Barynotus squamosus Germ.	b	—	—	+	+	+	+	—	—	(+)	—
Dorytomus taeniatus F.	m	+	+	+	+	—	+	+[8]	—	—	—
Lepyrus labradorensis Blair	b	—	—	—	—	—	—	—	+	+	—
Notaris aethiops F.	m	+	+	+	+	+	—	—	—	+	+
Otiorrhynchus arcticus O. Fbr. (fig. 41)	b	—	—	+	+	+	+	+	—	—	—
O. atroapterus DeG.	b	—	—	+	+	+	—	—	—	—	—
O. dubius Ström	b	—	—	+	+	+	+	+	—	—	—
O. rugifrons Gyll.	b	—	—	+	+	—	+	—	—	(+)	—
Phytonomus elongatus Payk.	b	—	+	+	+	—	—	+	—	—	—
Ph. pedestris Payk.	b	—	—	+	+	—	+	—	—	—	—
Sciaphilus asperatus Bonsd.	b	—	—	+	+	—	+	—	—	(+)	—
Strophosomus melanogrammus Först.	b	—	—	+	+	—	+	—	—	(+)	—
Tropiphorus obtusus Bonsd.	b	—	—	+	+	+	+	—	—	(+)	—

by Mäklin (1881, p. 42) for *dicksoni:* the broader 5th and the narrower 9–10th antennal segments, shorter elytra, and more shining abdomen, are by no means constant. The ♂ genitalia seems to be almost identical, though the penis (median lobe) is slightly shorter, more parallelsided and with blunter apex in Greenland specimens. The species (*dicksoni*) has also been reported from the Pribilof Islands off Alaska (*vide* Leng, Suppl. I, 1927) and thus apparently has a high-arctic circumpolar distribution. Mr. W. O. Steel, Maidenhead, Berks., who is revising the genus, informs me that probably two or three subspecies are involved, the population of the Pribilof Islands likewise deviating in some minor points.

6. *Simplocaria.* The Greenland species is apparently the North American *tessellata* Lec., according to a series from Churchill, Man. (det W. J. Brown, Mus. Ottawa), and not identical with the European *metallica* Sturm. The species are very closely related but in *tessellata* the pilosity of elytra is a little denser, forming more contrasting dark and light spots. The penis (median lobe) is slightly slenderer and a trifle more enlarged towards apex, the denticles along the sides in front of the flattened apex are more pronounced; but these differences are so slight that it is easily understood why Székessy (1936, p. 101) could declare the genitalia of Greenlandic and European ♂♂ as identical. — Apparently two species (other than *remota*

Brown) were confused under *"tessellata"* in North America. At least specimens from New-foundland belong to a third species.

7. *Caenoscelis.* Through the courtesy of Mr. Vibe I have been able to study 3 specimens collected by him in Greenland. They agree with the descriptions of *cryptophaga* Reitt. (1875, p. 87; 1911, p. 66). A comparison with a typical specimen (from "North America") would however be desirable. In Casey's key (1900, p. 104–107) they run to *macilenta* Csy. (New York, Penns.) which is probably a synonym. At least I have ventured to give the distribution as "E. North America".

8. After the above was set up for print the Greenland *Dorytomus* has proved to be distinct from *taeniatus* and probably a Nearctic species.

The *Nearctic* element (including two Holarctic species lacking in Europe) amounts to 6 species only:[1]

Colymbetes dolabratus groenlandicus	*Caenoscelis ? cryptophaga*
Gyrinus opacus blairi	*Simplocaria tessellata*
Micralymma brevilingue	*Coccinella transversoguttata*

Of these only the *Micralymma* is flightless. It inhabits the tidal zone and is no doubt easily dispersed by sea-water drift (cf. *M. marinum*, p. 244).

This point of view provides a satisfactory explanation for the unequal share of Nearctic species in Greenland within the different groups of animals to which attention was drawn above. They are most numerous in *Macro-Lepidoptera* (35 per cent) and *Birds* (28 per cent), with more or less developed powers of *active flight*, in the second place among *Spiders* (22 per cent, or 36, if "endemic" species are included), with their common habit of "ballooning" into the air. But in *Collembola* (Spring-tails) the Nearctic species amount to 11 per cent only, considerably less than in Coleoptera. Among comparatively able flyers, as the *Trichoptera* (Caddies-flies), 6 of 9 (or 10) species are Nearctic (Henriksen, 1939, p. 23–24; Vibe, 1950) but the *Neuroptera* (Lace-wings), with poorly developed powers of flight, are represented by one Holartic and two Palaearctic species.

The composition of the coleopterous fauna of *Baffin Island* is in complete accordance herewith. Of the 16 species[2] known so far from this island (Brown, 1937), only three species are common also to Greenland: the Water-beetles *Colymbetes dolabratus groenlandicus* and *Hydroporus melanocephalus*, both good flyers, and the Staphylinid *Micralymma brevilingue*, just mentioned as easily

---

[1] After the above was written, the *Dorytomus* from Greenland has proved to be a probably Nearctic species, different from *taeniatus* F. (*vide* table 7). It is fully winged.

[2] From Ellesmere Island in the high north (between about 76° and 83° north) only 5 species of Coleoptera are reported (Brown, 1937, and *in litt.*). Two, of the genera *Cryptophagus* and *Enicmus*, are accidental importations and the *Quedius "fulgidus"*, according to earlier practice of nomenclature within the genus, is no doubt *mesomelinus* Mrsh., a true synanthrop, common in the dwellings of the West Greenland esquimos. The two remaining species are *Micralymma brevilingue* Schiø. and one *Atheta*, which has been investigated by Dr. Brundin, who informs me that it represents a species unknown to him, possibly undescribed (unfortunately a female), and thus almost certainly a Nearctic element.

dispersed by sea-drift. The remaining 13 species, 7 of them lacking the power of flight (*vide* table 7), have been unable to get across to Greenland.

The character of the interjacent sea as a faunistic obstacle is best illustrated by maps of two functionally brachypterous species, the Ground-beetle *Amara alpina brunnipennis* Dej. (fig. 40) and the Weevil *Otiorrhynchus arcticus* O. Fbr. (fig. 41), both widespread on either side. It can be stated, without any exaggeration, that, *within the Arctic of the entire northern circumpolar area, the comparatively narrow strait between Baffin Island and Greenland has constituted the most effective barrier to the dispersal of soil-bound animals.* The Bering Strait has been far more sur-mountable (below, p. 293). Though it should of course be admitted that Green-land is a zoogeographical transition between the Palaearctic and Nearctic regions, this island—if a choice is necessary—must be regarded as Palaearctic (a good reason for continued Danish government!).

How is this surprising extension of the European fauna over the islands of the North Atlantic to be explained?

In the first place it must be stated that the possibilities of passive dispersal (and at least for the soil-bound, flightless fauna this is the effective agency) would seem to favour an *eastward* transport across the Atlantic. Not only the Gulfstream follows this course (fig. 32), the predominating winds are also western[1] and the barometric minima developed off the northeastern coast of North America, not-withstanding all irregularity too well-known to meteorologists, move eastward. Williamson (1954) has given good evidence for how stray birds on migration may be sluiced across from North America by the aid of subsequent minimum pressures (fig. 34). In exceptional cases, provided a minimum becomes immobilized to the south of Iceland (Lindroth, 1931, p. 524, fig. 42), favourable, mainly southeastern winds may last long enough to make air-borne transport at least theoretically possible, for instance from the British Isles to the Faeroes or Iceland. Salomonsen (1951) has shown quite convincingly how a wind-driven flock of Field-fares (*Turdus*

---

[1] The air movements at high altitude may be different from the winds immediately above the earths surface. Meteorological balloons, usually travelling above 20 kilometers, have crossed the Atlantic in both directions. In Europe, the summer winds at this altitude are usually eastern (Scherhag, 1948, p. 77 a. f.) but rather slow. The biogeographical consequences of transported air-plankton is a question of survival, which should be tested experimentally.

DIAGR. 7. Species of Coleoptera common to the Faeroes, Iceland, Greenland and Baffin Island, and selected regions of the Holarctis.

White = flying; black = flightless species.

Dimorphic species counted as flightless where (entirely or partially) represented by the short-winged form. — Different subspecies treated as species.

Summary of table 7.

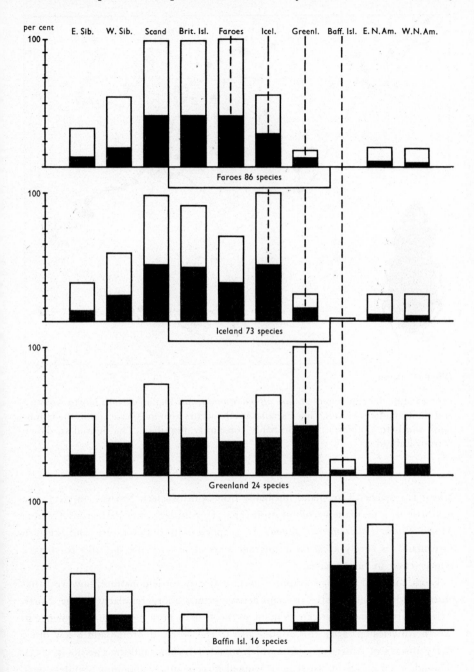

per cent

E. Sib. W. Sib. Scand Brit. Isl. Faroes Icel. Greenl. Baff. Isl. E. N. Am. W. N. Am.

Faroes 86 species

Iceland 73 species

Greenland 24 species

Baffin Isl. 16 species

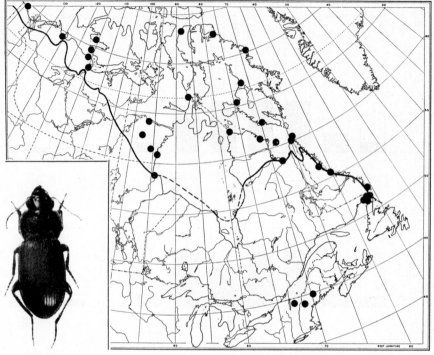

(Photo P. ARDÖ.)

FIG. 40. The distribution of *Amara alpina brunnipennis* Dej. in eastern North America and the Canadian Arctic. This Carabid beetle occurs also in Alaska and in the mountains south to Colorado. It is probably constantly flightless. The figured specimen is from Labrador.

pilaris L.) reached Greenland, probably from southwestern Norway, in 1937, and gave rise to a permanent colonization (fig. 42). Similarly, the Palaearctic Gamma Moth, *Plusia (Phytometra) gamma* L., captured in both eastern and western Greenland, is surely a casual immigrant since it is normally not able to survive winter even in Scandinavia.

From zoo- and phytogeographical facts it is easy to demonstrate, however, that *eastward* dispersal, passive or semi-active, occurs more regularly in the North Atlantic area. The American element in the British flora has little equivalence in North America (p. 251), this applies also to the Noctuid Moths and a few other flying insects of American origin which invaded Iceland and the Faeroes (p. 253). Though several Nearctic species of winged insects and "ballooning" spiders have

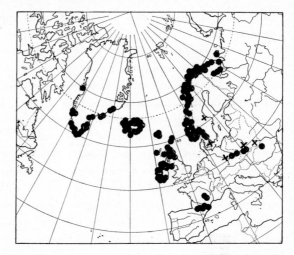

(From HOLDHAUS, 1924.)

FIG. 41. Distribution of the Weevil *Otiorrhynchus arcticus* O. Fbr., a flightless, sluggish, soil-bound insect with bisexual reproduction, and therefore not easily spread. The larva is subterraneous and feeds, like the imago, on various plants. Crosses = subfossils, earlier than Postglacial.

reached Greenland (p. 263) no Palaearctic species, as far as is known, have arrived in Baffin Island from the opposite direction.

To my mind, only two possibilities remain which, separately or by joint action, may account for the dominance of Palaearctic, in part strictly European, species in the faunas of Iceland and Greenland.

In the *first* place, *transport with man* may be responsible. Actually, voices have been raised to the effect that practically the entire lower terrestrial fauna of Iceland (*vide* Lindroth, 1931, p. 507) and the European element of the Greenlandic fauna and flora (Stephensen, 1921; Ostenfeld, 1926; Jensen, 1928) were introduced with the early Norse colonists and it cannot be doubted that human transport from Europe has played an important role in the composition of the fauna of these islands.

As far as Coleoptera are concerned, I have tried to exclude from the list above (table 7) all species for which this may be true, according to their choice of habitat &c., but it is of course by no means impossible that other species also, not at all connected with human culture, may have been brought over, by pure chance, for instance, in the Greenlandic fauna: *Atheta fungi* Gr. (60°59′–61°13′), *Lathrobium fulvipenne* Gr. (only one specimen known), *Quedius boops* Gr. (60°–62°), and *Scymnus limonii* Donis. (3 specimens in the extreme south), which are not found north of the old Norse colonization area (for this, *vide* "Atlas", 1921).

A removal of these species, however, does not appreciably change the zoogeo-graphical character of the island and I am completely unable to accept the idea that, for instance, the culture-avoiding, wingless, sluggish, and, contrary to the majority of species within the genus, obligatorily *bisexual* Weevil *Otiorrhynchus arcticus* O. Fbr. (fig. 41) should have been introduced into Greenland or Iceland (Lindroth, 1931, p. 514–515). Also, Porsild (1932) has published weighty argu-ments against the opinion of Ostenfeld, and others, that man is responsible for the European element of vascular plants in Greenland.

The trade from Europe to Iceland and Greenland from oldest times had a character essentially different from that with Newfoundland and the present Mari-time Provinces of Canada. From the very first time after discovery, the firstnamed island possessed a permanent population badly in need of all kinds of necessities (provisions, timber, metals, &c.) and there was certainly no use of ballast on the outward voyage. Consequently, the experiences gained from the study of the New-foundland trade (p. 154 a.f.) have no application at all to the naval connections of the northern islands. This explains why several species, for instance *Notiophilus biguttatus* F., *Amischa analis* Gr., *Coccinella 11-punctata* L., *Barynotus squamosus* Germ., *Otiorrhynchus rugifrons* Gyll., *Sciaphilus asperatus* Bonsd., *Strophosomus melanogrammus* Först., and *Tropiphorus obtusus* Bonsd., in table 7 are regarded as introduced in eastern North America, but as indigenous in Iceland, where they occur, in part or entirely, in the most inaccessible parts of the coast.

The most weighty objection to the opinion that the European element of the faunas of Iceland and Greenland was imported with man is the large amount of species *in common* among the species here regarded as indigenous.

From table 7 and diagr. 7, regarding *Coleoptera*, the following figures can be extracted: —

Of 11 native Palaearctic species in Greenland, 8 (73 %) are common also to Iceland.
Of 11 native Palaearctic species in Greenland, 6 (55 %) are common also to the Faeroes.
Of 56 native Palaearctic species in Iceland, 38 (68 %) are common also to the Faeroes.

The *introduced* species[1] of the same islands show a different picture: —

Of 23 introduced Palaearctic species in Greenland, 10 (43 %) are common also to Iceland.
Of 23 introduced Palaearctic species in Greenland, 9 (39 %) are common also to the Faeroes.
Of 99 introduced Palaearctic species in Iceland, 32 (32 %) are common also to the Faeroes.

---

[1] The records of introduced species among the Coleoptera of Greenland are from Hen-riksen (1939, p. 43–48), of Iceland from Lindroth (1931, p. 171–236) and S. G. Larsson (*in litt.*).

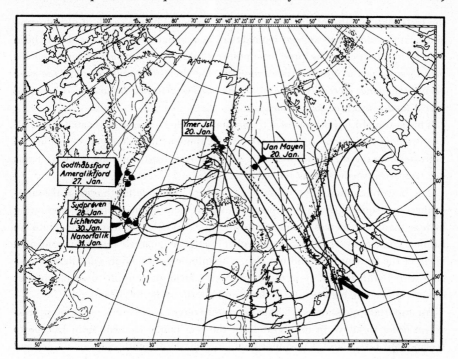

FIG. 42. Wind-drift of Fieldfares (*Turdus pilaris* L.) to Greenland in January, 1937.

Black circles = observed specimens. Broken line = probable course of flight.

Unbroken line = isobars of January 19 1937 (at 7 p.m.). Arrows = wind direction.

(From SALOMONSEN, 1951).   (From ROSENBERG, Fåglar i Sverige.)

A similar calculation, and with similar results, was carried out on the *Collemboles* of Iceland and the Faeroes (Lindroth, 1931, p. 516).

The accidental nature of introduction is thus clearly demonstrated. If this holds true for the unquestionably imported species with a more or less pronounced synanthropic habitat, how much more due to chance would not human transport be of species indifferent to or rather avoiding the neighbourhood of man! Yet within this latter faunal element the species common to the North Atlantic islands are *more*, not *less* numerous. This is the clearest possible proof that their presence is *not* due to human agencies.

We have thus rejected the idea that the pronouncedly European character of the Icelandic, but also of the Greenlandic fauna could be the result of introduction alone. At the same time we have denied that the said native element could have been able to immigrate during present conditions, with the extension of land and sea now existing in the North Atlantic region. One alternative only remains: *the main part of the fauna, especially of its soil-bound members, reached Iceland and Greenland over a land-connection now submerged.*

This is the old hypothesis of a transatlantic bridge, eagerly advocated above all by Sharff (1907, 1909, 1911), but with the fundamental divergence that it did not extend to the mainland of North America or at least, for some reason, it was not faunistically effective as far west.

The bottom configuration of the sea is rather favourable for the rise of the land-connection required (fig. 43). A positive displacement of the shore-line amounting to less than 600 meters would transform the Wyville-Thomson ridge into an isthmus connecting Iceland and Greenland with the enlarged European continent north of the present Scotland but also, it should be pointed out, *via* Ellesmere Island with Baffin Island. It would require very little more uplift to shape another direct connection between Greenland and southern Baffin Island.

An important question is whether an *un-interrupted* connection would be necessary in order to allow an immigration of the said faunal element from Europe to Iceland and Greenland. Considering its large share of flightless forms, in Iceland 26 species of 56 (46 per cent), in Greenland 6 of 11 (55 per cent), constituting the Palaearctic element, the answer seems to be in the affirmative. Ocean water of more than 30 pro mille salinity causes physiological desiccation of a terrestrial animal (Palmén, 1944, p. 155 a.f.; Lindroth, 1949, pp. 600, 613). Furthermore, the heavy Weevils, such as *Otiorrhynchus arcticus* O. Fbr., perhaps the zoogeographically most important member of the Iceland-Greenland fauna (fig. 41), soon are sunk to the bottom by the lapping waves (Lindroth, 1931, p. 485). Even the Channel, only 31 km. at its narrowest, constitutes a marked faunistic barrier (Lindroth, 1949, p. 613), though the British Isles were connected with the mainland in early postglacial times. The unbridgeable obstacle to flightless insects formed by the Davis Strait has just been demonstrated.

When it comes to *dating* the existence of the assumed Scotland-Greenland bridge a biologist is largely up in the air. This much is certain, however, from geological evidences: it cannot have persisted in late glacial or postglacial times. On the other hand, the faunas of Iceland and Greenland bear no sign of long isolation. Proposed endemic species all belong to insufficiently investigated animal groups, such as Diptera, Hymenoptera and Hemiptera Homoptera among the insects. The Coleoptera and Macrolepidoptera of these islands do not even contain clearly defined endemic *sub*species. Such, it is true, have been established among Mammals

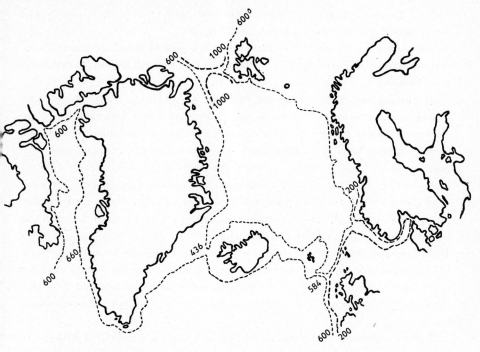

FIG. 43. The bottom configuration of the North Atlantic. The detailed figures give greatest depth of the ridge or plateau between the islands.

(From LINDROTH, 1931, supplemented by Dr BÖRJE KULLENBERG, Gothenburg, *in litt.*)

and Birds, especially of the Greenland fauna, but there is clear evidence in favour of the view that subspecies formation is often a rapid procedure among Vertebrates. The development into new "subspecies" of the Varying Hare, *Lepus timidus* L., and the House-Mouse, *Mus musculus* L., on the Faeroes, both introduced with man (Degerbøl, 1940), is a good illustration.

By a process of elimination we thus arrive at the opinion that the land connecting Greenland and Iceland with Europe must have existed in Pleistocene time and before the last glaciation (Würm, Wisconsin). This is also supported by the present distribution of the Icelandic fauna which clearly indicates survival of most of its indigenous members within two isolated glacial refuges in the south and southeast (fig. 46; Lindroth, 1931, pp. 489 a.f., 557–563).

Another remarkable fact is the discovery, in a fossiliferous *interglacial* layer in SW Iceland, of insect rests belonging to 6 species of Coleoptera (*Nebria gyllenhali* Schnh., *Patrobus septentrionis* Dej., *Pterostichus diligens* Sturm, *Agabus solieri*

Aubé, *Tachinus corticinus* Gr., *Byrrhus fasciatus* Forst.),[1] all of them members of
the present Icelandic fauna (Thorkelsson, 1935).

The powers which may have affected displacement of the shore-line in favour
of the extension of land in the North Atlantic area are eustatic, isostatic, and tectonic
movements.

(a) *Eustatic* movements of the sea, implying a world-wide change of the water
volume of the oceans, in Pleistocene time were caused first and foremost by the
glaciations. Part of the precipitation was stored on land in the form of glaciers and
thus withdrawn from the oceans, the level of which sank correspondingly. Cal-
culations of the vertical amount to which this happened are, as a matter of course,
highly diverging. They depend entirely on the estimated simultaneous volume
of all glaciers of the world during a certain phase of a glaciation. For the maximum
of the *last glaciation* (Würm, Wisconsin) the figures are usually given as something
between 90 and 100 meters (Zeuner, 1950, p. 129; WOLDSTEDT, 1954, p. 289).
During the last but one, the *"great glaciation"* (Riss, Illinoian), the regression of the
sea must have been more extensive but it cannot have amounted to more than one
fourth of the vertical distance necessary for realizing the postulated Scotland-
Greenland bridge. It may have contributed to its rise but was not alone responsible
for it.

Eustatic regression of the sea is perfectly and positively connected with glaciation (seen from a global point of view). Though this did not necessarily have its
maximum extension contemporaneously everywhere in the Northern Hemisphere,
countries situated as far north as Iceland and Greenland can never have remained
climatically unaffected by the ice during a glacial period. This means that, if eustatic regression has played a part in the existence of the Scotland-Greenland bridge,
this must have been realized during a period of arctic or at least subarctic climate on
the islands considered. This assumption may seem tempting because, if so, the
faunistic barrier between Greenland and Baffin Island could be explained as a
barrier of ice. Facts, however, argue against this. The coleopterous fauna of
Iceland contains one single arctic species, the Water-beetle *Colymbetes dolabratus*
Payk., immigrated from a western direction. The rest of the indigenous fauna is
boreal, not even subarctic; many of its members do not ascend to timber limit
anywhere on the earth. Among the Coleoptera of Greenland there are only two
Palaearctic species, the Staphylinids *Atheta hyperborea* Brund. and *Gnypeta cavi-
collis* J. Sahlb., which may be termed arctic; both are winged.

A satisfactory explanation of these conditions is found only in the assumption
that *the Scotland-Greenland land-bridge existed during a time of boreal climate* and

---

[1] In addition unidentified fragments of a *Hydroporus*, not living in Iceland of today.

eustatic movements of the sea have therefore played at most a quite inferior role in its formation.

(b) *Isostatic* movements are local and due to ice-pressure during periods of glaciation. In the central part of an inland ice they may amount to more than 200 meters, for instance in Scandinavia. If Greenland were cleared of ice, it would undoubtedly rise to a considerable degree but, as we have learned from investigations in Scandinavia, the "isobase 0", the line of equilibrium, with no postglacial upheaval and, consequently, no previous glacial down-pressure, runs close to the former ice-margin, or even inside it. The rise would affect only the immediately surrounding sea-bottom.

An increase of the Greenlandic inland-ice, on the other hand, and a contemporaneous ice-cap over Iceland, would possibly cause a slight upheaval of the interjacent sea-bottom but involve very little isostatic effect on the almost three times as long sea-bed between Iceland and Scotland. The proposed land-bridge could not arise, or even become considerably favoured, by isostatic movements.

(c) The possible influence of *tectonic* movements and *volcanic* activity remains to be considered.

Iceland is a country with still vividly living volcanic powers. In comparatively recent time, geologically speaking, these have been active within a much wider area. Basalt of the same kind as that which built up the frame of the Icelandic plateau occurs in parts of East Greenland, on the Faeroes, on some of the Inner Hebrides, and in northeastern Ireland. Certain fossiliferous layers of this system in Iceland, the Faeroes and Ireland have been regarded as homologous and contemperaneous. It is generally assumed that these now widely separated basalt occurrences are only remnants of a former continuous land, formed through volcanic eruptions in Tertiary time, from Eocene and onwards. Soon after its rise, this mighty basalt plateau became subject to violent tectonic movements and eventually was broken down to present conditions.

Geologists apparently are not able to answer the question most important to a biogeographer: at what time was the connection broken and the present isolation of these islands definite? According to Thoroddsen (1914), Iceland was already a separate island at the beginning of the Pliocene. Later geological students have thought that Thoroddsen generally overestimated the age of Icelandic geological formations but the current view seems to presume that the Tertiary transatlantic basalt isthmus was broken down almost to a definite extent before Pleistocene time.[1]

---

[1] Dr. Sigurdur Thorarinsson, the wellknown Icelandic geologist, informs me, however, (*in litt.*) that to his mind no definite facts seem to argue against the possibility that the Tertiary land-bridge persisted into part of the Pleistocene period.

Since the eustatic and isostatic movements of the shore-line in Pleistocene time apparently were insufficient to create a bridge connecting Greenland and Iceland with Europe, as described above, it is tempting to think of a prolonged persistence of the Tertiary basalt plateau into part of the Pleistocene. The absence of undoubtedly endemic species, and even true subspecies, in the insect fauna of Iceland and Greenland prevents the acceptance of survival *in situ* since Tertiary (Pliocene) time. Considering this, the present author (Lindroth, 1931, p. 550–557) arrived at the conclusion that the proposed land-connection most probably should be dated to the last (Riss-Würm) interglacial period.

Facts contradicting this view have since appeared in the form of the discovery of fossiliferous deposits in Central Sweden from the said period. The included insects (Lindroth, 1948) give evidence of a climate at least as warm as the present one during part of the Riss-Würm Interglacial in Scandinavia and this cannot be considered in accordance with a situation implying that the Gulfstream was prevented by a land-bridge from entering the Norwegian Sea[1].

It should also be considered in this connection that the fauna of Iceland is originally boreal, *not* arctic, the few exceptions (*Colymbetes dolabratus*, &c.) being easily dispersed animals independent of any land-connection. The invasion of this boreal fauna therefore took place in the warm middle part of some interglacial period. Such a violent oscillation, from one stage: "land-bridge, blockade of Gulfstream",—to another: "land-bridge sunk, 200 meters at least, Gulfstream free passage",—cannot be accepted to have taken place in a time so short as the temperate phase of an interglacial period.

It seems that a "removal" of the land-bridge one step further back in time, to the last but one Interglacial (Mindel-Riss), is the most likely solution. From a biological point of view, the difficulty in accepting this idea seems to me to lie not so much in the lack of endemics in Iceland-Greenland, as in the necessity of accepting survival in these islands through *two* subsequent glaciations, the first of them being the severe Riss.

Yet if the land-bridge existed in the Mindel-Riss Interglacial, the climatic influence of the dislocated Gulfstream, at least on Iceland, ought to have been highly increased and these favourable conditions may have lasted during part of the following Riss glaciation.

There is one special reason to think that in Iceland, to a lesser degree also in Greenland, local conditions may have been favourable enough, even during Riss, to make a survival possible: *the presence of volcanic hot springs*. Tuxen (1944, p. 189–199) has discussed this question and rightly concludes that a field of hot

---

[1] *Vide* also the table of climate and vegetation during the last interglacial period in Denmark by Jessen & Milthers (1928, p. 336).

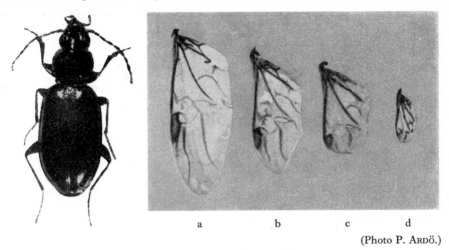

a   b   c   d

(Photo P. ARDÖ.)

FIG. 44. *Bembidion grapei* Gyll., a Carabid beetle showing polymorphism of the hind-wings. Types a–b are counted as macropterous, c–d as brachypterous. — Icelandic specimens.

springs, whatever its effect otherwise, will never be able to withstand an approaching land-ice. But thermal activity, in Iceland often giving the springs a temperature above boiling-point, may considerably ameliorate the loco- and microclimatical conditions of a possible ice-free refuge.

This opinion is confirmed by the occurrence of a Carabid beetle, *Bembidion grapei* Gyll., in Iceland. It shows dimorphism or, rather, polymorphism with respect to the hind-wings: in some specimens these are full and no doubt functioning (2 specimens were found in wind-drift material in Finland; Palmén, 1944, p. 37), in others they are more or less reduced and cannot be used (fig. 44). Breeding experiments with another Carabid beetle, *Pterostichus anthracinus* Ill. (Lindroth, 1946) have shown that the phenomenon has a heriditary base, "short wing" being a dominant. The full-winged individuals are therefore homozygotes and owing to their superior powers of dispersal usually form a genetically pure zone at the periphery of the species' area. At any rate, predominance of short-winged specimens is characteristic of *old* populations.

Possibly more than one gene mutation is involved in the case of *Bembidion grapei* (fig. 44), since different stages of wing-reduction occur, but the macropterous individuals also in this species are homozygotes, as is quite evident from the distribution in Fennoscandia (Lindroth, 1949, p. 401–405). The brachypterous form is predominant along the Norwegian coast, within the area of ice-free refuges

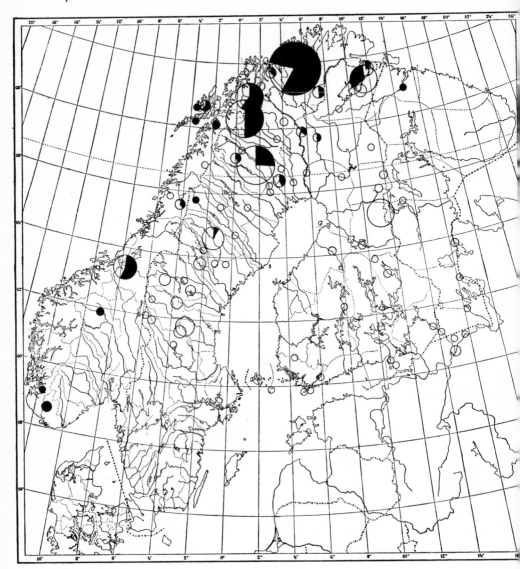

FIG. 45. Distribution of long-winged (white) and short-winged (black) specimens of the Carabid beetle *Bembidion grapei* Gyll. (fig. 44) in Fennoscandia. Cf. legend of fig. 14 (p. 153).

The occurrence of the short-winged form indicates survival on ice-free refuges of the western and northern coast during the last glaciation.

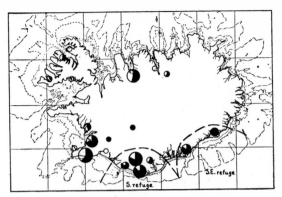

FIG. 46. Distribution of long-winged (white) and short-winged (black) *Bembidion grapei* Gyll. (fig. 44) in Iceland. The two main refuge areas during the last glaciation are indicated. Cf. fig. 45.

during last glaciation (Würm), whereas a purely macropterous population inhabits the eastern parts of Sweden and almost all of Finland (fig. 45).

Iceland is too small an area to have retained, in any part of the island, a purely macropterous population. The postglacial period has been sufficiently long to allow a universal colonization of the brachypterous form as well, and no obstacle comparable to the mountain range of Scandinavia has prevented its dispersal. The geographical distribution of the two forms (fig. 46) therefore, at first glance, seems rather confused and due to chance. That is not the case, however. The brachypterous form is most marked within two areas, around the Eyjafjallajökull in the extreme South and along the coastal margin of the Vatnajökull in the Southeast, which for other reasons are regarded as the main refuges during the Würm-glaciation (Lindroth, 1931, p. 489 a.f.). The index macropterous: brachypterous is here 0.2 and 0.1, respectively. For the rest of the island this figure is 0.7, slightly less in the Southwest, 0.6; in the North 0.9, in the isolated northwestern peninsula 1.5.

The interesting contribution to our present discussion is that in Iceland, outside the two main refuge areas, there is a marked contrast in the occurrence of the brachypterous form of *Bembidion grapei* in the immediate vicinity of *hot springs*, as compared with other localities. Apparently the species is favoured by the warm conditions. One would expect, then, that the hot springs would absorb in the first place the most easily dispersed individuals from the mixed populations of the surroundings and that consequently the macropterous form would be in the majority around them.

The exact opposite is the case. The index macropt.: brachypt. for individuals from the vicinity of hot springs is 0.3, for all others (outside the two refuge areas of the South), 1.3 (diagr. 8).

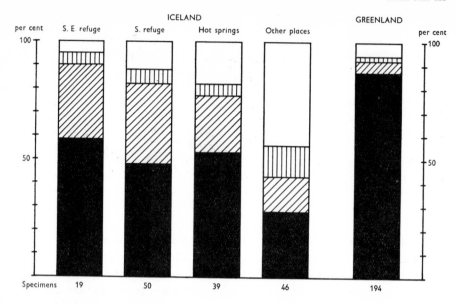

DIAGR. 8. *Bembidion grapei* Gyll. Distribution of four types of hind-wings (a–d, fig. 44) among four types of habitats in Iceland and in Greenland. White = full-winged; black = strongest wing-reduction.

In accordance with the current interpretation of the distribution of wing-dimorphic forms, the most likely explanation is that the surroundings of hot springs are inhabited by *old populations*. The index in favour of brachypterous forms is almost the same as for the two large refuge areas in southern Iceland. To my mind, this argues in favour of an assumption that, locally, small populations of terricolous animals were able to survive the last glaciation also in other parts of the island in the immediate neighbourhood of hot springs. For one of these localities, Krisuvík in the Southwest, where *Bembidion grapei* (25 specimens) shows an index of 0.5, the assumption of a glacial "micro-refugium" is confirmed by the isolated occurrence of the Staphylinid beetle *Othius melanocephalus* Gr., one of the most undoubted "survivors" of the Icelandic fauna (Lindroth, 1931, p. 484 a.f.).

In *Greenland, Bembidion grapei* occurs almost exclusively in the brachypterous form (fig. 47; diagr. 8). Apparently selection has been strongly in favour of flightless individuals in small, isolated populations, particularly during times when glaciation was more total than at present. A location of refuges based on the distribution of *Bembidion grapei* seems impossible but it should be mentioned that a large series of 65 exclusively short-winged individuals from Julianehaab in the South-west is from the vicinity of the most famous hot springs of Greenland.

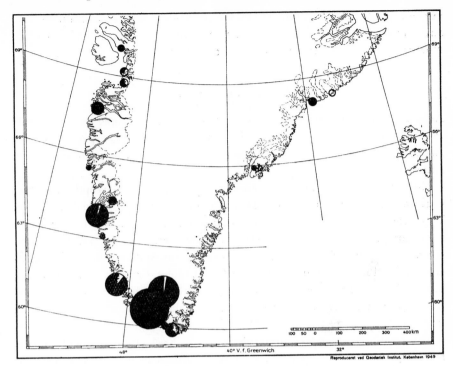

FIG. 47. Distribution of long-winged (white) and short-winged (black) *Bembidion grapei* Gyll. (fig. 44) in Greenland. Most of the few long-winged specimens are found near the periphery of the species' area, in the north and the south.

The best criterion for the existence of the Scotland-Greenland bridge during any of the interglacial periods would be the discovery of contemporaneous deposits in Scandinavia indicating an arctic climate contrasting with temperate, or warmer, conditions in central and western Europe. Until then the dating of this land-connection, which from a biogeographical point of view seems inevitable, must probably be postponed.

Meanwhile it is highly desirable that botanists reconsider the problems of "Westarctic" and other Amphiatlantic plants, and also of the Greenland flora, from a more realistic point of view. Above all these ought to be treated by careful investigation, including experiments, of seeds and other diaspores, in order to get a clear idea of their different modes of dispersal. Speculations founded exclusively on maps of distribution, as now often happens, do not give satisfactory results. In this way, botanists would also be able to approach the real nature of a possible high-arctic route of migration, Greenland–Spitzbergen, assumed by some authors (for instance Hansen, 1930, p. 226; Nordhagen, 1935, p. 157), to which zoologists seem to be unable to make a contribution.

Affinities in the south

Animal distribution shows a few spectacular instances of subtropic or "low boreal" forms indicating faunistic relationship between the southern parts of North America or the West Indies and Europe, including adjacent regions of North Africa and western Asia.

Usually the forms in question are not identical. Possible exceptions are two Carabid beetles, *Nomius pygmaeus* Dej. and *Blethisa eschscholtzi* Zoubk., and one Wood-louse (Terrestrial Isopod), *Tylos latreilli* Ad. & Sav. The latter inhabits the epilittoral zone of the sea-shore of the Mediterranean region and the Atlantic coast, north to central France, south to Dakar; on the American side, Florida, Atlantic Central America, the Bermudas and West Indies. Contrary to Vandel (1945, p. 229), I find the most probable explanation of this disjunct area to be introduction with ships from Europe into America. The habitat of the species quite invites transport.

The Centiped *Theatops erythrocephalus* C. L. Koch, from southern Europe, mentioned by Schmidt (1946, p. 145) as indigenous in western U.S.A., is no doubt introduced in the latter area.

One would perhaps feel inclined to apply the same view to *Nomius pygmaeus*, the more so since, in North America, it has repeatedly been observed in villages and towns, even indoors, as a famous "stink beetle". In the Old World it is a grand rarity and the assumption just mentioned would then necessarily imply introduction *from* North America. This, however, has become less probable since Basilewsky (1954) has described a very closely related species, *N. schoutedeni* Basil., from Ruanda Urundi in the interior of Belgian Congo. Now *Nomius* belongs to a quite isolated group (usually termed Tribus) among the Carabidae, the few genera of which have a pronouncedly disjunct, obviously relict, distribution, with several representatives in Australia (Emden, 1936, p. 50–51; Jeannel, 1941, p. 290–292). It may be suggested that not only subtribes and genera of this group, but also the actually existing species, are very old and the present distribution of *Nomius pygmaeus* may be regarded as a disjunct relict area which in itself gives no clue to the history of the species.

The same may be true for *Blethisa eschscholtzi* (fig. 56). One single specimen is known from North America, vicinity of Sanderson, SW Texas, but there seems to be no reason to doubt the correctness of the locality label or the indigenous

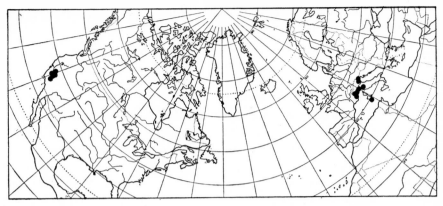

FIG. 48. World distribution of the Salamander genus *Hydromantes*, in California *H. platycephalus* Camp., in Europe *H. genei* Schleg. (*Spelerpes fuscus* Schreib.). The figured specimen is of the Californian species (from Stebbins, 1951).

occurrence on this far inland spot. Otherwise it is restricted to the steppe region north of the Caspian Sea and of western Siberia. *B. eschscholtzi* is the most primitive member of the genus *Blethisa* (Lindroth, 1945b, p. 13) and Semenov (1935, p. 275) regarded it as a "relictum faunae tertiariae elementum". It is an old species with disjunct relict area.

Among *Vertebrates*, the affinities in the south between Europe and North America are restricted to common *genera*, or higher taxonomic units. The most conspicuous cases are the following: —

Fam. *Umbridae*, fresh-water fishes, named Mud-minnows, with genus *Umbra*, has two species in North America and one in Europe, *U. krameri* Wahlb. (*lacustris* Gross), restricted to the basin of the Danube.

Among *Salamanders* (*Urodela*) there are two links suggesting a connection. — (1) The famous *Olm*, *Proteus anguineus* Laur., a true inhabitant of the karst-caves of SE Central Europe, possesses its closest relatives in the Mud Puppies, genus *Necturus*, with 7 free-living species in eastern North America. —(2) The *Plethodontidae*, abundant in North America, but lacking in Asia, are represented in Europe (SE France, N Italy, Sardinia) only by a species of *Hydromantes*, *genei* Schleg. (*Spelerpes fuscus* Schreib.), with two subspecies (Mertens & Müller, 1940,

p. 13). The genus occurs nowhere else on the earth, except in California (fig. 48), where the Mount Lyell Salamander, *H. platycephalus* Camp., is restricted to the Boreal zone of Sierra Nevada (Stebbins, 1951, p. 146).

The well-known genus *Emys*, among fresh-water *Turtles*, contains only two species, *orbicularis* L. of Europe, North Africa and Hither Asia, and *blandingi* Holbr., of central and eastern North America.

During present conditions a dispersal across the Atlantic of these Vertebrates, unable to endure salt water, is out of the question, except with the aid of man, and this again would be an absurd idea since in no case the same, only related species occur on both sides.

Similar instances of related, but not identical, animals of a southerly Amphiatlantic distribution are more numerous among Invertebrates but it is sufficient to mention a few examples.

Darlington (1934, p. 86–88) discovered and described two species of the Carabid genus *Perileptus*, from Cuba and Jamaica, a most surprising event since this was known as an entirely Old World genus and, moreover, the two species belonged to the *areolatus* group, confined to Europe, North Africa and the Macaronesian Islands; two further species were subsequently described from Hispaniola (Haiti) and Puerto Rico (Darlington, 1935). A quite similar distribution is recorded for the otherwise Old World Carabid genera *Stylulus*, with the species *nasulus* Schauf. on the island of St. Thomas, and *Lymnastis*, with two species in Cuba and Guatemala.

These cases were stressed by Jeannel (1937, p. 356 a.f.) as evidence of an earlier land-connection between the West Indies and the Mediterranean region. Darlington (1938) has strongly opposed this view. To his mind, all of them (or their ancestors) have been carried across to America with the trade winds. Though this may be true for *Perileptus* and *Lymnastis*, being constantly or (*Lymnastis*) individually long-winged, I cannot agree that this possibility exists for the flightless, blind *Stylulus*, subterranean in habit. The almost constantly very restricted distribution of the individual species of subterranean beetles, for instance in the Alps, where there are often heavy "Föhn"-winds, shows that their powers of dispersal are extremely poor. On the other hand, they are among the most difficult insects to collect and I am quite convinced that the *actual* distribution of genera and higher groups of subterranean Carabidae is known only in fragments. It should also be observed that the single West Indian species of *Stylulus* hitherto known belongs to a subgenus of its own.

However, Darlington is certainly right in rejecting Jeannel's idea of land-connection, and his suggestion that small *flying* Carabids may be carried by air currents at high altitudes was strongly confirmed by the investigations of "aerial plankton" by Glick (1939, p. 29–30), as only small species, of the genera *Bradycellus* (*Steno-cellus*), *Micratopus*, *Microlestes* (*Blechrus*), *Tachystodes*, and *Tachys*, were captured at 5,000 feet or higher, one specimen of *Microlestes pusio* Lec. (less than 2 mm.) at 10,000 feet.

Vandel (1945) has drawn attention to the almost Amphiatlantic distribution of the genera *Porcellio* and *Metaponorthus* and some other Terrestrial Isopods, and regards this (p. 265–266) as a proof of Wegenerian connection. His maps show, to my mind, that the world distribution of Wood-lice, notably in southern and eastern Asia, is not yet sufficiently investigated to allow for conclusions of this kind.

Jeannel (1942, p. 115) regards the Palpigrad Arachnid genus *Koenenia* as a case of direct transatlantic faunal exchange. Since one species is known also from Siam (Kästner, 1932, p. 98), this argument has lost its force.

The Cockroach (*Blattodea*) genus *Arenivaga* contains three subgenera, *Arenivaga s. str.* being strictly American (southern U.S.A., Mexico), whereas subgg. *Psammoblatta* and *Heterogamisca* are chiefly Mediterranean (S Europe, N & E Africa, Hither Asia). Bey-Bienko (1950, p. 300–323), who made a rearrangement of the genus, regards its distribution (p. 302) as the result of a direct contact, in Wegener's sense, across the present Atlantic, but the occurrence of species of *Psammoblatta* as far east as Baluchistan, Afghanistan and West Turkestan makes this assumption somewhat adventurous.

The *Oleacinidae*, a family of terrestrial Gastropod Molluscs, is restricted to America north to southern U.S.A., and the Mediterranean region (Pilsbry, 1946, p. 188). However, it is a very old type, known in fossil state right back to Upper Cretaceous of Europe, and it must be assumed that the family has undergone great, still unknown changes of area during the course of the Tertiary.

It is not surprising, with the above examples in mind, that several of the earlier zoogeographers, especially, have tried to explain this type of disjunct distribution by the assumption of some kind of land-connection also within the southern parts of the North Atlantic, usually thought to have joined the Iberian Peninsula and North Africa with the present West Indies (*vide* Scharff, 1911, pp. 173, 214, 220, 271 a.f., fig.14). Ihering (1927, pp. 26, 220) even boldly constructed one of "his" bridges, the "Archatlantis", exclusively for the convenience of Sirenians of the genus *Trichechus*, inhabitants of the sea, though as a rule, at least, of brackish water (*vide* Holdhaus, 1927–28, p. 1051). In later years the supporters of land-connections in this part of the Atlantic have usually been pronounced Wegenerians who in cases of distributional pattern of the type exemplified above find biological evidence in favour of the hypothesis of continental drift (*vide* next paragraph).

Yet it seems to me that there is no need at all for a land-connection to explain the cases here treated. We have to realize that they indicate an *old* contact, only in some few insects expressed through identity of *species, nota bene,* of a primitive and no doubt old type, otherwise in genera and families in common, and that we must go well back in Tertiary time for an explanation. Great faunal changes indeed have taken place since then.

This may be illustrated by an example. The *Cryptobranchidae* among the Salamanders are represented in the recent fauna of the earth only by the well-known "Giant Salamander", *Megalobatrachus maximus* Schleg., of China and Japan, and *Cryptobranchus alleghaniensis* Daud. from the Mississippi basin. But the European fossils from Miocene referred to genus *Andrias* (the famous *A. scheuchzeri* Tschudi, "*Homo diluvii testis*", and others), according to Herre (1935, p. 48), are generically, possibly even specifically, identical with the still living *Megalobatrachus.* Supposing the contrary had happened, that the European form had happened to survive but the East Asian had become extinct and no fossil remains discovered, —and we would have had a perfectly Eur-American family of Salamanders, with several false theories as a consequence.

The Baltic amber of Europe, usually considered of late Eocene age, contains numerous examples of genera, families or higher taxonomic categories, particularly of insects, now absent from the continent or even from the entire Holarctic region, examples of which are given below. As argued by Darlington (1948, p. 2 a.f.), recession and extinction plays a role equal to evolution and spreading in faunal history, and extinction usually starts with the division of one large area into small, separate ones.

The Amphiatlantic animals of the more southern type here treated apparently all have entered this stage of recession. They are remnants of a large, though not necessarily contemporaneous, area across the Asian continent. Thus I can add very little to the views expressed by Matthew (1915), Reinig (1937), Schmidt (1946), Simpson (1947), Darlington (1948), and others.

The present distribution of these animals is of pronounced relict character and necessitates no other change in extension of the present continents than the unanimously accepted Bering land bridge.

Wegener—pro and contra

The hypothesis of continental drift was in part based on biogeographical data by Wegener himself (1929, p. 99–124) and subsequent students accepting his idea have often used examples of animal distribution as confirmation.

Several zoologists and some botanists at first more or less enthusiastically accepted the theory, for instance Michaelsen (1922), Jaschnow (1925), Brehm (1926), Herre (1935), and others; among botanists, Böcher (1938), Steffen (1941), Walter (1954, p. 53 a.f.); *vide* also "Atlantisheft" (1939). In later years the critical voices have been in the majority but some zoologists are still ardent supporters. Thus, Modell (1943) thinks there is evidence for a Tertiary transatlantic connection in Wegenerian sense from the fossil Mollusc fauna of Europe, but the facts brought forth by him are quite in accordance with the late Tertiary European flora, as investigated by Szafer (1954), which needs no such explanation (below, p. 310).

His most loyal advocate among zoogeographers Wegener has found in Jeannel who, in a long series of books and papers, the most comprehensive being that of 1942, has tried to explain any imaginable pattern of animal distribution as the result of continental drift.

Jeannel's method is not one of science, but of faith. He simply "believes" in Wegener and, refusing to discuss any other explanation, makes "dogmatic statements with no distinction between fact and opinion". The last citation is from Darlington's excellent review (1949) of Jeannel's *"Genèse des Faunes Terrestres"* (1942), to which the interested reader is referred.

Since, according to Wegener (1929, p. 20), the Atlantic was the ocean latest formed and the continents bordering its northern part were the last to separate (in Pliocene or even Pleistocene time), one would expect to find particularly clear evidence of direct faunal exchange between Europe and North America, provided the theory is true. But this is not so.

As shown on preceding pages of this chapter, the number of Eur-American animal species lacking in Asia, which cannot easily be explained either by human transport or as the result of dispersal across the Atlantic under conditions similar to those of the present day, is so exceedingly small that any idea of general contact between the European and American faunas in Pleistocene or Late Tertiary time is sharply contradicted, other than through Asia and the present Bering Strait. This has already been pointed out, in part, by Økland (1927, pp. 361, 363) but, according to him, facts speak in favour of the "bridge theory". Actually, not even the assumption of a late (Pleistocene), complete transatlantic land-bridge, only of one joining Greenland and Iceland with the mainland of Europe, seems to be a zoogeographical necessity.

It must be frankly admitted that several single biogeographical facts would be more *easily* understood by resorting to Wegener's theory of continental drift: i.e., the distribution of the genera *Hydromantes* (p. 281) and *Umbra* (p. 281), of *Cepaea hortensis* O. F. Müll. (p. 234 a.f.) and *Tylos latreilli* Ad. & Sav. (p. 280), provided, in the latter cases, the idea of introduction has to be abandoned. But why should the (superficially regarded) *simpliest* explanation always be the true one? Widely scattered relict occurrences (*Hydromantes*, *Umbra*, &c.), usually a step towards extinction, do not necessarily imply earlier connection *at shortest distance*, the fossils often showing us the contrary.

It is questionable if, from the stand-point of a biologist, there is any need at all for transatlantic land-connection in *any* geological period. Simpson, on palaeo-zoological evidence, first (1940, p. 149) postulated "the inference of a wide-open corridor" between Europe and North America in the Lower Eocene but later (1947, pp. 658–659, 666, Footnote) regarded a substituting Pacific connection during this period as at least equally probable.

Whether the theory of continental drift is true, is a problem for geologists and geophysicians. The only contribution that can be delivered by a biogeographer is the declaration that, at least as far as the North Atlantic area is concerned, the continental drift, if considered a reality, took place in so early a period that its biological consequences cannot be traced. Also, the annual rate of drift supposed by Wegener for the North Atlantic is extravagantly high (Zeuner, 1950, p. 355).

Circumpolar animals

The word "Circumpolar" should not be interpreted too literally. No animal species inhabits all continents and islands surrounding the North Pole. The concept is here used to cover species occurring in the northern parts of Europe, Asia and North America without conspicuous interruptions of area. The term "Holarctic" is not a synonym because it only means that a species is indigenous in both the Palaearctic and the Nearctic region, without any demand for continuity. Yet all Circumpolar species are, of course, Holarctic at the same time.

Another question is how pronounced northerly a species' area is bound to be in order to be called Circumpolar. The "Circumtropical" species, such as the Dragonfly *Pantala flavescens* F. (Rensch, 1950, p. 136, fig. 109), must be excluded. A subtropical animal distributed round the earth at least belongs to either Hemisphere and may be included here, but the instances of this geographical type are so few that their placing has almost no interest.

As a matter of fact, the zonation of the circumpolar species from north to south, as well as vertically in the mountains, reveals interesting features. Carabid beetles are sufficiently known in this respect to serve as an illustration. The distribution of the 45 known circumpolar species among the vegetation belts as defined by Scandinavian botanists (*vide* Lindroth, 1949, p. 436–448), and corresponding zones of Asia and North America, is shown in table 8.

The table 8 gives clear evidence that the *subarctic* (subalpine) region contains

TABLE 8. Circumpolar Carabid beetles and their distribution among the climatically determined zones of vegetation.

Species with incomplete circumpolar area in brackets.[1]
Cross in brackets indicates rare, and perhaps not regular, occurrence.
The first column gives the state of the hind-wings, according to the following categories: **m** = macropterous (probably flying); **b** = brachypterous (flightless, doubtful cases in brackets); **d** = dimorphic (both forms represented within the species).

	Wings	Regio arctica			Reg. sub-arctica	Reg. coni-ferina	Reg. quer-cina	Southern regions
		superior	media	inferior				
gonum bogemanni Gyll.	m	—	—	—	+	+	+	—
consimile Gyll.	m	—	—	+	+	(+)	—	—
A. exaratum Mnh.)	m	—	—	+	+	—	—	—
mannerheimi Dej.	d	—	—	—	+	+	(+)	—
quadripunctatum DeG.	m	—	—	—	+	+	+	+
thoreyi Dej.	m	—	—	—	+	+	+	+
mara alpina Payk.	(b)	+	+	+	+	(+)	—	—
erratica Dft.	m	—	+	+	+	+	—	—
hyperborea Dej.	m	—	—	+	+	+	—	—
A. interstitialis Dej.)	m	—	—	—	+	+	(+)	—
lunicollis Schiø.	m	—	—	(+)	+	+	+	+
quenseli Schnh.	d	—	+	+	+	+	+	+
torrida Ill.	m	—	—	+	+	+	—	—
Bembidion dauricum Mtsch.)	d	—	—	+	+	—	—	—
grapei Gyll.	d	—	—	+	+	+	(+)	—
hasti C. R. Sahlb.	m	—	+	+	+	(+)	—	—
B. hyperboraeorum Munst.)	m	—	—	+	+	(+)	—	—
lapponicum Zett.	m	—	—	+	+	(+)	—	—
obscurellum Mtsch.	m	—	—	—	+	+	+	—
petrosum Gebl.	m	—	—	—	+	+	—	—
quadrimaculatum L.	m	—	—	—	—	+	+	+
transparens Gebl.	d	—	—	—	+	+	+	+
B. yukonum Fall)	d	—	—	+	+	—	—	—
lethisa multipunctata L.	m	—	—	—	+	+	+	+
alathus micropterus Dft.	b	—	—	+	+	+	+	+
Carabus truncaticollis Eschz.)	b	+	+	+	(+)	—	—	—
iachila arctica Gyll.	m	—	—	+	+	+	—	—
polita Fald.	b	—	+	+	+	—	—	—
yschirius helléni J. Müll.	b	—	—	+	+	+	—	—
laphrus lapponicus Gyll.	m	—	—	+	+	+	(+)	—
riparius L.	m	—	—	+	+	+	+	+

[1] The following species are possibly circumpolar though their distribution is insufficiently known: *Bembidion crenulatum* F. Sahlb., *B. mckinleyi* Fall, *Dyschirius politus* Dej.

	Wings	Regio arctica			Reg. sub-arctica	Reg. coni-ferina	Reg. quer-cina	Southern regions
		superior	media	inferior				
(*Harpalobrachys leiroides* Mtsch.)	m	—	—	+	+	+	—	—
Harpalus fuliginosus Dft. . .	m	—	—	+	+	+	+	+
(*H. nigritarsis* C. R. Sahlb.) .	m	—	—	+	+	+	—	—
Miscodera arctica Payk. . . .	m	—	+	+	+	+	+	+
Nebria gyllenhali Schnh. . .	(b)	(+)	+	+	+	+	+	+
N. nivalis Payk.	(b)	+	+	+	(+)	—	—	—
Notiophilus aquaticus L. . . .	d	+	+	+	+	+	+	+
Patrobus septentrionis Dej. . .	m	+	+	+	+	+	—	—
Pelophila borealis Payk. . . .	m	—	(+)	+	+	+	(+)	—
Pterostichus adstrictus Eschz. .	m	—	—	+	+	+	(+)	—
P. brevicornis Kby.	b	—	—	+	+	+	—	—
(*P. vermiculosus* Mén.) . . .	b	+	+	+	+	—	—	—
Tachyta nana Gyll.	m	—	—	—	(+)	+	+	(+)
Trichocellus cognatus Gyll. . .	m	—	—	+	+	+	+	+
Total 45 (36) species	—	6+(1)	12+(1)	33+(1)	44+(2)	33+(5)	17+(6)	13+(1)

most circumpolar species, actually all but one (*Bembidion quadrimaculatum* L.).
The unwooded *arctic* (alpine) zone is inhabited by 33 (or 34) species, that is 73
(or 76) per cent, the *conifer* belt (the "taiga" or highboreal zone) likewise by 33
(or even 38) species, that is 73(–84) per cent. The number sinks rapidly as the
climate grows milder toward the south (and downward).

A clearer and more correct picture is given if the circumpolar species are regarded as an element of the zone in which they live and their number is calculated
as a ratio of the total fauna of this zone. This is possible only for the Carabids
of Fennoscandia in northwestern Europe. Three species lacking there (*Carabus
truncaticollis, Harpalobrachys leiroides, Pterostichus vermiculosus*) must be excluded.
In table 8, as well as in the corresponding table 30 by Lindroth, 1949 (p. 440–448),
crosses in brackets are counted.

The circumpolar Carabids of Fennoscandia constitute:

in *regio arctica superior,*	5 species of	5, that is	100 per cent
,, *regio arctica media,*	11 ,, ,,	17, ,, ,,	65 ,, ,,
,, *regio arctica inferior,*	31 ,, ,,	75, ,, ,,	41 ,, ,,
,, *regio subarctica,*	41 ,, ,,	97, ,, ,,	42 ,, ,,
,, *regio coniferina,*	37 ,, ,,	271, ,, ,,	14 ,, ,,
,, *regio quercina,*	23 ,, ,,	315, ,, ,,	7 ,, ,,
,, more southern regions	14 ,, ,,	314, ,, ,,	4 ,, ,,

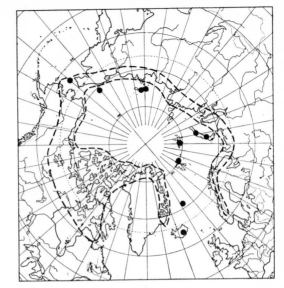

(From Rosenberg, Fåglar i Sverige.)

FIG. 49. Breeding area of the Snowy Owl, *Nyctea scandiaca* L., an arctic, circumpolar bird. The southern limit varies considerably according to supply of rodents.

(Compiled from Ekman, 1922, Pleske, 1928, "Check List", 1931, Stegmann, 1938, Timmermann, 1949, Salomonsen & Gitz, 1950.)

Thus, the circumpolar type dominates under high-arctic conditions and decreases relatively with decreasing latitude.

Examples of circumpolar distribution are here shown by maps of one *arctic* species, the Snowy Owl (*Nyctea scandiaca* L., fig. 49), one *subarctic-highboreal* species, the Three-toed Woodpecker (*Picoides tridactylus* L., fig. 50), and one *generally boreal* species, the Dragonfly *Libellula quadrimaculata* L. (fig. 51). This latter is an excellent flyer with strong migratory tendencies; it is able to cross even broad stretches of sea.

Several reasons may be given which could explain why no faunal element has been able to spread all around the globe to such a great extent as that of the High North: —

(a) The way along a given parallel is *shorter* the nearer it lies to the Pole.

(b) The continents lie everywhere *closer together* about the latitude of the Polar Circle than farther south. The most important distances are:

Bering Strait 90 km.   Greenland–Iceland 330 km.
Labrador–Greenland 750 km.   Iceland–Norway ca. 900 km.

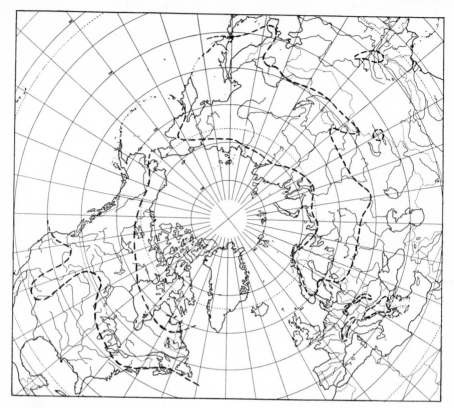

FIG. 50. The Three-toed Woodpecker (*Picoides tridactylus* L.). Breeding range of a subarctic-highboreal, circumpolar bird, boreoalpine in Eurasia.

(Mainly according to "Check List", 1931, STEGMANN, 1938, PETERS, 1948, and HOLDHAUS, 1954.)

(From ROSENBERG, Fåglar i Sverige.)

Yet these favourable conditions do not in themselves provide an exhaustive explanation, except for flying or otherwise easily dispersed forms. This was shown above (p. 264) regarding the Davis Strait which, though only 350 km. at its narrowest, has functioned as a highly efficient barrier against the dispersal of soil-bound animals.

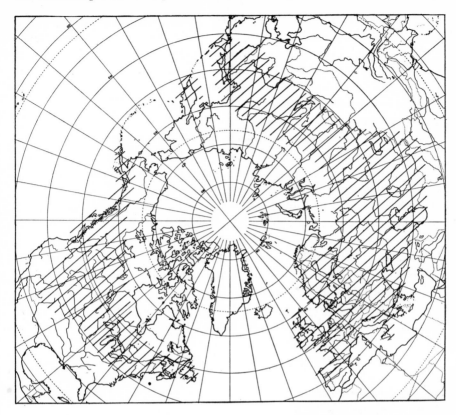

FIG. 51. *Libellula quadrimaculata* L., a generally boreal, circumpolar Dragonfly with excellent means of dispersal by active flight combined with wind-drift. It is a well-known migratory insect.

(According to BARTENEF, 1935, VALLE, 1952, NEEDHAM & WESTFALL, 1955.)

(From Svensk Insektfauna.)

(c) The sea and the sounds between the continents of the North are regularly *closed by drifting ice*, at least in the first half of the year, joining the Siberian coast with Novaja Zemlja and via Spitzbergen with Greenland and, usually, northern and eastern Iceland. On the American side, continuous drifting ice every spring goes right down to Newfoundland and the Bering Strait is regularly closed by ice.

The ice of the Polar basin, stable or drifting, is often traversed in winter by large warm-blooded animals. The Arctic Fox (*Alopex lagopus* L.) has been tracked on the ice at about 85° north (Braestrup, 1941, p. 19), also half-way between Greenland and Iceland (Saemundsson, 1939, p. 3). Proofs of still longer distances covered are available for the Reindeer (*Rangifer tarandus* L.) since animals with owner's mark on the ears have repeatedly been observed in Spitzbergen (Ingstad, 1948, p. 239 a.f.), which they must have reached travelling on the ice from Novaja Zemlja, at least, a distance of about 770 km. With this in mind it seems astounding that a special race of the Reindeer, sbsp. *pearyi* All., could establish itself on Ellesmere Island (fig. 53), separated from Greenland only by narrow ice-covered sounds. Perhaps this is due to a more complete isolation in earlier periods of the Pleistocene, and stragglers may not be accepted in the herds.

Cold-blooded and, probably, small warm-blooded animals, such as the Lemmings, cannot traverse the sea-ice actively. They may do so by passive ice-transport carried by currents, as has been suggested for the Waterbeetle *Colymbetes dolabratus* Payk. (from Greenland to Iceland; Lindroth, 1931, p. 529) and is still more probable for the high-arctic circumpolar Staphylinid *Micralymma brevilingue* Schiø. (*dicksoni* Mäkl.), inhabiting the tidal zone. Yet a general application of this kind of dispersal to the soil-bound fauna is made highly dubious by the existing faunal barrier between Greenland and Baffin Island, existing in spite of the fact that surface currents rather favour westward transport across the Davis Strait (Orchymont & Brown, 1940, fig. 1).

(d) *Extension of land* in the far north may have been *more favourable during earlier parts of the Pleistocene*, or in Tertiary time. This, to my mind, is *the clue to the circumpolar type of distribution*, or at least to the frequent occurrence of animals so distributed.

In a previous paragraph of this chapter (p. 253 a.f.) I have tried to show that Iceland and Greenland are so firmly linked to Europe, from a zoogeographical point of view, that the assumption of an uninterrupted land-connection (or almost so) with the European mainland seems unavoidable. At the same time, however, it was stressed that a westward prolongation of this "bridge", to Baffin Island, could not be traced on faunal evidence. This will be still more evident if we consider the pattern of subspeciation among circumpolar animals (below). It is a fact beyond any doubt that the circumpolar area of very few animal species, if any, has incorporated America from Eurasia, or *vice versa*, by way of Greenland–Baffin Island.

This being admitted, the Bering Strait, or rather the passage now occupied by this strait, is the historical link between the Palaearctic and Nearctic regions.

The idea is not at all revolutionary. It has been advocated by many skilled biogeographers (Matthew, 1915; Mayr, 1946; Simpson, 1947; &c.). And the conditions for a repeated firm connection between Asia and North America by this route are more favourable than between any second pair of continents on the earth.

The Bering Strait is only 90 km. at its narrowest and quite shallow, a land rise of 60–65 meters would be enough to shape a continuous bridge. This is no high figure. It lies within the limits of what is thought to be the normal world-wide eustatic regression of the sea during a glaciation. Even for the last glaciation (Würm, Wisconsin) this regression is usually calculated as something between 90 and 100 meters, somewhat more during at least one of the earlier ones (Zeuner, 1950, p. 129; Woldstedt, 1954, p. 289–291.

For other reasons, too, it is very likely that the Bering land-bridge existed during a period (or several periods) of glaciation. Alaska was little affected by the land-ice, the major part of it remained ice-free throughout the entire Pleistocene period (Flint, 1952) as did the opposite part of eastern Siberia (fig. 52). Therefore, no isostatic sinking of land caused by pressure of an ice-cap could affect the Bering area. The bridge furthermore prevented cold polar water from entering the North Pacific, and the south-coast of the isthmus, as well as the chains of islands off the coast, the present Aleutians, &c., were more under the influence of the warm Kuro Shivo current.

On the other hand, the Bering Isthmus was a pronounced "filter bridge" (Simpson, 1940, p. 148), certainly in the first place due to climate. It allowed passage to arctic and subarctic organisms but, as we just learned, there are very few circumpolar animals *not* able to endure at least subarctic conditions. This is well in accordance with the assumption made, that the Bering bridge developed and existed during *glacial* periods of the Pleistocene. Therefore very few organisms demanding a temperate, or warmer, climate are common to North America and Asia. For instance the Tiger-beetles, genus *Cicindela*, are very abundant in North America, amounting to almost one hundred different species (north of Mexico), but they do not enter the Arctic and none of them has reached countries outside the American continent.

In Tertiary time conditions may have been different. It is generally accepted that the Bering land-bridge existed throughout the main part of this period (Simpson, 1947) and thus under comparatively favourable climatic conditions. It remains doubtful, however, if they were warm enough to explain the distribution of Pantropical genera or groups (Mayr, 1946, p. 36). But, as we have seen, the actually living *species* which are supposed to have crossed the Bering bridge are northern in distribution, have low demands on climate and are no doubt Pleistocene migrants. *Blethisa eschscholtzi* Zoubk., among Carabid beetles (p. 280), may be a single surviving representative of Tertiary dispersal.

The following additional attempts (e–g) to explain the wide east-west distribu-

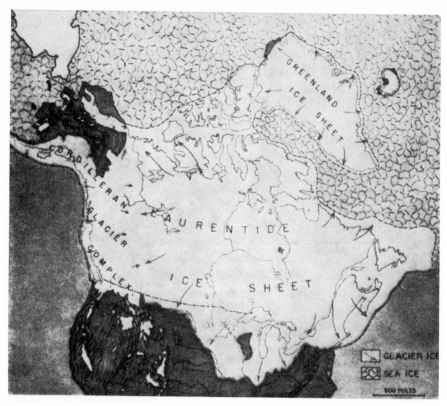

FIG. 52. Pleistocene glaciation of North America regardless of time.
(Reproduced by permission from "Textbook of Geology", Part I, by LONGWELL, KNOPF, & FLINT, published by JOHN WILEY & Sons.)

tion of arctic-subarctic species are mainly hypothetical but are mentioned as a possible incentive for further research.

(e) Arctic animals are more "hardy" than others, especially as regards low temperature. They may therefore be more liable to survive passive transport, above all as "aerial plankton" at high altitude. There would be no difficulty in testing this experimentally.

(f) Arctic (and subarctic) animals may generally be older as species and thus have had more time at their disposal for dispersal. This may be a direct consequence of climate (Van Dyke, 1939, p. 258), either because the rate of mutation decreases with temperature, as shown in *Drosophila* (Timoféeff-Ressovsky, 1947, p. 243), or because the number of generations per unit of time is smaller. The latter suggestion is more than a hypothesis: it is a common experience among

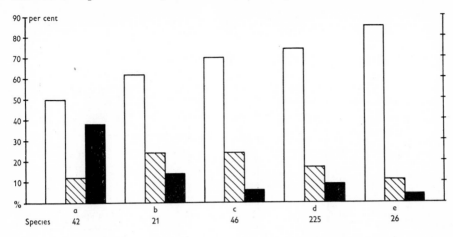

DIAGR. 9. Percentage of macropterous (white), dimorphic (striated) and brachypterous (black) species of Carabid beetles inhabiting Fennoscandia, arranged into different groups of distribution.

a = exclusively European
b = Euro-Caucasian & Euro-Mediterranean
(From Lindroth, 1949, p. 435.)

c = West-Palaearctic
d = generally Palaearctic
e = Circumpolar

entomologists that widespread insects in the northern part of their area or in high mountain regions turn to biennial development.

(g) Speciation may also be delayed, as an indirect result of climate, by decreased selection within the rather uniform arctic region with its generally low population density (reduced "competition"). This assumption, however, at least as far as insects are concerned, is purely theoretical.

A question worth raising is why some species reached the outermost limits of the continents, Scandinavia and/or the British Isles in Eurasia, Labrador and/or Newfoundland in America, and acquired a perfectly circumpolar area, and how these were selected from the far more numerous stock of other arctic species. The catch-word "aggressive" species, &c., gives no real explanation.

An investigation of the means of dispersal of every separate species may do so, at least in part. Circumpolar species of Carabid beetles as a rule have fully developed, functionary hind-wings, as shown in an earlier book (Lindroth, 1949, p. 435) on the Fennoscandian fauna. The diagram here reproduced (diagr. 9) is not quite up to date with respect to later discoveries of several species in North America, but it demonstrates the tendency.

TABLE 9. Circumpolar Carabidae, 45 species (*vide* table 8). Western limit in Europe plotted against eastern limit in North America.

W. limit in Europe

	40–60° E.	20–40° E.	W. of 20° E.	Brit. Isles
130–160° W.	3	1	2	0 species
80–130° W.	2	1	2	1 species
E. of 80° W.	0	1	3	1 species
Newfoundl.	0	3	9	16 species

(E. limit in North Amer.)

If the extension of area is primarily dependant on powers of dispersal, it is to be expected that a species occurring far east, in Newfoundland or Labrador, in North America, is usually at the same time among those which have spread farthest west, to the British Isles or Scandinavia in Eurasia. This is confirmed by the following simple arrangement (table 9).

Though circumpolar Carabids are thus, generally speaking, characterized by well developed powers of dispersal, they by no means constitute a homogenous group in this respect. A division of the species of each vegetational zone according to the development of wings, into *macropterous* (flying, or probably flying), *brachypterous* (flightless), and *dimorphic* forms (as in table 8), gives the following picture: —

Circumpolar Carabidae

	species total	macropt.	brachypt.	dimorph.
Regio arctica superior	7	1 = 14 %	5 = 71 %	1
,, ,, media	13	5 = 38 %	6 = 46 %	2
,, ,, inferior	34	20 = 59 %	9 = 26 %	5
,, subarctica	44	28 = 64 %	9 = 20 %	7
,, coniferina	38	28 = 74 %	5 = 13 %	5
,, quercina	23	16 = 70 %	2 = 9 %	5
More southern regions	14	10 = 71 %	1 = 7 %	3
Total	45	29 = 64 %	9 = 20 %	7

The decreasing number of flightless circumpolar species in the direction north-south is very striking. The explanation is probably that selection on the wind-swept barren land of the arctic region works in favour of flightless forms and species (the dominance of the constantly brachypterous subgenus *Cryobius*, of the Carabid genus *Pterostichus*, on the Siberian and Alaskan tundras is a good illustration); but also, that the Bering Isthmus was available as a trafficable bridge at any period of existence for animals enduring an arctic climate, and consequently that flightless *arctic* forms were at less disadvantage crossing it than the more fastidious forms of the forest regions. It is interesting to observe in this connection that no species of Conifer trees (provided *Picea glauca* Moench. is specificially distinct from *abies* L. and *obovata* Ledeb.) occurs on both sides of the Bering Strait (Hustich, 1953).

Many circumpolar animal species seem to be uniformous, from a taxonomical point of view, within their entire vast area, though this may be largely due to imperfect study of sufficient series from different localities. In others, two or more geographically separated forms, usually termed "subspecies", have been described. One instance of a multiformous complex is the Reindeer (*Rangifer tarandus* L.; fig. 53), in which the relationship between the different subspecies seems rather obscure.

The usual trend among circumpolar animals is that subspeciation, or whatever it may be termed, has the character of a sliding change of certain morphological properties which thus can be expressed as *clines* (in Huxley's sense) running from east to west. A good instance is provided by the Moose or European Elk (*Alces alces* L.; fig. 54), as investigated by Peterson (1952). Here, with respect to the shape of the palate bones, a double cline is formed, running in both directions from the E. Siberian—Alaskan area (diagr. 10).

The result is, in this case and in the character mentioned, that the forms *at the periphery* of the species' area, in Europe and eastern North America, are converging. A similar instance is provided by Davenport (1941) who, in his monograph of the butterfly genus *Coenonympha*, the "Ringlets" or "Heaths", analyses the distribution of the circumpolar, extremely multiformous *C. tullia* O. F. Müll. (fig. 55). He found two points of general interest: (a) that northwestern North America and northeastern Siberia are inhabited by the same form (sbsp. *mixturata* Alph.); and (b) that the Nearctic form occurring farthest east (sbsp. *inornata* Edw.) is strikingly similar to the forms of western Europe, especially to the Fennoscandian form (sbsp. *suevica* Hemm.). Davenport is probably right in his conclusion that both of these, *geographically* speaking, peripheral subspecies are similar, not because of direct historical connection, but because they have remained primitive and like the original ancestor of the species, whereas other forms situated closer to the centre and origin of its area (probably in eastern Asia), but near the *climatic*

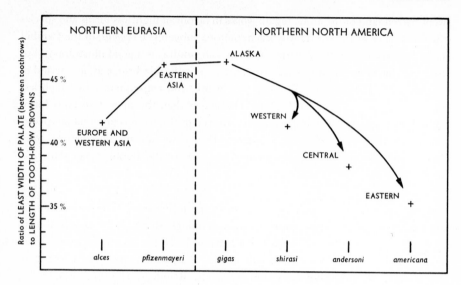

DIAGR. 10. Geographical relationships of the subspecies of Moose or European Elk (*Alces alces* L.) as indicated by the average relative shapes of the palates. (From Peterson, 1952.)

periphery, were exposed to heavier selection pressure and changed. The result of this procedure would be the same as through "elimination", in the sense of Reinig (1938), but attained in a different way.

The small Carabid *Bembidion* (*Chrysobracteon*) *lapponicum* Zett. behaves in a similar way (Lindroth, 1954a, p. 129–130), the *"forma typica"* of northwestern Europe and western Siberia being more like the form of the Mackenzie River region (*"bryanti* Carr") than specimens from Alaska and eastern Siberia (sbsp. *latiusculum* Mtsch.).

FIG. 53. Distribution of the Reindeer and Caribou (*Rangifer tarandus* L.) and its numerous subspecies.

1. *forma typica*
2. sbsp. *platyrhynchus* Vrol.
3. sbsp. *pearsoni* Lyd.
4. sbsp. *sibiricus* Murr.
5. sbsp. *valentinae* Fler.
6. sbsp. *angustirostris* Fler.
7. sbsp. *phylarchus* Holl.
8. sbsp. *arcticus* Rich.

9. sbsp. *dawsoni* Seton
10. sbsp. *montanus* Seton
11. sbsp. *caribou* Gmel.
12. sbsp. *caboti* Allen
13. sbsp. *terranovae* Bangs
14. sbsp. *pearyi* Allen
15. sbsp. *groenlandicus* Gmel.

(According to EKMAN, 1922, ANDERSON, 1946, ELLERMAN & MORRISON-SCOTT, 1951, BURT & GROSSENHEIDER, 1952, and FLEROW, 1952.)

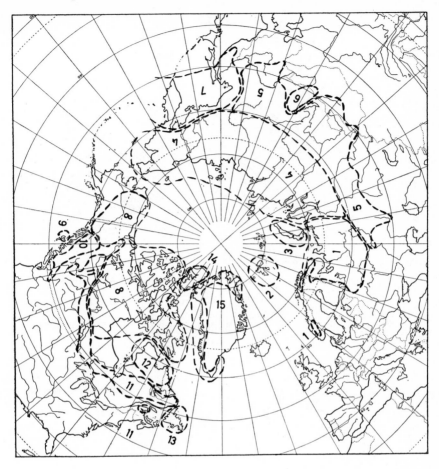

(From BURT & GROSSENHEIDER, 1952.)

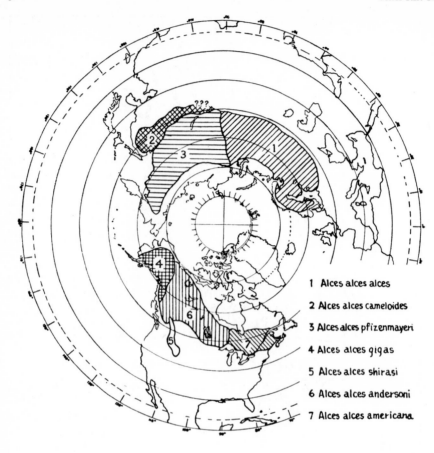

1 Alces alces alces

2 Alces alces cameloides

3 Alces alces pfizenmayeri

4 Alces alces gigas

5 Alces alces shirasi

6 Alces alces andersoni

7 Alces alces americana

FIG. 54. World distribution of the Moose or European Elk (*Alces alces* L.) and its subspecies.

(From PETERSON, 1952.)

(From BURT & GROSSENHEIDER, 1952).

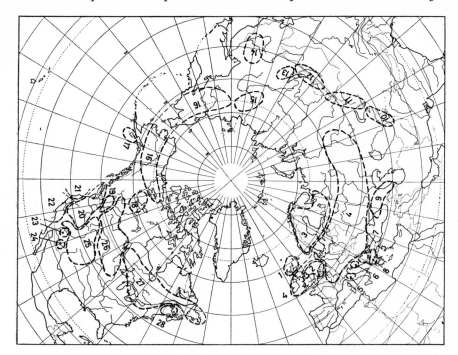

FIG. 55. The distribution of *Coenonympha tullia* O. F.
Müll. (*tiphon* Rott.) (The Ringlet or Large Heath),
an extremely multiformous butterfly.
The figured butterfly is of *forma typica* from S.
Sweden.

(According to DAVENPORT, 1941, FORD, 1946, &c.)

(Photo P. ARDÖ.)

1. sbsp. *scotica* Stgr.
2. sbsp. *philoxenus* Esp. (*davus* auctt.)
3. sbsp. *suevica* Hemm. (incl. *orstadii* Wahlgr.)
4. *forma typica*
5. sbsp. *italica* Vty.
6. sbsp. *bosniae* Davenp.
7. sbsp. *occupata* Reb.
8. sbsp. *rhodopensis* Elw.
9. sbsp. *chatiparae* Shelj.
10. sbsp. *caeca* Stgr.
11. sbsp. *eupompus* Stauder
12. sbsp. *subcaeca* Heyne
13. sbsp. *witimensis* Davenp.
14. sbsp. *sibirica* Davenp.
15. sbsp. *viluiensis* Mén.
16. sbsp. *mixturata* Alph.
17. sbsp. *kodiak* Edw.
18. sbsp. *mackenziei* Davenp.
19. sbsp. *columbiana* McD.
20. sbsp. *ampelos* Edw.
21. sbsp. *eryngii* H. Edw.
22. sbsp. *californica* Westw.
23. sbsp. *furcae* Brns. & Benj.
24. sbsp. *subfusca* Brns. & Benj.
25. sbsp. *ochracea* Edw.
26. sbsp. *benjamini* McD.
27. sbsp. *inornata* Edw. (incl. *mcisaaci* dos P.)
28. sbsp. *nipisiquit* McD.

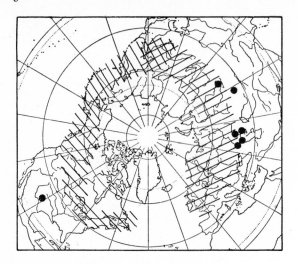

(From Faune de France.)

FIG. 56. Distribution of two species of the Carabid genus *Blethisa*.

Hatched area = *Blethisa multipunctata* L., in Europe and western Siberia *forma typica*, in North America sbsp. *aurata* Fisch.; overlapping or transgrading area in eastern Siberia.

Black dots = *Blethisa eschscholtzi* Zoubk.

The figured specimen belongs to *multipunctata f. typ.*

However, these are exceptions. The rule is that, provided a circumpolar species is at all inclined to subspeciation, the most differing forms appear in western or northern Europe on the one hand, in North America east of Hudson Bay on the other. This applies to the following Carabid beetles: *Agonum mannerheimi* Dej., *Amara alpina* Payk., *Blethisa multipunctata* L. (fig. 56), *Miscodera arctica* Payk., *Nebria gyllenhali* Schnh., *N. nivalis* Payk., and *Pelophila borealis* Payk.

Unfortunately, the lack of sufficient series of these species from northern Asia does not permit a description of existing cline systems, but the gradients as a rule seem not to be evenly sloping but to form a distinct step within a transitional zone on either side of the Bering Strait: in eastern Siberia at least for *Amara alpina*, *Blethisa multipunctata* (fig. 56), *Nebria gyllenhali* and *nivalis;* in Alaska or adjacent parts of Canada for *Miscodera arctica* and *Pelophila borealis*. Whether this is due to overlapping after previous isolation or to the transitional zone indicating the original centre of the species, I am not able to decide. But the presence, at least in other animal groups, of a common subspecies (*Coenonympha tullia*, fig. 55; also the sbsp. *leptura* Hbs. & Schtz. of the Burbot, *Lota lota* L.), or of two closely related subspecies (Moose, diagr. 10), on both sides of the Strait, from which other

FIG. 57. *Bembidion transparens* Gebl. Scandinavian specimens.

a = macropterous form (flying)

b = intermediate form (flightless) (very rare)

c = brachypterous form (flightless).

Short wing is a dominant and long-winged specimens are homozygotes.

subspecies radiate toward Europe and eastern North America, argues in favour of the "overlapping area" as an old centre.

When pronounced and geographically concentrated, this area is situated *west* of the Bering Strait, which supports the generally accepted idea that *the main Holarctic centre of speciation was in northeastern Asia* and that the traffic over the Bering land-bridge, irrespective of period, was most intense from the west to the east (Simpson, 1947, p. 628 a.f.).

Yet it is important to realise that a circumpolar area is not the "climax" stage of a perpetual and even dispersal from an ancient evolutionary centre of the species. It is but *one* stage in a complex procedure involving intermittent expansion and regression. Species may once have been circumpolar which now no longer are so, for instance the Muskox (*Ovibos moschatus* L.). The repeated glaciations prevented any species from being continuously circumpolar during the entire Pleistocene period, but at the same time they caused pulsating advances toward the south which in many cases, left permanent outposts in southern mountains. This gave rise to *boreoalpine* types of distribution (Holdhaus & Lindroth, 1939; Holdhaus, 1954), for instance in the Three-toed Woodpecker (*Picoides tridactylus* L.; fig. 50). It is difficult to establish the period in which the area of a boreoalpine species was formed, but it is reasonable to assume that the time of the largest ice-sheet, which,

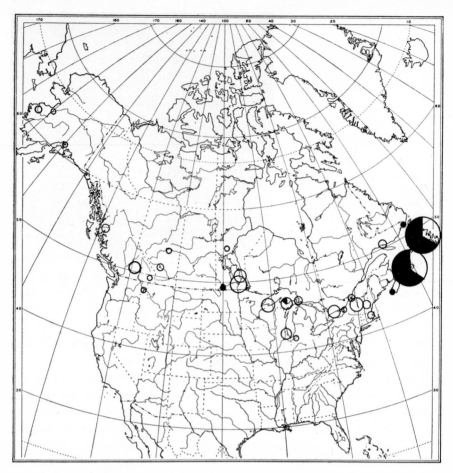

FIG. 58. *Bembidion transparens* Gebl. Distribution of long-winged (white) and short-winged (black) specimens in North America. The size of the circles is in proportion to the number of individuals examined. The circle for Newfoundland is strongly underdimensioned (*vide* fig. 59).

in Europe at least, was the last but one glaciation (Riss), had the greatest effect (Lindroth, 1935, p. 627).

The boreoalpine type of distribution is most frequent in Europe because a wide, continuous plain separates the southern mountains from the arctic-subarctic regions of the north. But it occurs also in Asia, as shown by the Three-toed Woodpecker (fig. 50) and the Carabid *Diachila polita* Fald. (Lindroth, 1954c, p. 9), though information as to its extent is not obtainable because of insufficient know-

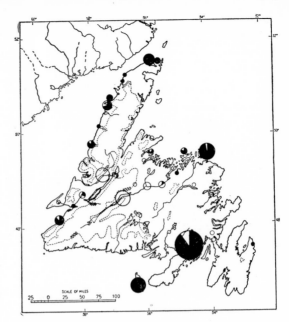

FIG. 59. *Bembidion transparens* Gebl. Distribution of long- and short-winged specimens in Newfoundland. For explanation, *vide* figs. 57, 58.

ledge. The Cordilleras of western North America are against boreoalpine distribution but in the northeast the St. Lawrence Valley cuts off from the main area an arctic-subarctic fauna on the highest mountains of New England, especially in the White Mountains of New Hampshire (Darlington, 1943). In some Diurnal Lepidoptera (Butterflies) the southern component of a boreoalpine species is supplemented or replaced by one or more subspecies ecologically connected with mires and bogs (Petersen, 1954).

The distribution of wing-dimorphic insects, here as in many other cases, may allow partial reconstruction of the troublesome history of circumpolar species.

The tiny Carabid beetle *Bembidion transparens* Gebl. (*sulcatum* Lec.) (fig. 57) apparently has an uninterrupted transamerican distribution and a traditional map of its area does not preclude the interpretation of a successive spread in a west-east direction across North America in Postglacial time. The distribution of long- and short-winged individuals (fig. 58) gives a contrary impression. From the western half of North America, west of longitude 100°, only macropterous specimens are known; the westernmost brachypterous specimen seen is from Aweme, Manitoba. A predominance of this form occurs only in Nova Scotia and Newfoundland and this region should therefore be regarded as a secondary centre of distribution. The picture may become slightly, but not decisively, altered if more abundant material available reveals the presence of brachypterous individuals in Alaska.

The following reconstruction of the history of *Bembidion transparens* in North America is the most plausible:—Immigration from northeastern Asia in early Pleistocene and subsequent spread to the Atlantic coast. Interruption of area during one or more glacial periods in the western and central parts. Survival, at least throughout the last glaciation (Wisconsin), in the Northeast. Postglacial re-colonization of lost area from the east, possibly also from the west.

The distribution in Newfoundland (fig. 59) suggests glacial refuges on the coast, in the northwestern, northeastern and southeastern parts.—A similar coastal refuge during the last glaciation was assumed for this species in northeastern Fennoscandia (Lindroth, 1949, p. 389 a.f., fig. 45).

The fossil evidence

The importance of reliably dated fossils to the reconstruction of faunal and floral history is immense. Our knowledge of what actually happened, and thus the interpretation of the present pattern of distribution, has often been radically altered by the discovery of a single fossil specimen.

The difficulties lie in a competent identification of the often fragmentary remains, but also in the scope of conclusions. Above all, considering what a futile fraction of organisms existing during a certain geological period was by chance fossilified, and how still more futile a fraction of them was discovered and came to the notice of a specialist, it is extremely dangerous to conclude anything from *negative* facts, from the seeming lack of a certain type of animal, in a certain area, from a certain period.

Yet fossils may show that many gaps in the present area of an animal group or species are secondary and that faunal connections once existed which are impossible to reconstruct from the recent distribution.

This applies very much to the question of faunal exchange between Europe and North America. The fossil faunas of both of these continents are the best known in the world and, partly—at least—for this reason, many fossil forms were regarded as Eur-American or a group of animals or plants now restricted to either continent was discovered as fossil in the other.

The resemblance of these faunas was apparently greater in remote times and this, as described above (p. 286), originally led Simpson to conclude, mainly from fossil Mammalia, that a broad transatlantic connection existed in the Lower Eocene; later he found this assumption unnecessary. It is worth mentioning in this connection that the insect fauna described by Henriksen (1922) from Lower

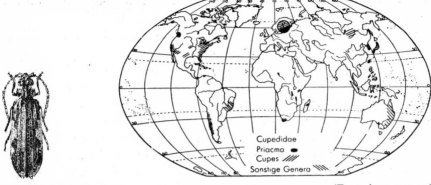

(From Traité de Zool.)   (From ANDER, 1942.)

FIG. 60. Distribution of the beetle family *Cupedidae*, recent and (in Europe) in Baltic amber. The figured specimen is of *Cupes raffrayi* Fairm. from Madagascar.

Eocene Diatom-earth in Denmark has its closest geographical connection with Southern Asia.

Now, the distribution of existing species, and usually even of genera, is little affected by what happened in the early Tertiary. The first period in which *possibly* still existing species had developed within the terrestrial fauna was the time of the Baltic amber, usually referred to Upper Eocene (or Lower Oligocene), that is more than 40 million years ago. It happens that one of the most famous insect specimens of the amber, a Tiger-beetle of genus *Tetracha* (*Megacephala*), has a special bearing upon our problem. It is often regarded as the single instance of an insect species still living unchanged since that time (Ander, 1942, p. 26)[1], since W. Horn (1906), though with some doubt, declared it as identical with the American *T. carolina* L., distributed from Virginia through Central America to northern Chile. The genus has a wider occurrence (S Spain, Africa, Hither Asia, Australia) but the group or subgenus to which *carolina* belongs is strictly American and Walter Horn was so skilled a specialist in Tiger-beetles that he could not possibly have identified the wrong *group*. It is therefore easily understandable that some students (at least verbally!) expressed their doubts as to the authenticity of the specimen.[2] — On other proposed North American elements from Baltic amber, *vide* Kolbe (1925).

The main impression of the Baltic amber fauna, if climatic differences from present European conditions are disregarded, is its importance as a connecting link

[1] However also a small Silphid beetle, *Nemadus colonoides* Kr., is reported to have remained unchanged since the time of the Baltic amber (Jeannel, 1942, p. 192).
[2] The specimen belonged to the Berendt collection of the Geol.-Palaeont. Inst., Humboldt University, Berlin, but seems to have been lost.

between highly disjunct present areas of old taxonomical groups. The primitive beetle family *Cupedidae* (fig. 60) is a good example.

As more and more recent species appear from the course of the Tertiary, the geographical character of the different faunas and floras becomes more easy to fix; and elements, often identified to species, of an indisputable "American" type—judged from present distribution—were discovered in Europe.

The Tertiary development of the European fauna of terrestrial and limnic *Molluscs* is notably well known and has been summarized by Ehrmann (1914). From the *Eocene* no recent species is known; the connections, according to present distribution of genera or groups, were largely towards the Tropics, including, but not favouring, South and Central America. Of particular interest is the family *Oleacinidae* (p. 283), now restricted to tropical America, subtropical North America and the Mediterranean, but found as fossil in Europe as early as in Upper Cretaceous.

In the *Oligocene* more decidedly American types appear, among these genus *Strobilops* (*Strobilus* auctt.), now chiefly American but also occurring in East Asia (fig. 61). It persisted in Europe at least to Middle Pliocene. Pilsbry (1948, p. 853) assumes an Asiatic centre of origin for *Strobilops*, with subsequent radiation, west into Europe, east across the Bering bridge into America.

Other Oligocene Molluscs also show relationship with America, for instance several freshwater Bivalves. Modell (1943) therefore postulates a direct Transatlantic land-connection in this period, which was probably of "Wegenerian" type. Yet the so-called American forms of Oligocene Molluscs in Europe are constantly associated with other extra-European elements, mainly with recent occurrence in Asia.

In the *Miocene* and *Pliocene* periods genera and species groups suggesting American and South or East Asian connections gradually and contemporaneously disappear. The Upper Pliocene contains an almost entirely European fauna and no "American" Molluscs; nor are any known from the Pleistocene.

A most interesting light has quite recently been thrown upon the late Tertiary and early Pleistocene history of the European *flora* through the intense investigations in Polonia by Szafer (1954). In Lower Pliocene the American element was twice—but the East Asian four times (!)—as numerous in species as the generally Eurasian group. The balance changed gradually in favour of Eurasian plants but not until the first Pleistocene glaciation (Günz) did this element take a clearly dominating position. In the first part of the following Interglacial period the East Asian group was well represented (11 species) but it disappeared completely during the course of this period, whereas two species (*Tsuga* sp. and *Osmunda*

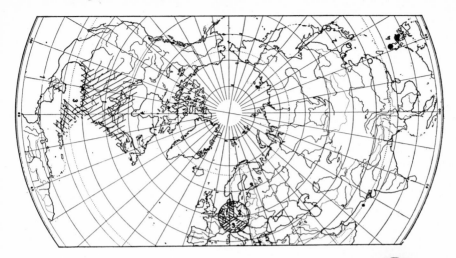

FIG. 61. Recent and (in Europe) Tertiary distribution of the Mollusc genus *Strobilops* (*Strobilus* auctt.) in the Northern Hemisphere. (Outside the map found in South America only.)

1. *Strobilops s. str.* (America) 3. subg. *Discostrobilops* (America)
2. subg. *Eostrobilops* (E. Asia) 4. subg. *Enteroplex* (Philipp.)

The figured specimen is of the North American *Strobilops* (After PILSBRY, 1948.) (*s. str.*) *labyrinthica* Say.

claytoniana L.[1]) of the American group survived the whole Günz-Mindel Interglacial.

From investigations in other parts of Europe the persistence of some of the American plants can be followed into later parts of the Pleistocene. Three species of the sedge genus *Dulichium*, now restricted to America, are recorded from Upper Pliocene (Vlerk & Florschütz, 1953; Szafer, 1954), two of these survived the first glaciation and one, *D. spathaceum* Rich., still grew in Denmark during the last (Riss-Würm) Interglacial (Jessen & Milthers, 1928, p. 348). The water-fern *Azolla filiculoides* Lam. likewise persisted into Pleistocene time. Similarly, the fern *Osmunda claytoniana*, just mentioned, or some closely related non-European form, has quite recently (Lundqvist, 1955, p. 321) been discovered in Swedish deposists from the last interglacial period.

A very interesting discovery was that reported from "glacial" deposits (without exact dating)[2] at Deuben, Saxonia, (Nathorst, 1894), of an elytron of *Carabus*

---

[1] *Osmunda claytoniana* is not strictly American. It still grows in Himalaya and East Asia.
[2] Woldstedt (1954, p. 248) dates the Deuben fossils as early Würm or, possibly, Riss.

chamissonis Fisch. (*groenlandicus* Dej.), a beetle now restricted to arctic-subarctic North America (the record for Greenland being erroneous). Since the elytral sculpture is very characteristic in this species, a wrong identification seems out of the question.—For a review of the late Tertiary and Pleistocene fossil insects of Europe, *vide* Henriksen (1933, p. 265 a.f.).

The key to a proper understanding of the now extinct American element, not only of the European flora but also of the contemporaneous *fauna*, seems to be given by the balance between American and East Asian plants in the different periods investigated by Szafer (diagr. 11). Until, and inclusive of, the first part of the Günz-Mindel Interglacial *the curves for these two elements run perfectly parallel, the East Asian element being clearly in the majority*. This is definitely *not* what could be expected if the presence of the American plants was due to a Transatlantic land-connection. In that case, the American element would have increased *at the cost* of the East Asian. The parallel development of the said elements can only be explained under the assumption *that the "American" plants were simply part of the East Asian group*, that they invaded Europe together from the east.

The longer persistence in Europe of some few members of the American type (*Dulichium, Osmunda,* &c.) does not contradict this opinion, because it must be expected that these plants, being able to reach *both* Europe *and* eastern North America from a centre in Asia, belonged to the most hardy and most easily dispersed plants of the group which, in full, ought to be called "East Asian". The only obscure point is why they later, entirely or in part, became extinct in Asia.

The opinion here stressed, that northeastern Asia has served as an evolution centre for circumpolar animals, is quite in accordance with Hultén's view (1937) of the development of the Holarctic flora. But to my mind, Hultén has underestimated, (a) the possibility of transatlantic dispersal without the aid of land-connections, and (b) the importance of an element of original (endemic) species in Europe and North America. Then it is evident that the mountains of both regions possess a rich element of indigenous species though, for some reason, these have almost failed to spread outside their area of origin.

The reasons may be tentatively indicated as follows:—The main areas of speciation were mountains. They possess a great variety of habitats and the strong shortway zonation shapes small isolated population areas, thereby favouring speciation. The Tertiary mountain ranges, the Alps, the North American Cordilleras, &c., are young. They have existed long enough to allow for speciation but not for the development of really new "inventions", higher taxonomic units, essentially new

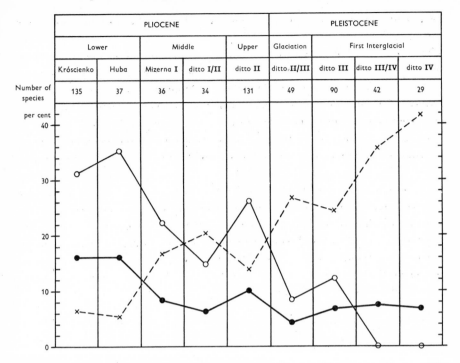

	PLIOCENE				PLEISTOCENE			
	Lower		Middle		Upper	Glaciation	First Interglacial		
	Krościenko	Huba	Mizerna I	ditto I/II	ditto II	ditto II/III	ditto III	ditto III/IV	ditto IV
Number of species	135	37	36	34	131	49	90	42	29

DIAGR. II. Three main elements of the Pliocene–Lower Pleistocene flora of SW Polonia.

Black dots = the American element. Open dots = the East Asia element.
Crosses = the Eurasian element

Elements of a generally Holarctic or more southern character omitted.
(After Szafer, 1954.)

types of organisation. And the species arisen in these mountains had comparatively too short time to spread.

Older mountains, of Palaeozoic (Carboniferous-Permian) age, the Hercynians of Europe, the Appalachians, &c., have been more important centres of evolution. Apparently it was the fauna of such mountains, in northeastern Asia, that provided the main source of circumpolar animals. Considering that the Bering Strait during the entire Tertiary and Quaternary periods has formed only a temporary obstacle to dispersal, the fauna (and flora) of northeastern Asia was in the best imaginable position, in the centre of the Holarctic region, for sending branches in both directions, towards Europe and towards North America.

But this is not sufficient explanation. Why, for instance, did the Appalachians not provide a similar old faunal element, spreading west across the Bering land bridge?

The most acceptable hypothesis seems to be that the old mountains of north-eastern Asia, simply because they were situated farther north, the Hercynian ranges reaching at least 60° north in the Jablonoj Mountains, and probably farther northeast (Obrutschew, 1926, p. 445), and because they probably always had a more continental climate, gave rise to a Tertiary fauna with a high amount of hardy species[1] which, more than any other contemporaneous fauna, were fit for subsequent dispersal across two continents, and later to survive the critical glacial periods. Thus they became circumpolar.

The original faunas of Europe and North America—and it should be realized that these regions were certainly never "empty"—were less adapted to arctic-subarctic conditions, were perhaps largely inhabitants of mountain woods, and therefore had no chance of becoming members of a cold-adapted Holarctic fauna. It is possible, though, that the Ural Mountains once served as a centre similar to that of northeastern Asia but, if so, the following Pleistocene glaciations swept away the traces of their original fauna.

---

[1] Kusnezov (1935, p. 130) tries to explain this phenomenon by proposing a Miocene glaciation of Alaska and NE Siberia.

Bibliography of Chapter III

ALEXANDER, W. B. & FITTER, R. S. R., 1955. American land birds in western Europe. — Brit. Birds. 48. Watford, Herts., p. 1–14.

ANDER, K., 1942. Die Insektenfauna des baltischen Bernsteins nebst damit verknüpften zoogeographischen Problemen. — K. Fysiogr. Sällsk. Handl. (N.S.) 53:4. Lund, p. 1–83.

ANDERSON, R. M., 1946. Catalogue of Canadian recent Mammals. — Bull. Nation. Mus. Can. 102. Ottawa, pp. I–V, 1–238.

ARNDT, W., 1928. Der Süsswasserschwamm Heteromeyenia ryderi Potts auf den Fär Öern. Zugleich ein Überblick über die Spongilliden-Fauna der Inseln des Atlantik und seiner Neben- und Randmeere. — Zool. Anz. 77. Leipzig, p. 156–166.

Atlantisheft, 1939. — Geol. Rundschau. 30. Stuttgart, p. 1–400.

Atlas til Bind I og II, 1921. Grønland i 200-aaret for Hans Egedes Landing. — Copenhagen.

BARTENEF, A., 1935. Über die Gattung Libellula und besonders über ihre paläarktischen Arten. — Zeitschr. wissensch. Zool. (Arch. f. Naturgesch.) (N.S.) 4. Leipzig, p. 274–290.

BASILEWSKY, P., 1954. Description d'un Carabique nouveau du Ruanda-Urundi, représentant d'une sous-famille inédite pour l'Afrique Noire. — Ann. Mus. Congo. 4. Zool., 1. Tervuren, p. 301–303.

BEY-BIENKO, G. J., 1950. Blattodea. — Fauna SSSR (N.S) 40. (Russian.) Moscow & Leningrad, p. 1–343.

BLAIR, K. G., 1933. Coleoptera collected by the Oxford University Expedition to Akpatok Island, Ungava Bay, Aug.–Sept. 1931. — Ann. Mag. Nat. Hist. (10) 12. London, p. 93–96.

BLASIUS, W., 1903. Der Riesenalk, Alca impennis L. — Naumann: Naturgesch. Vögel Mitteleuropas. 12. Gera-Untermhaus, p. 169–208.

BÖCHER, T. W., 1938. Biological distributional types in the flora of Greenland. — Medd. om Grønl. 106:2. Copenhagen, p. 1–339.

— 1948. Contributions to the flora and plant geography of West Greenland. I. Selaginella rupestris and Sisyrinchium montanum. — Ibidem. 147:3, p. 1–26.

BOETTGER, C. R., 1950. Analyse einer bemerkenswerter Population der Schnirkelschnecke Cepaea hortensis Müller. — Abh. Braunschw. Wiss. Gesellsch. 2. Braunschweig, p. 1-12.

BOYCOTT, A. E., 1936. The habitats of fresh-water Mollusca in Britain. — Journ. Anim. Ecol. 5. London, p. 116–186.

BRAENDEGAARD, J., 1946. The spiders (Araneina) of East Greenland. A faunistic and zoogeographical investigation. — Medd. om Grønl. 121:15. Copenhagen, p. 1–128.

BRÆSTRUP, F. W., 1941. A study on the Arctic Fox in Greenland. — Ibidem. 131, p. 1–101.

BREHM, V., 1926. Amerikanische Typen in der Organismenwelt Europas. — Die Erde. 4. Braunschweig, p. 315–325.

BRINCK, P., 1940. Beitrag zur Kenntnis der Wasserkäfer Grönlands. — Opusc. Ent. 5. Lund, p. 37–41.

BROOKS, S. T. & B. W., 1940. Geographical distribution of the recent Mollusca of Newfoundland. — Ann. Carn. Mus. 28. Pittsburgh, p. 53–75.

BROWN, W. J., 1937. The Coleoptera of Canada's Eastern Arctic. — Can. Ent. 69. Guelph, p. 106–111.

BRUNDIN, L., 1943. Zur Kenntnis einiger in die Atheta-Untergattung Metaxya M. & R. gestellten Arten (Col. Staphylinidae). — K. Fysiogr. Sällsk. Handl. (N.S.) 54:4. Lund, p. 1–38.

BURT, W. H. & GROSSENHEIDER, R. P., 1952. A field guide to the Mammals. — Boston, p. 1–200.

CASEY, T. L., 1900. Review of the North American Corylophidae, Cryptophagidae, Tritomidae and Dermestidae, with other studies. — Journ. N. Y. Ent. Soc. 8. New York, p. 51–172.

Check-List of North American Birds, 1931. 4. ed. — Amer. Ornith. Union. Lancaster, Pa., p. 1–525.

CLAPHAM, A. R., TUTIN, T. G. & WARBURG, E. F., 1952. Flora of the British Isles. — Cambridge, pp. I–LI, 1–1591.

CREIGHTON, W. S., 1950. The ants of North America. — Bull. Mus. Comp. Zool. 104. Cambridge, Mass., p. 1–585.

CROSBY, C. R. & BISHOP, S. C., 1936. Aeronautic spiders with a description of a new species. — Journ. N. Y. Ent. Soc. 44. New York, p. 43–49.

DALL, W. H., 1910. Land and fresh water Mollusks. — Harriman Alaska Exp. 13. Smiths. Inst. Washington, D. C., pp. I–VII, 1–171.

DARLINGTON, P. J., Jr., 1934. New West Indian Carabidae, with a list of the Cuban species. — Psyche. 41. Cambridge, Mass., p. 66–131.

— 1935. West Indian Carabidae II.: Itinerary of 1934; forests of Haiti; new species; and a new key to Colpodes. — Ibidem. 42, p. 167–215.

— 1938. Was there an Archatlantis? — Amer. Naturalist. 72. New York, p. 521–533.

— 1943. Carabidae of mountains and islands: data on the evolution of isolated faunas, and on atrophy of wings. — Ecol. Monogr. 13. Durham. N. C., p. 37–61.

— 1948. The geographical distribution of cold-blooded vertebrates. — Quart. Journ. Biol. 23. Baltimore, pp. 1–26, 105–123.

— 1949. Beetles and continents. (A review of La Genèse des Faunes Terrestres by R. Jeannel.) — Ibidem. 24, p. 342–345.

DAVENPORT, D., 1941. The butterflies of the Satyrid genus Coenonympha. — Bull. Mus. Comp. Zool. 87:4. Cambridge, Mass., p. 215–349.

DEEVEY, E. S., Jr., 1949. Biogeography of the Pleistocene. I. — Bull. Geol. Soc. Amer. 60. New York, p. 1315–1416.

DEGERBØL, M., 1940. Mammalia. — Zool. of the Faroes. III:2. Copenhagen, p. 1–133.

EHRMANN, P., 1914. Grundzüge einer Entwicklungsgeschichte der Tierwelt Deutschlands. (Lit.-Gesellsch. Neue Bahnen.) — Leipzig, pp. I–VIII, 1–213.

EKMAN, S., 1922. Djurvärldens utbredningshistoria på skandinaviska halvön. — Stockholm, pp. I–XVII, 1–614.

ELLERMAN, J. R. & MORRISON-SCOTT, T. C. S., 1951. Checklist of Palaearctic and Indian Mammals. — (Brit. Mus.) London, p. 1–810.

EMDEN, F. VAN, 1936. Bemerkungen zur Klassifikation der Carabidae: Carabini und Harpalinae piliferae. — Ent. Blätter. 32. Krefeld, p. 12–52.

FERNALD, M. L., 1925. Persistence of plants in unglaciated areas of Boreal America. — Mem. Amer. Ac. Arts & Sci. 15:3. Lancaster, Pa., p. 237–342.

FISHER, J., 1952. The Fulmar. — (The New Naturalist.) London, pp. I–XV, 1–496.

FISHER, J. & VEVERS, H. G., 1943. The breeding distribution, history and population of the North Atlantic Gannet (Sula bassana). — Journ. Anim. Ecol. 12. Cambridge, p. 173–213.

FLEROW, C. C., 1952. Mammalia. I:2. — Fauna SSSR. 55. Moscow & Leningrad, p. 1–256.

FLINT, R. F., 1952. The Ice Age in the North American Arctic. — Artic. 5. Ottawa, p. 135–152.

FORD, E. B., 1946. Butterflies. — The New Naturalist. London, pp. I–XIV, 1–368.

FRIES, T. C. E., 1913. Botanische Untersuchungen im nördlichsten Schweden, &c. — Uppsala, p. 1–361.

GIBSON, A., 1920. Lepidoptera. — Rep. Can. Arct. Exp. 1913–18. III:1. Ottawa, p. 1–58.

GISLÉN, T., 1940. The number of animal species in Sweden with remarks on some rules of distribution especially of the microfauna. — K. Fysiogr. Sällsk. Handl. (N.S.) 51:2. Lund, p. 1–23.

GLICK, P. A., 1939. The distribution of insects, spiders and mites in the air. — U.S. Dept. Agric., Techn. Bull. 673. Washington, D. C., p. 1–150.

HAANSHUS, K., 1933. Fortegnelse over Norges Lepidoptera. — Norsk Ent. Tidsskr. 3. Oslo, p. 165–216.

HAMMER, MARIE, 1953. Investigations on the microfauna of northern Canada. II. Collembola. — Acta Arctica. 6. Copenhagen, p. 1–108.

HANSEN, A. M., 1929. Bre og biota. — Norsk. Vid. Akad. Skr., Mat.-Naturv. Kl. 5. Oslo, p. 1–255.

HENRIKSEN, K. L., 1922. Eocene insects from Denmark. — Danm. Geol. Unders. (II) 37. Copenhagen, p. 1–36.

— 1933. Undersøgelse over Danmark-Skånes kvartære Insektfauna. — Vid. Medd. Dansk Naturh. Foren. 96. Copenhagen, p. 77–355.

— 1939. A revised index of the insects of Greenland. — Medd. om Grønl. 119:10. Copenhagen, p. 1–112.

HENRIKSEN, K. L. & LUNDBECK, W., 1917. Grønlands Landarthropoder (Insecta et Arachnida Groenlandicae). — Ibidem. 22, p. 483–823.

HERRE, W., 1935. Die Schwanzlurche der mitteleocänen (oberlutetischen) Braunkohle des Geiseltales, &c. — Zoologica. 87. Stuttgart, pp. I–VI, 1–85.

HESLOP-HARRISON, J., 1953. The North American and Lusitanian elements in the flora of the British Isles. — In: Lousley, J. E. (editor), The changing flora of Britain. — Arbroath, p. 105–123.

HOLDHAUS, K., 1927–28. Die geographische Verbreitung der Insekten. — In: Schröder, Handb. d. Ent. II:6. — Jena, p. 592–1058.

— 1954. Die Spuren der Eiszeit in der Tierwelt Europas. — Abh. Zool.-bot. Gesellsch. 18. Wien, p. 1–493.

HOLDHAUS, K. & LINDROTH, C. H., 1939. Die europäischen Koleopteren mit boreo-alpiner Verbreitung. — Ann. Naturh. Mus. 50. Wien, p. 123–293.

HORN, W., 1906. Über das Vorkommen von Tetracha carolina L. im preussischen Bernstein und die Phylogenie der Cicindela-Arten. — Deutsch. Ent. Zeitschr. Berlin, p. 329–336.

HUBENDICK, B., 1947. Die Verbreitungsverhältnisse der limnischen Gastropoden in Südschweden. — Zool. Bidr. 24. Uppsala, p. 419–559.

HULTÉN, E., 1937. Outline of the history of Arctic and Boreal Biota during the Quaternary Period. — Stockholm, p. 1–168.

— 1950. Atlas of the distribution of vascular plants in NW. Europe. — Stockholm, pp. 1*–119*, 1–512.

HUSTICH, I., 1953. The boreal limits of conifers. — Arctic. 6. Montreal, p. 149–162.

HYNES, H. B. N., 1954. Identity of Gammarus tigrinus Sexton 1939. — Nature. 174. St. Albans, p. 563.

IHERING, H. VON, 1927. Die Geschichte des Atlantischen Ozeans. — Jena, pp. 1–IX, 1–237.

INGSTAD, H., 1948. Landet med de kalde kyster. (Spitzbergen.) — Oslo, p. 1–422.

JASCHNOW, W. A., 1925. Crustacea von Nowaja Zemlja. — Ber. Wissensch. Meeres-inst. 12. Moscow, p. 50–76.

JEANNEL, R., 1937. Les Bembidiides endogés. — Revue Franç. d'Ent. 3. Paris, p. 241–399.

— 1941. Coléoptères Carabiques. I. — Faune de France. 39. Paris, p. 1–571.

— 1942. La genèse des faunes terrestres. — (Bibl. Inst. Marit. & Colon.) Paris, pp. I–VIII, 1–513.

JENSEN, A. S., 1928. Grønlands Fauna. Et Forsøg paa en Oversigt. — Festskr. Kbhvns Univ. Copenhagen, p. 1–88.

JESSEN, K., 1949. Studies in late Quaternary deposits and flora-history of Ireland. — Proc. R. Irish Ac. (B) 52. Dublin, p. 85–290.

JESSEN, K. & MILTHERS, V., 1928. Stratigraphical and palaeontological studies of interglacial fresh-water deposits in Jutland and northwest Germany. — Danm. Geol. Unders. (II) 48. Copenhagen, p. 1–380, Atlas.

JOHANSEN, H., 1955. Die Jenissei-Faunenscheide. — Zool. Jahrb., Abt. Syst., Ökol., Geogr. 83. Jena, p. 237–247.

JOHNSON, C. W., 1906. On the distribution of Helix hortensis Mueller, in North America. — Nautilus. 20. Philadelphia, p. 73–80.

— 1915. Helix hortensis from a Maine shell heap. — Ibidem. 28, p. 131.

KÄSTNER, A., 1932. Palpigradi Thorell. — In: Kükenthal, Handb. d. Zool. III:2, 1. Berlin, p. 76–98.

KEVAN, D. C. McE., 1943. Study of an introduced North American freshwater Mollusc, Stagnicola catascopium (Say). — Proc. R. Soc. B. 61. Edinburgh, p. 430–461.

KLOET, G. S. & HINCKS, W. D., 1945. A check list of British insects. — Arbroath, pp. I–LIX, 1–483.

KOLBE, H., 1925. Vergleichender Blick auf die rezente und fossile Insektenwelt Mitteleuropas, &c. — Deutsch. Ent. Zeitschr. Berlin, p. 147–162.

KROGERUS, H., 1954. Investigations on the Lepidoptera of Newfoundland. I. Macro-lepidoptera. — Acta Zool. Fenn. 82. Helsingfors, p. 1–80.

KULLENBERG, B., 1946. Über die Verbreitung und Wanderungen von vier Sterna-Arten. — Ark. f. Zool. 38 A :17. Stockholm, p. 1–80.

KUSNEZOV, N. J., 1935. The origin of the Lepidopterous fauna of the Arctic Eurasia. — Arctica. III:3. Leningrad, p. 115–136.

LAUTERBORN, R., 1927. Beiträge zur Flora der oberrheinischen Tiefebene und der benachbarten Gebiete. — Mitt. Bad. Landesver. Naturk. & Naturschutz (N.S.) 2. Freiburg i. Br., p. 77–88.

LENG, C. W., 1920. Catalogue of the Coleoptera of America, north of Mexico. — Mount Vernon, N.Y., pp. I–X, 1–470.

LINDROTH, A., 1942. Garfågeln i Sverige. — Vår Fågelvärld. 1. Stockholm, p. 138–140.

LINDROTH, C. H., 1931. Die Insektenfauna Islands und ihre Probleme. — Zool. Bidr. 13. Uppsala, p. 105–589.

— 1935. The Boreo-British Coleoptera. A study of the faunistical connections between the British Isles and Scandinavia. — Zoogeogr. II:4. Jena, p. 579–634.

— 1946. Inheritance of wing dimorphism in Pterostichus anthracinus Ill. — Hereditas. 32. Lund, p. 37–40.

— 1948. Interglacial insect remains from Sweden. — Sver. Geol. Unders. C 492. Stockholm, p. 1–30.

— 1954a. Random notes on North American Carabidae (Coleopt.). — Bull. Mus. Comp. Zool. 111:3. Cambridge, Mass., p. 117–161.

— 1954b. Carabidae common to Europe and North America. — Coleopt. Bull. 8. Washington, D. C., p. 35–52.

— 1954c. A revision of Diachila Motsch. and Blethisa Bon. — K. Fysiogr. Sällsk. Handl. (N.S.) 65. Lund, p. 1–28.

— 1955. The Carabid beetles of Newfoundland, including the French islands St. Pierre and Miquelon. — Opusc. Ent., Suppl. XII. Lund, p. 1–168.

LOHAMMAR, G., 1954. Matsmältningens inverkan på Potamogeton-frönas groning. — Fauna o. Flora. 49. Uppsala, p. 17–32.

LÖWE, Á., 1950. Some innovations and nomeclatural suggestions in the Icelandic flora. — Bot. Notiser. Lund, p. 24–60.

LUNDQVIST, G., 1955. Stocken i Öje. Ett säkert interglacialfynd. — Geol. Fören. Förh. 77. Stockholm, p. 317–322.

MÄKLIN, F. W., 1878. Diagnoser öfver några nya sibiriska insektarter. — Öfvers. Finsk. Vet.-Soc. Förh. 19 (1876–77). Helsingfors, p. 15–32.

— 1881. Coleoptera insamlade under den Nordenskiöld'ska expeditionen 1875, &c. — K. Sv. Vet. Ak. Handl. 18:4. Stockholm, p. 1–48.

MATTHEW, W. D., 1915. Climate and evolution. — Ann. N.Y. Ac. Sci. 24. New York, p. 171–318.

MAYR, E., 1946. History of the North American bird fauna. — Wilson Bull. 58. Ann Arbor, Mich., p. 3–41.

McDUNNOUGH, J. H., 1950. Species of Euxoa of eastern North America, &c. — Bull. Amer. Mus. Nat. Hist. 95:6. New York, p. 355–408.

MERTENS, R. & MÜLLER, L., 1940. Die Amphibien und Reptilien Europas. — Abh. Senck. Naturf. Gesellsch. 451. Frankfurt a. M., p. 1–56.

MICHENER, C. D. & M. H., 1951. American social insects. — New York, pp. I–XIV, 1–267.

MICHAELSEN, W., 1922. Die Verbreitung der Oligochäten im Lichte der Kontinental-verschiebung, &c. — Verh. Naturw. Verein. (3) 29 (1921). Hamburg, p. 45–79.

MODELL, H., 1943. Tertiäre Najaden. III. Nordamerikanische Najaden im bayrischen Oligozän. — Arch. f. Molluskenk. 75. Frankfurt a.M., p. 107–117.

NANNFELDT, J. A., 1940. On the polymorphy of Poa arctica R. Br., with special reference to its Scandinavian forms. — Symb. Bot. 4. Uppsala.

NATHORST, A. G., 1894. Die Entdeckung einer fossilen Glacialflora in Sachsen, am äussersten Rande des nordischen Diluviums. — Öfvers. K. Vet. Ak. Förh. 51. Stockholm, p. 519–543.

NEEDHAM, J. G. & WESTFALL, M. J., Jr., 1955. A manual of the Dragonflies of North America (Anisoptera). — Berkeley & Los Angeles, p. 1–615.

NORDHAGEN, R., 1916. Ranunculus Cymbalaria Pursh. fundet i Norge. — Nyt Mag. f. Naturv. 55. Oslo, p. 119–145.

— 1933. De senkvartære klimavekslinger i Nordeuropa og deres betydning for kulturforskningen. — Inst. Sammenlign. Kulturforskn. A. 12. Oslo, p. 1–246.

— 1935. Om Arenaria humifusa Wg. og dens betydning for utforskningen av Skandinavias eldste floraelement. — Berg. Mus. Årbok. Bergen, p. 1–183.

OBRUTSCHEW, W. A., 1926. Geologie von Sibirien. — Fortschr. Geol. & Palaeont. 15. Berlin, pp. I–XI, 1–572.

OEKLAND, F., 1925. Die Verbreitung der Landgastropoden Norwegens. — Skrift. Norsk. Vid.-Ak., I. Mat.-Naturv. Kl. 8. Oslo, pp. I–VIII, 1–168.

— 1927. Einige Argumente aus der Verbreitung der nordeuropäischen Fauna mit Bezug auf Wegeners Verschiebungstheorie. — Nyt. Mag. f. Naturv. 65. Oslo, p. 339–367.

ORCHYMONT, A. DE & BROWN, W. J., 1940. Helophorus arcticus Brown, a living fossil. — Can. Ent. 72. Ottawa, p. 1–4.

OSTENFELD, C. H., 1926. The flora of Greenland and its origin. — Biol. Medd. K. Dansk. Vid. Selsk. 6:3. Copenhagen, p. 1–71.

PALMÉN, E., 1944. Die anemohydrochore Ausbreitung der Insekten als zoogeographischer Faktor, &c. — Ann. Zool. Soc. Zool. Bot. Fenn. Vanamo. 10:1. Helsingfors, pp. I–V, 1–262.

PETERS, J. L., 1948. Check-List of birds of the world. VI. — Cambridge, Mass., pp. I–XI, 1–259.

PETERSEN, B., 1954. Some trends of speciation in the cold-adapted Holarctic fauna. — Zool. Bidr. 30. Uppsala, p. 233–314.

PETERSON, R. L., 1952. A review of the living representatives of the genus Alces. — Contr. R. Ont. Mus. Zool. & Palaeont. 34. Toronto, p. 1–30.

PILSBRY, H. A., 1894. Helicidae. — Manual of Conch. (Tryon & Pilsbry). 2. Pulmonata. IX. — Philadelphia, pp. I–XLVIII, 1–366.

— 1939, 1946, 1948. Land Mollusca of North America (north of Mexico). I:1, II:1–2. — Ac. Nat. Sci., Monogr. 3. Philadelphia, pp. I–XVII, 1–573; I–VI, 1–1113.

PIROŽNIKOV, P. L., 1937. A contribution to the study of the origin of the northern elements in the fauna of the Caspian Sea. — C. R. Ac. Sci. URSS. 15. Moscow, p. 521–524.

PLESKE, T., 1928. Birds of the Eurasian tundra. — Mem. Bost. Soc. Nat. Hist. 6:3. Boston, p. 11–485.

POULSEN, E. M., 1939. Freshwater Crustacea. — Zool. of Icel. III:35. Copenhagen, p. 1–50.

PRAEGER, R. L., 1932. Recent views bearing on the problem of the Irish flora and fauna. — Proc. R. Irish Ac. B. 41. Dublin, p. 125–145.

— 1934. The botanist in Ireland. — Dublin.

REINIG, W. F., 1937. Die Holarktis. Ein Beitrag zur diluvialen und alluvialen Geschichte der zirkumpolaren Faunen- und Florengebiete. — Jena, pp. 1–VII, 1–124.

— 1938. Elimination und Selektion. — Jena, pp. 1–VIII, 1–146.

REITTER, E., 1875. Beitrag zur Kenntniss der aussereuropäischen Crytophagidae. — Coleopt. Hefte (E. v. Harold). 13. München, p. 73–87.

— 1911. Fauna Germanica. III. — Stuttgart, p. 1–436.

RENSCH, B., 1950. Die Verteilung der Tierwelt im Raum. — Handb. d. Biol. V:1. Potsdam, p. 125–172.

SÆMUNDSSON, B., 1939. Mammalia. — Zool. of Icel. IV:76. Copenhagen, p. 1–38.

SAHLBERG, J., 1880. Bidrag till Nordvestra Sibiriens insektfauna. Coleoptera, &c. — K. Svensk. Vet. Ak. Handl. 17. Stockholm, p. 1–115.

SALOMONSEN, F., 1951. The immigration and breeding of the fieldfare (Turdus pilaris L.) in Greenland. — Proc. X. Intern. Ornith. Congr. (1950). Uppsala, p. 515–526.

SALOMONSEN, F. & GITZ-JOHANSEN, 1950. Grønlands Fugle. The Birds of Greenland. — Copenhagen, p. 1–608.

SANN, J., 1952. (On Penguinus [Alca] impennis.) — Fauna. 5. (Norsk Zool. Foren.) Drammen, p. 74–75.

SCHARFF, R. F., 1907. European animals: their geological history and geographical distribution. — London, pp. 1–XIV, 1–258.

— 1909. On the evidence of a former land-bridge between Northern Europe and North America. — Proc. R. Irish Ac. 28 B. Dublin, p. 1–28.

— 1911. Distribution and origin of life in America. — London, pp. 1–XVI, 1–497.

SCHERHAG, R., 1948. Neue Methoden der Wetteranalyse und Wetterprognose. — Berlin, pp. 1–XII, 1–424.

SCHMIDT, K. P., 1946. On the zoogeography of the Holarctic region. — Copeia. Ann Arbor, Mich., p. 144–152.

SEGERSTRÅLE, S. G., 1954. The freshwater Amphipods, Gammarus pulex (L.) and Gammarus lacustris G. O. Sars, in Denmark and Fennoscandia, &c. — Comment. Biol., Soc. Sci. Fenn. XV:1. Helsingfors, p. 1–91.

SEMENOV, A., 1935. Analecta coleopterologica. XXI. — Rev. Russ. d'Ent. 25. Moscow, p. 275.

SIMPSON, G. G., 1940. Mammals and land bridges. — Journ. Wash. Ac. Sci. 30. Washington, D.C., p. 137–163.

— 1947. Holarctic Mammalian faunas and continental relationships during the Cenozoic. — Bull. Geol. Soc. Amer. 58. New York, p. 613–687.

SMITH, M. R., 1951. Formicidae. — In: Muesebeck, Krombein, Townes, Hymenoptera of America, &c. — U. S. Dept. Agric., Agric. Monogr. 2. Washington, D. C., p. 778–875.

SPÄRCK, R., 1934. Freshwater Sponges. — Zool. of the Faroes. I:1, 4. Copenhagen, p. 1–3.

STEBBINS, R. C., 1951. Amphibians of Western North America. — (Univ. Calif. Press.) Berkeley & Los Angeles, pp. I–XVII, 1–539.

STEGMANN, B., 1938. Principes généraux des subdivisions ornithogéographiques de la région paléarctique. (Russ.) — Fauna SSSR. (N. S.) 19. Moscow & Leningrad, p. 1–157.

STEPHENS, JANE, 1920. The fresh-water Sponges of Ireland. — Proc. R. Irish Ac. 35. Dublin, p. 205–254.

STEPHENSEN, K., 1921. Grønlands Dyreverden. — Medd. om Grønl. 60. Copenhagen.

STERNER, R., 1945. Nordiska havsstrandsväxter. En växtgeografisk överblick. — Fauna o. Flora. Uppsala, p. 28–43.

SZAFER, W., 1954. Pliocene flora from the vicinity of Czorsztyn (West Carpathians) and its relationship to the Pleistocene. — Prace Inst. Geol. 11. Warszawa, p. 1–238.

SZÉKESSY, V., 1936. Revision der boreoalpinen Koleopteren auf vergleichend-anatomischer Grundlage. II. — Ent. Tidskr. 57. Stockholm, p. 97–126.

TAMBS-LYCHE, H., 1937. Forekomsten av Ranunculus Cymbalaria Pursh i Østfold og Bohuslän. — Nyt Mag. f. Naturv. 77. Oslo, p. 15–38.

TAYLOR, J. W., 1906–14. Monograph of the land & freshwater Mollusca of the British Isles. III. — Leeds, p. 1–522.

THIENEMANN, A., 1950. Verbreitungsgeschichte der Süsswassertierwelt Europas. — Stuttgart, pp. I–XVI, 1–809.

THORODDSEN, TH., 1914. An account of the physical geography of Iceland, &c. — Bot. of Icel. I, 2. Copenhagen.

THORKELSSON, TH., 1935. A fossiliferous interglacial layer at Elliðaárvogur, Reykjavík. — Greinar (Soc. Scient. Isl.) I:1. Reykjavík, p. 1–14.

TIMMERMANN, G., 1938–49. Die Vögel Islands. I:1–2. — Vísindafélag Íslendinga (Soc. Scient. Isl.) 21. 24. 28. Reykjavík, p. 1–524.

TIMOFÉEFF-RESSOVSKY, N. W., 1947. Das Treffersprinzip in der Biologie. — Biophysik. I. Leipzig, pp. I–XII, 1–317.

TUXEN, S. L., 1944. The hot springs of Iceland, their animal communities and their zoogeographical significance. — Zool. of Icel. I:11. Copenhagen, p. 1–216.

VALLE, K. J., 1952. Die Verbreitungsverhältnisse der ostfennoskandischen Odonaten. — Acta Ent. Fenn. 10. Helsingfors, p. 1–87.

VANDEL, A., 1945. La répartition géographique des Oniscoidea (Crustacés Isopodes terrestres). — Bull. Biol. France & Belg. 79. Paris, p. 221–272.

VAN DYKE, E. C., 1939. The origin and distribution of the Coleopterous insect fauna of North America. — Proc. 6. Pac. Sci. Congr. 4. San Francisco, p. 255–268.

VIBE, C., 1950. Some insects new to Greenland. — Ent. Medd. 25. Copenhagen, p. 419–420.

VLERK, I. M. VAN DER & FLORSCHÜTZ, F., 1953. The palaeontological base of the subdivision of the Pleistocene in the Netherlands. — Verh. K. Nederl. Ak. Wet., Afd. Naturk. (I) 20:2. Amsterdam, p. 1–58.

WAHLGREN, E., 1919. Västarktiska element i Skandinaviens fjärilfauna. — Ent. Tidskr. 40. Stockholm, p. 22–32.

WALTER, H., 1954. Einführung in die Phytologie. III. Grundlagen der Pflanzenverbreitung. II. Arealkunde. — Stuttgart, p. 1–245.

WEGENER, A., 1929. Die Entsthehung der Kontinente und Ozeane. 4. Aufl. — Die Wissenschaft. 66. Braunschweig, pp. I–X, 1–231.

WEST, A., 1930. Coleoptera. — Zool. of. the Faroes. 40. Copenhagen, p. 1–92.

WHEELER, W. M., 1900. The habits of Ponera and Stigmatomma. — Biol. Bull. Marine Biol. Lab. Woods Hole. 2. Boston, p. 43–69.

— 1915. The ants of the Baltic amber. — Schr. Phys.-Ökon. Gesellsch. Königsberg. 55. Leipzig & Berlin, p. 1–142.

WILLIAMSON, K., 1954. American birds in Scotland in autumn and winter, 1953–54. — Scott. Nat. 66. Aberdeen, p. 13–29.

WOLDSTEDT, P., 1954. Das Eiszeitalter. Grundlinien einer Geologie des Quartärs. 2. Aufl. — Stuttgart, pp. I–XV, 1–406.

— 1955. Norddeutschland und angrenzende Gebiete im Eiszeitalter. (Geogr. Handb.) — Stuttgart, pp. I–XII, 1–467.

WURTEMBERG, W. J., 1919. Helix hortensis. — Nautilus. 33. Philadelphia, p. 71.

ZEUNER, F. E., 1945. The Pleistocene Period, its climate, chronology and faunal successions. — (Ray Soc.) London, pp. I–XII, 1–322.

— 1950. Dating the past. An introduction to geochronology. — London, pp. I–XVIII, 1–474.

Conclusions

The animal species common to Europe and North America are numerous. If conditions among the groups here treated in Chapter I, comprising altogether 908 species in common, are regarded as representative, a calculation on the basis of the Swedish fauna (Gislén, 1940), in which these groups make 17,3 per cent of the entire terrestrial and limnic fauna, would lead to the conjecture that the actual number of Eur-American non-marine animal species amounts to more than 5,000. The true figure is probably higher because the microfauna, here disregarded, includes forms with a distribution above average.

A large part of the species in common are regarded as introduced with man into either continent, or both, this element amounting to between 41 and 46 per cent (375–417 species). As the birds, with no unintentionally introduced species, are among the groups treated, these figures are probably not too high, if applied to the calculated total of Eur-American species.

Species introduced from Europe into North America are about ten times as numerous as those transported in the opposite direction. This is explained by the peculiar character of ballast traffic in olden times, sailing vessels going almost exclusively in ballast on their way *west*, to Newfoundland and the Maritime Provinces of Canada on the one hand, to the Pacific Northwest on the other. The main area of departure for these animals, mostly belonging to the soil fauna, was southwestern England.

A contributory reason why the contingent of introduced European animals is particularly large in the coastal regions of northeastern and northwestern North America is, of course, that the climate of these parts of the continent is most similar to that of western Europe.

Among groups treated, the number of animal species undoubtedly indigenous in both continents exceeds 500. Most of them possess a more or less continuous circumpolar distribution. A special interest, however, is connected with the so-called Amphiatlantic (incl. "Westarctic") species, which are lacking or have a broadly interrupted area on the Pacific side of the globe. They have often been used as an argument in favour of earlier transatlantic land-connections.

Attempts are made to demonstrate that the cases of Amphiatlantic, and similar, distribution can be understood, partly by over-sea dispersal under present conditions, partly as remnants of a broken-up area of circumpolar type. From a bio-geographical point of view, the necessity for any kind of land-connection in the past, directly joining the European with the North American continent, is thus denied. Like Simpson (1947, p. 666, footnote) I started my investigation "with a feeling that a north Atlantic bridge was probable" and like him I dare hope that abandoning this prejudice reduces the subjectivity of opinion.

On the other hand, it seems unevitable to assume that part of the fauna of Greenland and Iceland immigrated across a Pleistocene land-bridge from the European mainland. An interesting point is that this invasion did not at all affect the fauna of Baffin Island, which is completely devoid of a European element. Actually, the narrow strait between Greenland and Baffin Island is the most pronounced north-south barrier within the arctic region of the Holarctic area.

Since the Bering land-bridge, repeatedly at work during Tertiary and Pleistocene time, was the most important link toward evolution of the circumpolar fauna, a detailed comparative study of the Alaskan and Northeast Siberian faunas is the most important task for the future.

Index

OF CHAPTER II AND III

Species, Genera and certain Families

Animals

yukonum, Bembidion

Zelotes pedestris, 190
zetterstedti, Anarta

zibethicus, Fiber
Zonitoides arboreus, 213
Zyras limbatus, 187, 206

Plants

Achillea millefolium, 174, 180, 197
Agrostis sp., 181
Alchemilla filicaulis, 146
  minor, 146
  pastoralis, 146
Alliaria officinalis = petiolata
  petiolata, 180, 197
Alopecurus ventricosus, 146
  sp., 176
Ammophila arenaria, 178, 198
Anagallis arvensis, 178, 198
Anisantha sterilis, 174, 197
Artemisia vulgaris, 174, 176, 197, 198
Atriplex sp., 176
Azolla caroliniana, 212, 241
  filiculoides, 309

Ballota nigra, 174, 197
Bellis perennis, 173, 180, 197
Beta vulgaris, 183, 198
Brassica nigra, 178, 197
Bromus = Anisantha

Calystegia sepium, 174, 197
Capsella bursa-pastoris, 174, 177, 197
Cardamine flexuosa, 146
Carduus crispus, 180, 197
Carex fulva = hostiana
  hostiana, 251
Centaurea nigrescens, 146
Cerastium vulgatum, 174, 180, 197
Chaerophyllum temulum, 180, 197
Chamaenerium = Epilobium
Chrysanthemum leucanthemum, 147, 180, 197
Cirsium arvense, 173, 174, 178, 180, 197, 198
  lanceolatum = vulgare
  palustre, 146
  vulgare, 174, 180, 197

Cochlearia danica, 146
Convolvulus = Calystegia
Coronopus didymus, 174, 197
Crepis sp., 176, 178, 180
Cynoglossum officinale, 178, 198
Cytisus = Sarothamnus

Dactylis glomerata, 173, 178, 180, 197
Daucus carota, 178, 197
Dulichium spathaceum, 309
  spp., 309, 310

Elodea canadensis, 212, 241
Entomophthora sphaerosperma, 222
Epilobium adenocaulon = glandulosum
  glandulosum, 212
  hirsutum, 174, 197
  latifolium, 253
Equisetum arvense, 174, 197
Erigeron canadense, 212
Eriocaulon septangulare, 240, 241, 250
Erodium cicutarium, 178, 198
Euphorbia paralias, 178, 198
  portlandica, 178, 198

Festuca ovina, 178, 197
Fragaria vesca, 146
Funaria hygrometrica, 176

Galium aparine, 146, 180, 197
  saxatile, 146
Geranium dissectum, 174, 180, 197
  ibericum, 146
  robertianum, 180, 197, 198
Glaux maritima, 183, 198
Gnaphalium sylvaticum, 146

Habenaria hyperborea, 253
  straminea, 253
Halimione pedunculata, 183, 198